Tiny Earth

A Research Guide
to Studentsourcing Antibiotic Discovery

Simon Hernandez
Tiffany Tsang
Carol Bascom-Slack
Nichole Broderick
Jo Handelsman

XanEdu

Printed in the United States of America

ISBN 13: 978-1-59399-493-8

Second Printing, May 2019

Cover Image Credit: Dr. Victor J. Cid of the Complutense University of Madrid

4750 Venture Drive, Suite 400
Ann Arbor, MI 48108
800-562-2147
www.xanedu.com

Contents

Tiny Earth
studentsourcing antibiotic discovery

Acknowledgments

Thank you to our partner instructors (our TEPIs) for their thoughtful feedback and helpful suggestions. Special thanks to the hard work of Todd Kelson of Brigham Young University, Sachie Etherington from University of Hawaii, Michael Buckholt from Worcester Polytechnic University, Erica Suchman from Colorado State University, Barbara Murdoch from Eastern Connecticut State University, Ann Buchmann from Chadron State College, Ana Barral from National University, Kristen Butela from Seton Hill University, Jean Schmidt from University of Pittsburgh, Karen Pelletreau from University of Connecticut, Mutafa Morsy from University of West Alabama, and Neil Enis from Tulsa Community College.

Also, thanks to Sam Rikkers, **Tiny Earth** Executive Director, and Patricia Pointer, Multimedia Coordinator for the Wisconsin Institute for Discovery, for their help in producing these materials.

Finally, thanks to all our **Tiny Earthlings** across the world for sharing the journey of discovery and learning.

Introduction

Tiny Earth is a global network of students and instructors conducting research on soil and antibiotics. The network has four goals:

1. Educate students about the antibiotic crisis.

2. Educate students about the soil crisis.

3. Engage students in original scientific research.

4. Discover new antibiotics from soil!

Goal 1. The Antibiotic Crisis

There is a crisis brewing with potential for enormous health, economic, and political consequences. Many diseases caused by bacteria are becoming untreatable due to the proliferation of pathogens resistant to the effects of antibiotics. The World Health Organization (WHO) reports that, in the European Union, about 25,000 patients die each year due to infection with agents that are resistant to multiple antibiotics (WHO, 2011). In the United States, the Centers for Disease Control and Prevention (CDC) reports that over 2 million people acquire serious resistant infections and at least 23,000 die as a direct result of these infections, with many more dying of conditions complicated by the antibiotic-resistant infection (CDC, 2013).

The pace of antibiotic discovery is not keeping up with the rapid evolution of resistance in microbes. Many of the major pharmaceutical companies that had driven the antibiotic discovery process for decades have eliminated or reduced their discovery programs. The United States Food and Drug Administration approval of new antibacterial drugs decreased by 56 percent between 1998 and 2002 (Spellberg, 2004). So, while the crisis escalates, the commitment to drug development is declining.

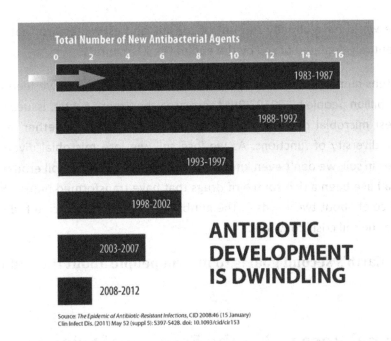

Total Number of New Antibacterial Agents

ANTIBIOTIC DEVELOPMENT IS DWINDLING

Source: *The Epidemic of Antibiotic-Resistant Infections,* CID 2008:46 (15 January)
Clin Infect Dis. (2011) May 52 (suppl 5): S397-S428. doi: 10.1093/cid/cir153

Tiny Earth's first goal is to educate students and the public about the antibiotic crisis.

Goal 2. The Soil Crisis

Most of us take for granted the Earth's crust that we call soil, but it is a precious and rapidly diminishing resource. Soil is well-known as the substrate in which we grow our crops, but it has shaped the course of human history by providing us with lifesaving drugs. In particular, most of the antibiotics we use to treat infectious disease come from bacteria in soil.

But despite its importance to our nutrition and health, we have squandered the Earth's soil. Disrupting it with plowing has degraded its structure, making it vulnerable to wind and water erosion. Many uses have depleted the soil's nutrients making it unhealthy and further vulnerable to damage by wind and water. When soil erodes, it moves from the place it was produced to the atmosphere or waterways. It can be transported to the other side of the Earth or into a river or other waterway. When soil releases its nutrients into water, the ecosystem becomes unbalanced and some organisms grow out of control. This has happened in the Gulf of Mexico where rich soil that eroded from farmland in the Midwestern United States is deposited after traveling down the Mississippi River. The nutrients that are carried along have caused massive blooms of algae that have depleted much of the Gulf of oxygen, producing a 7,900 square mile hypoxic (oxygen-free) zone where few organisms can grow—essentially a dead zone. So soil erosion is a serious problem both where the soil is lost and where it is deposited.

Soil forms slowly but erodes quickly. Most soil is produced at a rate less than 0.5 ton/acre/year, or less than one mm/acre/year. Some estimates suggest that it takes more than 100 years to produce one centimeter of soil. The frightening truth is that much of the world's soils erode at least 10 times this rate, and in some areas as much as 100 times as fast as the soil is produced. This is not sustainable.

Tiny Earth
studentsourcing antibiotic discovery

Many areas of the world have already run out of topsoil, and estimates are that much of the United States is likely be entirely depleted of soil by the end of the 21st century.

Soil erosion threatens human existence. The obvious question is how will we feed a population that is predicted to top 9 billion people by 2050? But there are other, more subtle, issues that arise. Soil is the home to the richest microbial resource on Earth. Species are packed together at a high density and contain a fantastic diversity of functions. As we lose soil, we lose microbial diversity. Since we don't know all the species in soil, we don't even know what we are losing as the soil erodes. What we do know is that soil bacteria have been a rich source of drugs that have transformed human health. In particular, the soil is the source of about two-thirds of the antibiotics we use in medicine today. This is where the antibiotic crisis and the soil crisis converge.

Tiny Earth's second goal is to inform people about the soil crisis.

Goal 3. Original Research—the Essence of Science

The third goal of Tiny Earth is to engage students in original research. It is impossible to learn what science is and what scientists do without conducting research. Many students never experience science in its authentic form, but rather, read about what other scientists have discovered in textbooks. Knowledge discovered by others is important and scientists depend upon previous discoveries to guide and inspire their own research, but it is difficult for many people to get truly excited about the facts and concepts of science before they have experienced the thrill of research. There is nothing in the world like making a discovery. For a moment, you are the only person in the world that knows that tiny piece of information about the world around us. Cherish those moments. And then you get to share your finding, which has its own satisfaction. This is what being a scientist is about—having ideas, discovering new knowledge, sharing that knowledge, and putting in context with what is already known.

Tiny Earth's third goal is to engage students in original research.

Goal 4. Antibiotic Discovery from Soil

Although the antibiotics from soil microbes have been mined for decades, making them the premier source of antibiotics on the market today, they remain a rich treasure-trove of more drugs.

It may seem odd that the class of organisms intended as the target of antibacterial compounds is also a source of these lethal compounds, but it may also be that antibiotics serve functions other than as killer molecules in soil communities. Producing organisms may use antibiotics as signals to other species or they may provide specialized food sources. Whatever their roles in Nature, antibiotics have tremendous value to people for managing infectious disease, so we are fortunate that soil bacteria produced so many different compounds that we call antibiotics.

One of the challenges of identifying antibiotic-producing organisms is isolating the right ones in laboratory culture and then inducing them to produce their antibiotics. Much remains to be learned about the conditions that trigger antibiotic production, but we know that a small percentage of soil microbes produce inhibitory compounds under laboratory conditions quite readily—these are easy to find. One of your challenges will be to figure out new ways to induce other microbes to express normally silent pathways so that we can find the antibiotics that have remained hidden until now.

Can a team of student researchers solve the antibiotic crisis? The answer is a resounding, "yes!" To understand why we are so sure that **Tiny Earth's** students can discover new antibiotics, it's worth examining why antibiotic discovery has slowed to a trickle.

Pharmaceutical companies have said that the probability of identifying novel compounds is too low to be worth investment. The "low-hanging fruit," so to speak, has been picked. We disagree. There is copious evidence that there are many antibiotics waiting to be discovered, and students in our network have already identified novel compounds. We think it more likely that drugs prescribed for chronic conditions such as anxiety, depression, heart disease, and elevated cholesterol—drugs that people take for a lifetime—lured much of the pharmaceutical industry away from antibiotics that are prescribed for a relatively short duration.

While discovering and bringing an antibiotic to market is more than a semester-long process, we can certainly discover and characterize potential candidates in a few months—and learn about the research process along the way. By harnessing the power of undergraduate researchers, we can extend the discovery process to a wide range of geographic locations and a worldwide community of volunteers where every individual has the potential to make novel discoveries.

Tiny Earth's fourth goal is to discover new antibiotics.

Comments on "Tiny Earth"

"**Tiny Earth**" was chosen as the name of our network for several reasons. It captures both the small and the large—small microbes on a large planet, individual researchers part of large network, and many small discoveries that have a large cumulative impact. **Tiny Earth** also refers the Earth as a planet—which houses our network—and earth as soil, the precious resource that we study.

Perhaps the most important significance of **Tiny Earth's** name is that it alludes to how our network makes the Earth seem smaller because we knit together a global community of students and instructors with a common mission. Through our common database, we all work on the same dataset, created by our collective results, which could not be created by any one researcher or a small research team. This dataset will be informative, regardless of the outcome in terms of antibiotic production. Entries from around the world will help to identify trends about microbes that produce antibiotics and delineate geographic regions or biological habitats where antibiotic producers are abundant.

Science today is usually a collaborative effort by individuals in many laboratories. **Tiny Earth** takes that model to a new level, engaging tens of thousands of student researchers in antibiotic discovery and discovery about antibiotics.

References

Bulletin of the World Health Organization 2011;89:390–392
http://www.who.int/bulletin/volumes/89/5/11-088435/en/index.html

Antibiotic Resistance Threats in the United States, 2013. U.S. Department of Health and Human Services, Centers for Disease Control and Prevention (2013).

Spellberg, B., Powers, J. H., Brass, E. P., Miller, L. G., Edwards, J. E., Jr. (2004) Trends in antimicrobial drug development: implications for the future. Clin Infect Dis 38:1279–1286 doi: 10.1086/420937 pmid: 15127341.

How to Use the Research Guide

This research guide is designed to provide background information for each experiment in your research project. As a student researcher, you will be tasked with formulating your own hypotheses, designing your own experiments, picking which protocols to use, and interpreting and presenting your findings. As with every authentic research project, you will not have all the answers upfront. This guide is not meant to give you a set of instructions on how to execute your experiment or tell you everything you need to know about the subject. Instead, it will provide you with general **concepts**, **principles**, and **prompts** to guide you through the project.

Concepts

The **concepts** include a small selection of general biological and microbiological information, brief descriptions of what you would normally find in your textbook and gain from the lecture portion of your course. Each section, we will give you enough information to start thinking about the topic at hand and give you a basis to pursue more information. Use this opportunity to pursue information in a more targeted and goal-oriented manner. Ask yourself, what else would be relevant to know for this experiment or to answer the biological questions? By doing so, you will start to think like a scientist and take ownership of your research.

Principles

The **principles** are general microbiological guidelines to perform your experiments. We provide you with examples of microbiological techniques to show you some of the traditional approaches to answer the biological questions. The protocols section at the back of the book contains an assortment of traditional microbiological methods. After reading each section, you will be prompted to pick a protocol. In some cases, your instructor will provide a protocol or you will be asked to design your own or find one in the literature. While some experiments will have well-established protocols associated with them, you must always determine what you are trying to accomplish with your experiment and formulate your idea of "best results." Maybe you disagree with the traditional approach and can think of alternative ways to design the experiment and obtain even better results. We encourage this evaluation process because it will help you practice the kind of scientific thinking needed to execute any type of research. This is also how you will contribute to the collective creativity of the **Tiny Earth** network.

Prompts

Finally, each section in the research guide will feature several **prompts**. They will be scattered in the section or be presented as Biological Questions or Experiment prompts. At the end of every section, you will come across the topic or the goal of the experiment at the heading and the Biological Questions below it. This is where the *guiding* part of the research guide comes in. With every phenomenon we want to understand, or issue scientists wish to address, we come up with a list of questions. *Why is the*

sky blue? How will I solve world hunger? What is the matter with dung beetles? We present some of the main questions for you, which should be evident after reading the background information in the section and browsing through some of your course materials. <u>Use these questions to make informed hypotheses and design your experiments with specific outcomes in mind.</u> The prompts will encompass the premise and the objective of the experiment, but you must tease those things apart yourself to start thinking like a scientist about own your project. Which takes us to the Experimental prompts. With every experiment, you will need to answer prompts, which are necessary to keep track of and record your research as well as validate your scientific approach and your findings. Should you need more room to write answers than what is provided (you probably will), use your own lab notebook. The following prompts are examples of the main anatomy of the Experimental Sheet at the end of every section:

- **Background:** What led to the biological questions at hand? What is the issue or the phenomenon you want to learn more about?
- **Objective:** List the objective(s) of the experiment. What do you wish to learn about the issues or phenomena at hand?
- **Hypothesis:** Come up with a temporary answer to your question and propose an outcome for your experiment. What do you propose is the explanation for the issue or the phenomenon at hand?
- **Experimental design:** Use text and graphics to explain your scientific approach. How will you go about testing your hypothesis?
- **Techniques/protocols used:** List the protocols you will refer to in the protocols section, or give a detailed description of alternative protocols (designed by you, provided by your instructor, or acquired from the literature). If you make any modification to the protocols provided, make sure you list them here.
- **Results:** Describe the findings of your experiment. What observations did you make? What data did you collect? Do not leave out your negative results—sometimes they are the most important part of your experimental findings that tell you which hypothesis is wrong or which new directions to pursue.
- **Interpretations**: What do your results mean? Speculate as to why you obtained the results you did, referring back to the original question and hypothesis. This will be the place to describe similar trends in your class results or the literature, and come up with insights about what your results tell you. This will also be the place to reevaluate your hypothesis and propose future directions.
- **Conclusion:** Wrap up your experiment with a brief summary and some of the new things you learned.

Use this resource to guide you through the research project and capture your sense of inquiry, observation, critical thinking, problem solving, and creativity. This is a guide into uncharted territory and only you will be the expert on your findings. Enjoy the ride!

Lab Safety and Best Practices

Knowledge and awareness of rules for personal and biological safety are highly important to creating a safe, organized, collaborative, and productive lab environment. Working in the laboratory requires constant surveillance for hazardous materials and practices. It also requires that we be able to identify potential hazards and prevent or manage them properly without compromising our safety and the safety of others. Lab etiquette informs us on how to behave properly in the lab by developing safe practices and habits, as well as effective responses to potentially hazardous activities and outcomes.

General Lab Safety and Etiquette

Entering and Leaving the Lab

1. Always wash your hands before and after doing lab work, and immediately after removing gloves. Never leave the lab without washing your hands first.
2. Never place personal belongings on benchtops or surfaces used for lab work. Keep clothing, backpacks, and other personal belongings in specified locations.
3. Food and drink are strictly prohibited in the lab!
4. Never use personal belongings, such as cameras, tablets, or utensils, for lab work. If use of personal cameras or tablets is required, ensure that they are completely sealed in bags or plastic wrap. When finished, dispose of bag or plastic wrap in designated waste containers before leaving the lab. Personal belongings that become contaminated with microbiological materials need to be properly sterilized (for example sprayed with a 70% ethanol solution) before leaving the lab.
5. Never remove lab materials, reagents, or cultures from the lab. Lab materials could introduce biologically and ecologically hazardous materials to the environment.
6. Know the equipment and supplies on your bench at all times. When in doubt about the identity of lab materials, ask your instructor.
7. For your own safety and the safety of others, know where eyewash and emergency shower stations, fire extinguishers, and emergency exits are located.

Personal Protection

1. Wear proper clothing. Closed-toed shoes and long pants are mandatory to enter the lab. Ensure that your hair is held in pace or tied back. Avoid clothes that expose too much skin or that are too loose. Clothes and hair can get in the way of flames, lab materials, and experiments.
2. Inform your instructor if you are immunocompromised, have allergies (e.g., latex allergy), or feel ill. Should you have any minor cuts or non-intact skin, ensure that they are covered with waterproof bandages. When in doubt, inform your instructor.
3. When carrying out experiments and handling lab materials, it is mandatory to wear personal protective equipment (PPE):

    a.   gloves

    b.   protective eyewear (goggles or spectacles)

    c.   lab coat

4. Always check gloves for integrity. Gloves provide only a thin layer of protection and may contain holes or pores that could allow the passage of fluids and solid materials.

5. Avoid touching shared surfaces, such as light switches, door knobs, and handles, while wearing gloves.

6. When removing PPE, avoid touching the outside of the gloves or your lab coat. Dispose of used gloves in designated waste containers, not regular trash, and immediately wash your hands. Remove eyewear with clean hands.

Handling Lab Materials and General Precautions

1. Handle Bunsen burners or flames with caution: before lighting flame, remove flammable objects (paper, plastic, solvents) from its range.

2. When working with chemicals, such as organic solvents, work in a fume hood and never near a flame.

3. Avoid bringing samples, cultures, reagents, and hazardous equipment close to the face or skin. Never ingest, inhale, lick, or taste materials in the lab!

4. Practice proper pipetting and never mouth-pipette. Never point the pipette toward your body or others. Dispense liquids down the sides of tubes/containers and as close to the content as possible to minimize splashing.

5. Keep test tubes and microcentrifuge tubes in racks at all times.

6. Minimize aerosols by handling liquid cultures, reagents, and solutions carefully. Avoid excessive shaking and forming bubbles in uncapped tubes when pipetting, pouring, decanting, mixing, etc.

7. Cap liquids when not in use, and always cap when mixing, vortexing, or inverting. This measure will help prevent cross-contamination and avoid you coming into contact with potentially hazardous biological materials, fluids, and aerosols.

8. Cap or cover samples, cultures, and specimens when not in use, and keep in specified locations. Avoid close contact with face, skin, and clothes. Avoid stacking plates and leaving them in the middle of the benchtop when not in use.

9. Label samples and cultures with your name, date, and content (See notes on labeling in next section). Make sure that all samples, cultures, media, reagents, solutions, and used test tubes, microcentrifuge tubes, and conical tubes, have proper labeling. Avoid using unlabeled materials.

10. Disinfect surfaces before and after every lab activity. Wipe benchtops and large exposed surfaces with disinfectant solution. Apply 70–85% ethanol or 1–10% chlorine bleach solution, or any disinfectants provided by instructor. Never apply disinfectant solution via spray or squirt bottles near an open flame!

Disposal and Spills

1. Place used or contaminated lab supplies in proper waste containers. Locate the regular trash, biological waste containers, sharps, and broken-glass containers. Any lab supplies that come

into contact with cultures, media, reagents, or any potentially hazardous material should not be left on the benchtop.

    a. Place used reusable equipment in proper receptacles for autoclaving; this includes metal loops, hockey sticks, glass beads, forceps, and glassware.

    b. Dispose of samples, cultures, and media in designated biological waste receptacles.

    c. Dispose of used weigh boats, Petri dishes, and other disposables in designated biological waste receptacles.

    d. Dispose of used sharps (slides, coverslips, Pasteur pipettes, broken glass, toothpicks, wooden sticks, plastic tips, etc.) in designated sharps and/or broken-glass containers. Ask your instructor about glass (e.g., microscope slide) and/or broken-glass disposal.

    e. Ask instructor where to dispose of large pointy objects, such as serological pipette tips.

2. Properly dispose of contaminated media and plates.

    a. Do not remove the lid from plates with fungal growth. Plates with yeasts or molds disseminate spores, which can rapidly spread and contaminate the lab. Consult your instructor for inspection and proper disposal.

    b. Do not use agar plates (solid media) or liquid media that are supposed to be sterile but appear to have microbial growth. Consult your instructor for inspection and proper disposal.

3. Immediately clean spills by flooding the area with disinfectant for a few minutes and wiping with appropriate absorbent material. For large spills, immediately inform your instructor.

Behavior

1. Always be respectful of your lab mates and their workspaces.

2. Do not distract or obstruct lab mates when they are carrying out an experiment as this can compromise their safety and the integrity of their experiments.

3. Communicate questions or doubts about lab safety and proper technique at all times. Also, say something when others are not adhering to lab safety rules and nonhazardous techniques.

4. Always keep written records of your experiments. If you are lost or confused, do not hesitate to ask.

5. Be aware of yourself and your surroundings at all times.

American Society for Microbiology Guidelines for Biosafety

When working with environmental samples, we are always faced with unknown microorganisms. Based on what we know of soil bacteria, most will probably be harmless or nonpathogenic. These bacteria are treated as low-risk or biosafety level 1 (BSL1) microorganisms. However, bacteria that are normally nonpathogenic may become pathogenic under unusual conditions or environments. Furthermore, we can never disregard the possibility of isolating a pathogen. These bacteria are treated as moderate to high risk or biosafety levels 2 or 3 (BSL2/3), respectively. **For these reasons, we should always treat bacterial isolates in the lab as potential pathogens.**

Another risk of isolating unknowns is increased bacterial load. Every time we plate a soil sample, we are allowing individual bacterial cells to reproduce exponentially under optimal conditions. Colonies contain millions of cells, where only a small number may be necessary for infection. Students with a greater risk of infections – due to compromised immune systems or prolonged sickness – should inform their instructor.

The following guidelines, based on the ASM *Guidelines for Biosafety in Teaching Laboratories* (2012) contain precautionary measures that we must take when working with unknown isolates:

1. Treat all unknown bacterial isolates regardless of sample source (nature, household items, human skin) as potential pathogens or microorganisms that may need BSL2 containment, and, in rare cases, BSL3 containment.
2. BSL1 labs may plate bacteria from environmental samples; however, these plates must remain covered and sealed or stored in a secure location. Isolates must remain enclosed at all times, and only observed through the lid. After observation, plates must be decontaminated by autoclaving and properly discarded.
3. BSL2 labs may subculture, or transfer, unknown bacterial isolates from the original medium (described above) to a fresh medium for further testing.

Adherence to the aforementioned guidelines, along with other best-practice suggestions, aseptic technique, and general laboratory safety and etiquette, will help promote a safe and productive lab environment.

For more information:

- **Please read through the ASM *Appendix to the Guidelines for Biosafety in Teaching Laboratories*:** http://www.asm.org/images/Education/FINAL_Biosafety_Guidelines_Appendix_Only.pdf

- **Please visit the following URL for more information on guidelines for biosafety teaching:** http://www.asm.org/index.php/education2/22-education/8308-new-version-available-for-comment-guidelines-for-best-biosafety-practices-in-teaching-laboratories

- Emmert, E. Biosafety guidelines for teaching laboratories. 2013. JMBE. 82, 14. Available at http://jmbe.asm.org/index.php/jmbe/article/view/531

Safety Rules

1. Treat all environmental samples as a potential source of pathogenic microorganisms.
2. Whenever culturing from soil, the use of selective media with an antifungal agent (50 µg/ml cycloheximide) is recommended.
3. Never culture environmentally isolated and unidentified microorganisms at 35 °C or higher to reduce (but not eliminate) the chance of culturing human pathogens, many of which require 37°C for growth.
4. Never culture environmentally isolated and unidentified microorganisms in broth (liquid culture). All experiments with unknown microorganisms must be done on agar.
5. Properly dispose of plates with fast-growing microorganisms, which spread from a single colony to cover most of the surface of the plate.
6. Keep plates covered at all times. Plates can only be observed through the lid.
7. When handling bacteria:
   - Follow "Aseptic Technique" section.
   - Wear appropriate PPE and follow the lab safety rules.
   - Keep a reasonable distance between your body and the plate.
   - Keep the lid at an angle over the plate to insert a pipet tip, toothpick, inoculating loop, or any other sterile inoculating supply.
   - Dispose of or place any used or contaminated supplies in designated BSL1/2 waste container or ethanol/bleach solution.
   - If your gloves touch any bacterial growth or become compromised, quickly cover the plate, stop what you are doing, dispose of your gloves, and thoroughly wash your hands with disinfectant soap.
8. Do colony PCR and sequencing of unknown antibiotic-producing microorganisms before performing biochemical tests or chemical extractions.
9. Clean the workspace with ethanol or bleach solution at the end of lab session.
10. When in doubt, do not do anything you feel is unsafe and contact your instructor or lab safety officer.

TinyEarth
studentsourcing antibiotic discovery

Aseptic Technique

Aseptic or sterile technique is a central concept in microbiology and may be the most important part of working in a microbiology lab. The goal of aseptic technique is to promote practices that (1) prevent the contamination of cultures, lab supplies, and equipment with bacteria or fungi from the environment, and (2) prevent the contamination of individuals working in the lab with potentially pathogenic bacteria. Aseptic technique requires constant attention until it becomes second nature. Practice and strict adherence to these practices is crucial to making proper aseptic technique a habit; the health of individuals in the lab and the integrity of experiments depend on these principles. Here are some general guidelines for practicing aseptic technique:

- Remember that bacteria are ubiquitous in the environment and our bodies.
- When possible, light a Bunsen burner or flame when working with both solid and liquid bacterial cultures. The Bunsen burner will create an umbrella of sterility by creating an upward airflow in your workspace and preventing debris from falling on your sterile materials. Work at a safe distance from your flame without risking burning yourself or anything in your workspace.
- Handle lab materials sensibly, avoiding unnecessary motions or contact with contaminated objects/surfaces or things that are not pertinent to the protocol at hand. Inoculating loops, sticks, toothpicks, pipette tips, serological pipettes, agar plates, media, and other previously sterilized materials are packaged and stored under aseptic conditions. Should you inadvertently touch any items used in the protocol, the item is no longer sterile and must be resterilized or discarded (if the item is disposable).
- Keep in mind that Petri dish lids prevent particulate matter and airborne bacteria from contacting the plate surface, while allowing the diffusion of air around the edges. Whenever a plate lid is removed, it should be held over the plate as a shield. Do not place the lid face down on the benchtop; avoid placing it on the bench all together. Do not leave plates uncovered. Do not walk around the room with an open plate.
- When working with cultures in test tubes, work diligently and as fast as possible. If Bunsen burners are available, pass the uncapped mouth of test tubes through the flame to prevent air from coming into the test tube. Keep tubes open for a minimum amount of time. While lids are removed, hold the tube at a slight angle so that airborne contaminants cannot fall into the open tube. Point tubes away from your face and body while working with them.

Recordkeeping

An important aspect of scientific research is effective communication of one's findings. Today's scientific problems are not solved in isolation but rather by groups or communities of researchers working together or building on the results of others. Methods of communication include publication in peer-reviewed journals, presentation of results at public forums through posters or seminars, submission of data to databases such as GenBank, and communication to the public through media outlets or informal gatherings. In order for research to be accepted by other scientists it must be reproducible. Good recordkeeping is imperative for ensuring that others can replicate one's experimental procedure. **Tiny Earth** is a real research project with a worldwide community of undergraduate researchers. To this end, it is important to keep accurate records. This includes the upload of required information to the database, documenting experimental procedures in your lab notebook, and recording digital photographs of results.

Tips for keeping a laboratory notebook

- Notebook entries should be made in ink and in chronological order. Entries should not be erased or whited out. If an entry contains an error, a line should be drawn through the error and new text should continue in the next available space.
- Start each entry with a title and a clear description of the objective of the experiment.
- Date each experiment. The dates when the work was begun and completed should be recorded.
- Record all materials used in the experiment.
- Record experimental design as well as protocols used. Any modifications to existing protocols should be thoroughly explained. Never assume that any protocol is common knowledge. Be sure to write your own descriptions and definitions.
- Record all data collected and observations made in the experiment. If possible, include photos and diagrams.
- At the end of the record, evaluate your experimental results in an interpretation or discussion section. Draw conclusions and future directions, if possible.
- Explain all abbreviations and terms that are nonstandard. Explain in context, in a table of abbreviations or a glossary.
- Document everything; take detailed notes and photographs during lab. Immediately download and annotate photos to capture accurate data.
- Record negative results. Scientists, especially novice scientists, can learn a great deal from negative results. Reviewing the protocol, brainstorming where the error occurred or reasons for the negative results are key teaching and learning moments. Take advantage of them.
- In general, a good practice is to organize your report as soon as you obtain data. Summarize protocols, experimental designs, and results, make presentable tables, and incorporate the photos taken during lab.

Labeling

Labeling materials and supplies is a critically important aspect of science and lab safety. With multiple plates, tubes, and samples, it is easy to become confused and lose track of things between and within experiments without the proper labeling practices. Here are a few guidelines for labeling:

- Always label the back of the Petri dish, never the lid, because the lid may become separated from the actual dish containing the growth medium (for example, if plates are dropped).
- Always add a date. Dates help orient the scientist as to when the experiment was performed and provide information about the quality of materials.
- Write as legibly as possible – others may need to find your materials or experiments.
- Label experiments with your initials and experiment number and number of trials, for example: TMT 2.1 – experiment 2 performed the first time.
- Label isolates with the your initials, type of medium used, and an identifying number. For example: SS-PDA-5 stands for Sam Smith, potato dextrose agar medium, isolate number 5. If the identity of the organism is known, label with scientific nomenclature: genus, species, and strain.

Entering Data into the Tiny Earth Database (TED)

The power of **Tiny Earth's** student research is substantially greater than the sum of its parts. When student research data are recorded in TED, **Tiny Earth's** Database, our network's discovery potential expands well beyond new antibiotics. Given **Tiny Earth's** global footprint and the diversity of soils mined by **Tiny Earth** student-scientists, soil collection and soil isolate data entered into TED will help us answer questions and better understand factors influencing antibiotic production in soil. With TED's help, **Tiny Earth's** potential for *studentsourcing antibiotic discovery* swells.

Section 1: Living on a Bacterial Planet

Microbes and the Environment

Microbes live in diverse natural habitats, ranging from hot hydrothermal vents deep in the ocean to the insides of our guts and the surfaces of our computer keyboards. The ubiquity and versatility of microbes is the result of their long, intimate relationship with our planet, dating back nearly four billion years. Throughout this long journey, microbes have been active contributors—perhaps the most important drivers—in the transformation of our planet and evolution of its inhabitants. They have shaped the biosphere, driving the evolution of complex cells and multicellular organisms that continue to be largely dependent on the specialized products made by bacteria. Microbes have influenced the Earth's biogeochemical systems, driving the cycling of elements that would otherwise be inaccessible to other systems and organisms. Elements such as carbon and nitrogen would only exist in forms we cannot assimilate into our bodies without them. Microbes living more than 2 billion years ago produced the oxygen that made the Earth's atmosphere transition from anaerobic (oxygen free) to aerobic (oxygen rich), and created the ozone layer that protects the Earth from UV radiation. Microbes might even play a role in forming water droplets that produce rain in clouds.

Definitions

Microbial ecology is the study of microbes' interactions with each other and with their environments. Microbes are part of complex ecosystems, and the communities within those ecosystems teem with life and bustle with activity. Microbes communicate, exchanging and sharing instructions to make new compounds. They may compete for a limited resource or cooperate to maximize the availability of another. Two major focuses of microbial ecology relate to the **biodiversity** and **bioactivity** in an ecosystem. These terms refer to the types of organisms present in an ecosystem and what their activities entail, respectively.

Microbe is a general term for an organism that cannot be seen with the naked eye, and is therefore microscopic. Microbes include **bacteria** and **archaea** (**prokaryotes**), and microscopic **eukaryotes**, such as yeasts, molds, and protists. **Viruses** and **prions** are also lumped into the broad category of microbes. However, these agents do not meet the all the basic requirements for life, such as the ability to reproduce on their own, and are therefore considered nonliving. Prokaryotes and eukaryotes differ in their level of complexity and cellular organization. Eukaryotes package their genetic material inside a compartment called the **nucleus,** whereas prokaryotes do not. Prokaryotes do not contain intracellular compartments or organelles and maintain their genetic material in the cytoplasm.

Living on a Bacterial Planet

The number of individual prokaryotic cells in soil across the planet has been estimated to be 26×10^{28} (260 billion billion billion) (Whitman, Coleman, & Wiebe, 1998). The collective impact of prokaryotes,

Tiny Earth

such as bacteria, on our planet cannot be overstated.This course will focus primarily on bacteria because:

- *Bacteria are virtually everywhere on the planet and are highly abundant – in many ways we live on a bacterial planet;*
- *Bacteria are great research tools because, in comparison with other organisms, they are simple but make specialized chemical compounds, many of which have human applications;*
- *And bacteria greatly impact our health – some may cause infectious disease and others protect our bodies from invasion by harmful bacteria.*

Getting Started

In this course, we will conduct research involving soil bacteria and ask questions pertaining to microbial ecology such as:

- *What types of bacteria are present in our soil samples?*
- *How can we accurately count bacteria and tell them apart from one another?*
- *How many different types and/or individual bacteria of a given type are there?*
- *How do environmental factors influence these numbers?*
- *Does isolation in culture influence bacterial activity?*
- *Are the activities of a particular bacterium beneficial or harmful to another bacterium?*
- *Do they produce specialized molecules like pigments, toxins, or antibiotics?*
- *How active are their antibiotics and what do they target?*
- *Are they resistant to the effects of other antibiotics?*
- *Can we manipulate their production of antibiotics?*
- *Are these antibiotics useful for humans?*
- *Are they known or novel antibiotics?*

We will design and execute experiments to answer these questions, test hypotheses, and develop new insight into the microbial world. As microbiologists, we will refer to many disciplines in the natural sciences, ranging from cell biology to biochemistry to analytical chemistry to genetics. Tools developed in these disciplines will be very important for us over the following weeks as we assess the biodiversity and bioactivity in our soil samples. We will be challenged to think critically about microbial interactions and functions, as well as about ways that we can apply our newly acquired knowledge to enrich the existing body of knowledge and improve human welfare.

References

Whitman, W. B., Coleman, D. C., & Wiebe, W. J. (1998) Prokaryotes: the unseen majority. Proc Natl Acad Sci U S A 95(12):6578–6583.

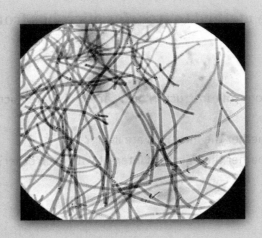

Living on a Bacterial Planet

This photo, taken through a light microscope eyepiece, shows the unique shape and color of the **photosynthetic cyanobacteria** (also known as blue-green algae). Cells form long chains (filaments) and inhabit a variety of habitats, including soil and oceans. Cyanobacteria produce oxygen through photosynthesis and also chemically modify gaseous nitrogen from the atmosphere, which they use for growth. The evolution of cyanobacteria 2.5 billion year ago was perhaps the most transformative event in earth's evolutionary history. Massive amounts of oxygen were released into our planet's atmosphere for the first time, drastically changing its composition. This event triggered the mass extinction of many oxygen-sensitive microorganisms, enabled evolution of oxygen-dependent respiration, and gave rise to the ozone layer, which allowed life to migrate to land and evolve into the wide biodiversity (the human species included) we see on earth today.

Photo source: commons.wikimedia.org

Experiment 1: Devise a method to transfer microbes from a soil sample to a medium in the lab

Biological Questions:

1. Given a soil sample from your instructor, how can you isolate microbes from soil into a medium in the lab?
2. How will you know whether the microbes are living?
3. How will you know whether the microbes interact with each other?

Background:

Objective of the experiment:

Hypothesis and rationale:

Isolation method used:

Observations:

Evaluation and conclusions:

Notes:

Section 2: More Than Just "Dirt"

Soil

Throughout human history, humans have looked at soil with a sense of mysticism and spirituality, in appreciation for its necessity for life. Soil sustains humans through agriculture and provides a platform for our daily activities. In many respects, soil not only sustains us, but also makes us who we are. The development of civilizations has depended upon soil health; poor soils have resulted in the collapse of entire civilizations, whereas fertile soils have enabled civilizations to flourish. As a symbol of fertility and the raw materials of life, soil has inspired many of the world's religions and traditions.

Soil is an extensive natural body covering most of the Earth's terrestrial surface and mediating the Earth's systems in the biosphere, atmosphere, hydrosphere, and lithosphere. Most evident of all, soil supports forests and plant life, which in turn produces half of the oxygen in the atmosphere and 95 percent of the world's food. Soil greatly influences the planet's ecosystems but is itself affected by natural forces and human, or anthropogenic, activities as well. Humans have rapidly extracted large quantities of soil constituents that were accumulated over millions of years through soil genesis and mineral weathering and sedimentation. Human activity can disrupt the natural cycling of elements and can pollute the soil with extraneous chemicals that natural ecosystems are not well-suited to remove or not well-suited to remove or degrade. All these external factors greatly influence the life that depends on soil and can produce predictable changes in the biodiversity, bioactivity, and biomass we observe. This is because soil is itself an ecosystem for some of the most numerous, diverse, and dynamic organisms on Earth.

Soil Characteristics

The main characteristics defining soil are its physical structure, chemical composition, and association with plant roots or other resident organisms. The association of soil with plant roots creates a distinction between soil types that is often referenced by microbiologists and agronomists. We can distinguish between the **rhizosphere**, or soil that is in direct contact with living plant roots and their secretions, and **bulk soil**, which constitutes everything else. The microbial profile of the rhizosphere differs starkly from that of bulk soil. Root systems create microenvironments that favor the growth of specific bacteria. These microenvironments affect the way nutrients and energy are delivered, how water drains, and how temperature fluctuates. Different plants and microbes have specific chemical and metabolic signatures, which in turn change the chemical properties of soil. This interplay between living and nonliving entities defines the characteristics of their respective environments.

The physical structure of soil is determined by the proportions of three main particle types: sand, silt, and clay. These particles clump together to form aggregates of different sizes and textures. Soil with large, coarse particles (sand) or clumps is more permeable than finer soil, allowing the passage of water and faster leaching of soluble molecules. This can deplete the soil of necessary nutrients and limit the

amount of life that can be sustained by it. Conversely, soils containing more fine particles (silt and clay) or smaller clumps are less aerated than coarse soils, restricting the growth of microbes that need oxygen gas (O_2) below the surface.

The rates at which materials are deposited into the soil and subsequently removed or processed by natural forces, such as living organisms and water, drastically impacts the spatial composition of soil. As we dig into the soil, getting further away from the surface, we encounter differences in physical and chemical composition, as well as differences in the microbial populations found at each depth. Cross-sections of most soils reveal that they are divided into distinct layers called **horizons** (Figure 2-1). Understanding the different horizons is important to categorizing soils. The structure of horizons is also a good predictor of the nutritional characteristics of the microbes living within them. Generally, as we descend from one horizon to the next, the abundance of organic components, as well as the exposure to light and oxygen, declines.

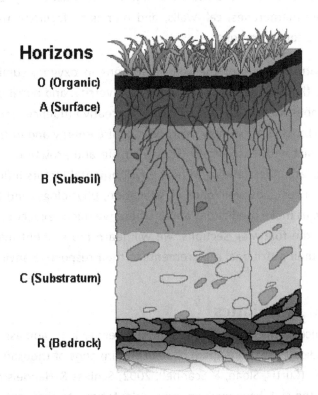

Horizons

O (Organic)
A (Surface)
B (Subsoil)
C (Substratum)
R (Bedrock)

Figure 2-1. Soil Horizons: Soil is divided into layers called horizons, which vary in their physical and chemical characteristics. As we descend from one horizon to the other, organic matter and microbial life decrease and we approach greater accumulations of inorganic materials such as minerals and rock. Source: https://en.wikipedia.org/wiki/Soil_horizon

The **O Horizon** sits at the surface of the soil profile, where un-decomposed plant matter is directly exposed to the elements. This is what we typically see on the forest floor. Right below this thin layer sits the **A Horizon,** or **topsoil**, which is rich in organic matter and contains most soil life. Microbes actively

Tiny Earth
studentsourcing antibiotic discovery

decompose organic material to form humus, and intimately interact with plant roots and other organisms such as fungi, insects, and worms. Some of the organic and inorganic components of this layer are easily drained by water and accumulate in the subsequent **B Horizon**, or subsoil. The B Horizon contains lower levels of microbial life and a greater proportion of anaerobic bacteria that do not require oxygen for respiration. Inorganic matter such as minerals and partially weathered parent material constitute the **C Horizon**. In this layer, microbial life is low in abundance but nevertheless present. Researchers have even found microbes in bedrock, thriving in an environment free of sunlight, oxygen, organic molecules, and with very little available water.

pH is a significant factor in shaping microbial life in soil. Plants and microbes can only survive within a specific pH range. This means that pH can be viewed as reflective of soil health. After comparing different environments across the globe, Fierer and Jackson found that soil pH was the best predictor of microbial diversity. Arid soils, which are poor in water and nutrients but generally have a near-neutral pH, were richer in microbial diversity than rainforest soils, which are usually more acidic (2006). This is in spite of the fact that rainforests comprise incredible amounts of diversity at the **macroscale**. Another important factor is the ionic concentration of the soil. Microbes must be equipped to withstand **osmotic forces** with well-adapted membranes, cell walls, and pumps to facilitate the movement of ions and resist fluctuations in ionic concentrations.

As we approach the bottom layers of the soil, limitations in oxygen, sunlight, carbon sources, and changes in pressure drastically affect microbial biomass, diversity, and nutrition. It is important to know which layer of soil microbes are isolated from since this greatly influences microbial growth conditions. Furthermore, soil characteristics affect how microbes acquire energy and nutrients, how they adhere to surfaces, how they interact with each other, what their life and growth cycles are like, and how they evolve over time. Having an understanding of how environmental factors influence microorganisms can help when making inferences about microbial classification, physiology, and basic cellular biology. This knowledge can also help us make predictions about where we might expect to find the most biodiversity and active microbes. In the following sections, we will learn more about microbial nutrition and how microbes have adapted their nutritional requirements to their respective environments.

Soil Microbes and Antibiotics

Soil harbors an abundance of microbes in terms of biodiversity and biomass (the number of individual organisms). Research indicates that <u>one gram of soil contains tens of thousands of bacterial species and billions of individual cells</u> (Curtis, Sloan, & Scannell, 2002; Schloss & Handelsman, 2006). **Soil microbes**, or microbes that live in the soil, have evolved many adaptations to their environment. They synthesize an arsenal of biochemicals used for bacterial warfare, signaling, or acquiring nutrients. They break down complex molecules, such as those present in decaying plant matter or carcasses, and cycle nutrients and elements back into their ecosystems. In addition, many soil processes that decompose biological materials release greenhouse gases and characteristic odors. It is no wonder that humans have ascribed so many mystical qualities to soil.

Soil bacteria live in a crowded and highly competitive environment where conditions constantly change and resources are limited. In order to cope with a changing and competitive environment, many microbes have evolved specialized molecules that mediate their interactions with their surroundings. Pigments, toxins, and antibiotics are specialized molecules known as secondary metabolites. **Secondary metabolites** are organic compounds produced by bacteria that enhance their chances for survival, while remaining nonessential for fundamental growth processes (unlike structural molecules and DNA, for example). Antibiotics are secondary metabolites that inhibit the growth of other microorganisms. In their natural habitat, some microbes may produce antibiotics to reduce competition for resources; these same antibiotics save human lives when used as drugs to treat infectious disease (more on secondary metabolites and antibiotics in Section 9).

The majority of antibiotics in commercial and clinical use today are derived from soil bacteria. Actinomycetes, which are common soil bacteria, produce 60 percent of clinically important antibiotics. There is still tremendous potential for finding new antibiotics among the immense soil reservoir of microbes and molecules; in fact, the more scientists study soil, the more we realize just how little we know about the chemistry of soil microbes. The vast unknown features and intricacy of the soil makes this ecosystem a fascinating place to study microbes, which is the focus of our research project. We will collect soil and bring it to the lab to explore the capabilities of the microbes living in it. Keep in mind that a soil sample you collect represents the most complex ecosystem on Earth. Your soil sample may not encapsulate the full range of biology and chemistry of soil, or even of the soil immediately adjacent to the sample you removed, but it will be very, very complex. So pay close attention to the characteristics of the soil ecosystem and what they might indicate about the microbes inhabiting it.

- *How will we know whether our sampling location is rich in abundance and diversity of antibiotic-producing bacteria?*

As a collaborative network of student researchers and instructors across the globe--from Botswana to Connecticut, U.S.A, **Tiny Earth** is poised to collect data at a scale never before reported. By documenting detailed information about your sample location and keeping records of your observations (the number of microbes isolated, the number of those that produce antibiotics, etc.) we will begin to amass a large and useful data set that may reveal trends in soil. This information may prove helpful, not only for future classes, but also for the research community as a whole, to distinguish likely sources of new antibiotics from those that have a low probability of yielding antibiotic producers.

Experiment 2: Find a local soil environment you wish to sample

Biological Questions:

1. What soil environments will give us the most unique and greatest diversity of bacteria to study in the lab? Define what unique and diverse means to you.
2. What local soil environment will you choose for sampling and why?
3. What do you hypothesize about the abundance and diversity of microbes in your soil sample and why? How will you test this? Think of controls to use in your experiment.

Background:

Objective:

Criteria for picking soil sample:

Soil sample site:

Hypothesis and rationale:

Technique used for collecting your soil sample:

Notes:

Tiny Earth
studentsourcing antibiotic discovery

Soil Sample Data Collection Sheet

Worksheet also available in protocols section. Your instructor may only want you to record data on some of these or may indicate additional data they want you to record.

Collected By:	
Date of Collection:	
Depth:	
Type of Soil:	
Temperature of Air:	
Temperature of Soil:	
Weather Conditions on Day of Collection:	
General Location:	
GPS Coordinates via Google Earth:	
Sample Site Descriptors:	
Additional Data to be Collected in Lab:	
pH of Soil:	
Water Content:	
Organic Content:	

Additional Documentation:
- Photo of sampling site
- Identification of any plant species observed near site
- Photo of soil in collection tube

Soil Sampling Kit Contents:
- Data sheets
- 50-mL conical tubes
- Lab marker
- "Scientific Soil Sample Collection Device" (plastic knife or spoon)
- Alcohol pads (used to disinfect collection device, thermometer, ruler before taking each sample)
- Thermometer
- Site-marking flag (if return to site necessary)
- Plastic ruler

Printout of "Guide of Texture by Feel": http://soils.usda.gov/education/resources/lessons/texture/

Section 3: Redefining "Growth" and "Culture"

Bacterial Growth

Bacterial cells "grow," in the sense of getting larger, to a limited extent (generally doubling in size before dividing), but this is not what microbiologists usually refer to when using the term "growth." We use **"growth"** to describe an increase in the size of a microbial population. In other words, when talking about single-celled organisms, "growth" usually means "reproduction." Reproduction is critical to the survival of any species, and bacteria are true survivors, reproducing exponentially under optimal growth conditions.

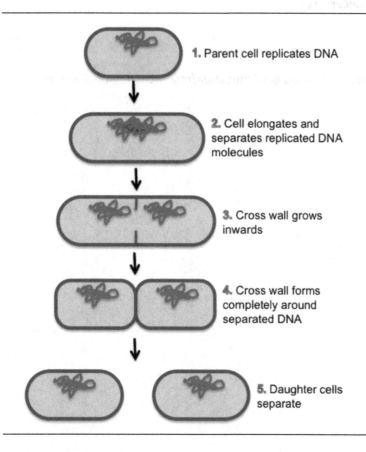

1. Parent cell replicates DNA

2. Cell elongates and separates replicated DNA molecules

3. Cross wall grows inwards

4. Cross wall forms completely around separated DNA

5. Daughter cells separate

Figure 3-1. Schematic of binary fission, the process of bacterial cell division whereby a parental cell gives rise to two daughter cells. Every successive round of cell division doubles the size of the bacterial population. This results in exponential growth under optimal conditions.

The bacterial growth cycle is driven by complex intracellular and extracellular signals, which tell the cell when it is time to replicate. The first step in the process is DNA synthesis, in which a bacterium makes an extra copy of its chromosome, which contains all the genetic information necessary to give a cell its instructions for life. The cell then increases in size and elongates, pulling two identical chromosomes apart. Once the chromosomes are localized at the opposite ends of the elongated cell, the plasma membrane and cell wall start forming an "equatorial septum," which splits the parental cell into two

daughter cells. This type of symmetrical cell division is known as **binary fission** (Figure 3-1). A few bacteria reproduce by an alternative mechanism known as **budding**, in which a small daughter cell "buds off" a larger mother cell. In either case, daughter cells remain genetically identical to the parent.

In any given population of bacteria, some cells will be dividing, others may be between stages or quiescent, and others may be dying. Yet when conditions are optimal for growth, such as a warm environment with just all the right nutrients, most cells will be dividing rapidly. The time it takes for a population of bacteria to double in size is called the **doubling,** or **generation, time**. In rich nutrient environments, *Escherichia coli* populations may double every 20 minutes, whereas other species of bacteria, such as *Mycobacterium tuberculosis*, may take up to 16 hours. "Optimal growth" conditions, however, are virtually nonexistent in natural habitats, where bacteria are kept in check by competing microbes and limited resources. Optimal growth conditions are typically created in the lab, where microbiologists have developed nutrient-rich environments to support the growth of some bacteria.

Bacterial Cultivation

To promote the growth of bacteria in the lab, which is referred to as **culturing** or **cultivating**, we need a medium to provide them nutrition and a place to live and reproduce. **Media** (plural of the word medium) are "bacteriological foods," which are mixtures of nutrients contained in liquid or solid form (more on media and nutrition in Section 4). When a microorganism is introduced into a liquid medium or the surface of a solid medium and allowed to reproduce, we refer to the resulting mixtures as **cultures**. Liquid media are typically referred to as broths, and solid media as agar plates (agar is the solidifying agent that is used to make the media solid in a Petri dish) (Figure 3-2) (more in Section 4). Culture conditions are carefully controlled parameters, such as temperature, humidity, and oxygen levels. However, there is no *one* food for bacteria. Just as bacteria are taxonomically diverse, so are their nutritional requirements. Every discovery of a new organism requires a careful assessment of the nutrients and conditions necessary to support its growth.

The greatest limiting factor in studying microbes is the small number of bacterial species that grow in culture. Until the 1990s, most of our knowledge of bacteria was based on the small number of so-called **culturable** bacteria, or bacteria that can be cultured in the lab based on current knowledge. This **culture-dependent** approach has been the basis for studying bacteria in most traditional microbiology labs. However, microbiologists have developed alternative approaches to get a wider and more accurate representation of bacteria living in the environment. These **culture-independent** approaches do not require bacteria to reproduce in the lab or exist in large numbers. It relies on advanced and expensive equipment to detect and analyze millions of microscopic entities individually. **Metagenomics**, the study of all the genetic material present in a given environment, allows us to sample soil and analyze all the DNA present in it as a signature for all the organisms living in it, whether or not they grow in the lab. These methods indicate that <u>only 0.3 percent of all bacteria in soil can be cultured in the lab</u> (Amann, Ludwig, & Schleifer, 1995). This means that only 3 in 1,000 bacteria can be studied in the laboratory by using a culture-dependent approach.

Tiny Earth
studentsourcing antibiotic discovery

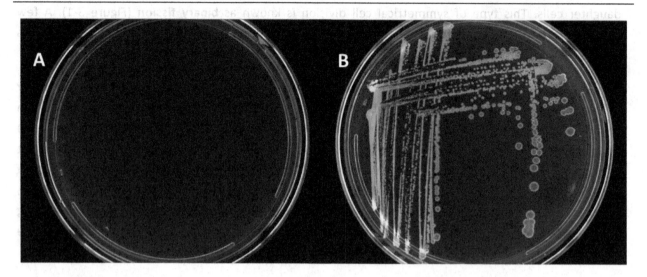

Figure 3-2. (A) A solid medium, composed of a mixture of nutrients, water, and agar (a solidifying agent) with no bacterial growth. (B) The same solid medium with a culture of *Staphylococcus cohnii* after 48 hours of incubation at 28°C.

The limitations of the culture-dependent approach result from inadequate knowledge of conditions that favor bacterial growth in natural habitats. Studying the soil metagenome in many ways has led to more questions than answers. Although the metagenome represents the complexity of the microbial world, its functional diversity remains difficult to study without culturing bacteria. In our lab, we will rely on the culture-dependent approach to study soil bacteria because it gives us functional information, can lead directly to antibiotic discovery, and has not been used to fully mine the soil or the antibiotic producing bacteria that inhabit it. Just remember that we won't be visualizing the entire microbial world with culture methods.

CFUs and Bacterial Colonies

The most important feature of the culture-dependent approach is that it allows us to study microscopic entities at the macroscopic scale. However, it is important to keep in mind the requirements and limitations of this approach:

1. *Only **viable** (alive and capable of reproducing) cells will grow. Dead and/or dormant cells will not be detected.*
2. *Only cells that are **culturable** (capable of growth on the selected culture medium and under the prescribed incubation conditions) will be detected. Cells that cannot grow under the selected laboratory conditions will not be detected.*

In order to detect a microorganism in the lab, we need a visual cue that will tell us whether the microorganism meets the above requirements. We are familiar with the appearance of molds on bread and other food, and we use the visual cue to avoid eating contaminated food. Similarly, when we grow bacteria in the lab, we typically look for the formation of colonies. In the field of microbiology, a **colony**

Tiny Earth
studentsourcing antibiotic discovery

is a collection of genetically identical cells that arise from a single cell. This can be any one cell in the environment or in a soil sample. Single cells that give rise to a colony are referred to as **CFUs (colony forming units)**. As a CFU reproduces, the mass of dividing cells eventually becomes large enough that a macroscopic colony becomes visible to the naked eye. Colonies enable us to see into the microscopic world, each colony revealing characteristics that are unique to its species and which, in many cases, can be easily recognized by experienced microbiologists (more on colony morphology in Section 5).

An important step in isolating soil bacteria is obtaining **single colonies**. We know that, by definition, a colony arises from a single CFU. Therefore, we can expect all the cells present in the colony to be of the same genetic composition. By studying bacterial species discretely, we can truly appreciate the diversity of microbes and their unique characteristics.

How do we go from millions of individual cells and species living in soil to single colonies on a solid medium? Even if only 3 in 1,000 bacteria in the soil will grow in the lab, culturing from even a speck of soil will result in tens and hundreds of thousands of colonies growing on the surface of a solid medium all crammed together. The outcome of this will be a nondescript mass of contiguous and overlapping colonies that provides no useful information about the types of microorganisms in the sample. The logical solution would be to spread them out, but how much room do we need to spread out thousands of CFUs so they grow into non-overlapping, distinct colonies?

Microbiologists use dilution methods to reduce the number of cells present in a given sample. We may dilute them in pure water or in salty solutions to keep the cells in an isotonic environment. Once we obtain a desired dilution, which can only be determined on a case-by-case basis, we can spread a small volume of the dilution (in the range of microliters) on a plate. The spreading step separates and disperses cells all over the surface of the plate. Each CFU will be randomly deposited on a spot on the plate where it will proliferate and give rise to a single colony. Colonies will be sparse and separated when the appropriate dilution is achieved (Figure 3-3).

Since colonies represent the unique qualities of the bacteria reproducing in them, we must ensure that they are not contaminated with other species that may obscure our observations (Figure 3-3C). To confirm that a colony contains a single species of bacteria, microbiologists use other spreading methods to further separate cells and observe differences in morphology (more on colony morphology in Section 5). Obtaining **pure cultures**, which each contain a single strain of bacteria, is important for conducting controlled experiments and is the basis of making comparisons, reliable observations, and measures in scientific research. By observing the response of a pure culture to different variables (e.g., type of medium used, temperature, incubation period, technique used, chemicals applied), we can make inferences about the characteristics of the individual cells that constitute it.

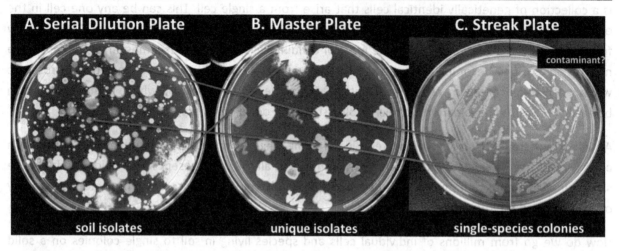

A. Serial Dilution Plate	B. Master Plate	C. Streak Plate

contaminant?

| soil isolates | unique isolates | single-species colonies |

Figure 3-3. (A) A serial dilution plate of a rich soil sample. Bacteria in the soil sample were suspended in sterile water and diluted 10,000-fold (10^{-4}) to obtain a distribution of cells that produces discrete colonies, while representing a wide diversity of bacteria. After incubating the plate 24–72 hours, single colonies can then be picked from the dilution plate and smeared on a new medium plate to create a master plate. (B) The master plate serves as a catalogue of the visibly distinct bacteria that were isolated from a sample. The blue arrows show the transfer of cells from colonies in the dilution plate to a clear spot on the master plate. After 24–72 hours of incubation, the smear grows onto a dense patch of cells that is visible to the naked eye. From this collection of cells, we start new cultures and do further testing. (C) The unique isolates on the master plate are "streaked" onto a new plate to isolate single colonies. A streak of one of the isolates (far right) reveals a second species of bacteria interspersed in the patch. The streaking method allows us to separate them and start pure cultures of each.

Milestones in Microbiology

Selman Waksman coined the term "antibiotic" and pioneered exploration of the prolific antibiotic producers of the soil during the 1940s and 1950s. Along with his student Albert Schatz, he discovered and developed the antibiotic streptomycin, produced by the actinomycete *Streptomyces griseus*. Streptomycin was the cure for tuberculosis. Wakman's discovery, along with the commercialization of penicillin, ushered in the golden age of antibiotics, a time in which the rate of antibiotic discovery was rampant, with dozens of antibiotics being discovered and brought to the market every year. By the beginning of the 1980s, it was believed that antibiotics had eliminated the threat of infectious disease.

Photo source: commons.wikimedia.org

Alma Whiffen, a contemporary of Waksman, was a mycologist who discovered the antifungal agent cycloheximide during the mid-1940s, produced by *S. griseus* (the same bacterium that produced the antibiotic streptomycin). Because of its toxicity to eukaryotic cells (such as human cells), cycloheximide is normally used for research applications, such as inhibiting the growth of fungi in bacterial cultures rather than for treatment of disease in people.

Photo source: commons.wikimedia.org

References

Amann, R. I., Ludwig, W., & Schleifer, K. H. (1995). Phylogenetic identification and in situ detection of individual microbial cells without cultivation. Microbiol Rev, 59:143–169.

Curtis, T. P., Sloan, W. T., & Scannell, J. W. (2002). Estimating prokaryotic diversity and its limits. Proc Natl Acad Sci U S A, 99:10494–10499. doi: 10.1073/pnas.142680199

Schloss, P. D., & Handelsman, J. (2006). Toward a census of bacteria in soil. PLoS Comput Biol, 2:e92. doi: 10.1371/journal.pcbi.0020092

Experiment 3: Find a method to isolate single colonies of bacteria from your soil sample

Biological Questions:
1. What is the significance of single colonies? How can you obtain single colonies on a medium plate from a soil sample?
2. How will you enumerate the culturable microorganisms present in your soil sample?
3. Once you obtain single colonies, can you identify morphologically distinct microorganisms?
4. What would you like to learn about the microorganisms you isolated?

Background:

Objective:

Hypothesis and rationale:

Procedure for obtaining single colonies on plate:

Draw a schematic of the procedure used:

Data and observations:

Interpretations and conclusions:

Notes:

Tiny Earth
studentsourcing antibiotic discovery

Assignment: Calculating CFU/g soil
Objective:

Sample	Number of colonies per sample					
Media	No dilution		10^{-1}	10^{-2}	10^{-3}	10^{-4}

CFU/g soil calculations:

How does this compare with estimates in the literature?

Notes:

Section 4: Bacteria Are What They Eat, Too

Composition of Living Things

We have considered methods to maximize the number of bacteria in a sample. But did those efforts also capture the number of different species? Will all species present in the soil grow equally well on a single type of media? To answer these questions, we must consider how microorganisms obtain the energy needed to support biological processes and proliferation.

Like all other organisms, microorganisms use energy to produce organic molecules that perform specific biological functions and allow them to grow, proliferate, and engage with their environments. Organic molecules by definition contain carbon (C) atoms, the core elemental building block of life, and are the main constituents of cellular components and energy sources. Some organic molecules can be joined together to form complex macromolecules (see Table 4-1), which perform their own specific functions, or be further modified by reactions within the cell to form secondary metabolites. Organic molecules are largely constructed from only a few elements. Of these elements, carbon (C), hydrogen (H), oxygen (O), nitrogen (N), phosphorus (P), and sulfur (S) are most abundant and required for life. A variety of additional elements are also needed by living cells but in lesser quantities (see Table 4-2).

Organic molecule	Elemental components	Macromolecule
Amino acids	C, H, O, N, S	Proteins
Nucleic acids	C, H, O, N, P	DNA and RNA
Fatty acids	C, H, O	Lipids
Sugars	C, H, O	Carbohydrates

Table 4-1. Macromolecules and their constituents.

Sodium (Na^+)	Magnesium (Mg^{2+})	Calcium (Ca^{2+})
Iron (Fe^{2+}/Fe^{3+})	Potassium (K^+)	Chloride (Cl^-)

Table 4-2. Trace elements. Table adapted from Slonczewski & Foster (2011)

Classifying Bacteria Based on Nutrition

Bacteria can be classified based on how they obtain carbon and energy from their environments to make biological molecules (Table 4-3). Some organisms produce organic molecules by obtaining or "fixing" carbon from inorganic sources, such as CO_2. They are known as **autotrophs** and are the primary producers in food chains. Photosynthetic organisms, such as plants, algae, and cyanobacteria, are good examples of autotrophs. Conversely, **heterotrophs** obtain carbon from organic molecules formed by other organisms. Animals, protozoa, fungi, and many bacteria and archaea are heterotrophs.

42

Bacteria can also be classified based on their tolerance for oxygen. Many (but not all) bacteria that live in contact with the atmosphere, which is approximately 21% oxygen gas (O_2) by volume, are **aerobic**, which means they can grow and survive in the presence of O_2. In contrast, O_2 is toxic to some anaerobes, many of which thrive only in strictly O_2-free environments.

Living organisms use oxidizing substances, such as O_2, sulfate (SO_4^{2-}), and pyruvate, as electron acceptors in fueling reactions that oxidize "food" molecules to free usable energy. These processes of respiration (using oxygen as a source of electrons) and fermentation (using organic molecules as a source of electrons) ultimately capture and store released energy in the form of **adenosine triphosphate (ATP)**, the "energy currency" common to all life.

		Energy Source	
		Light (photo-)	**Chemical compounds (chemo-)**
Carbon Source	**Carbon dioxide (auto-)**	**Photoautotrophs** • Plants, algae, cyanobacteria • Green sulfur and purple sulfur bacteria	**Chemoautotrophs** • Hydrogen, sulfur, nitrifying bacteria
	Organic (hetero-)	**Photoheterotrophs** • Green nonsulfur and purple nonsulfur bacteria	**Chemoheterotrophs** • Aerobic respiration: most animals, fungi, and protozoa; many bacteria

Table 4-3: Metabolic types of organisms are categorized on the basis of how they obtain their energy and carbon. Table adapted from Bauman, Microbiology 1st ed., Figure 6.1

Media and Culture Conditions

In the lab, microbes are grown on many different types of media that contain mixes of essential nutrients suspended in water (e.g., broths and infusions). Some media are solidified with agar, gelatin, or another jelly-like substance. Media ingredients range from dehydrated extracts of plant, animal, or fungal material to synthetic compounds made in the lab. Media can be enriched with a variety of organic molecules, macromolecules, and vitamins to support the growth of **fastidious** bacteria, which have complex nutritional requirements. They can also be minimal, composed mainly of simple sugars, salts, and water. Over the years, microbiologists have developed standard media formulations that can be purchased from commercial vendors and used for many different applications.

Other **physical parameters**, such as light exposure, temperature, and tonicity, can drastically affect the assortment of microbes that grow in culture. The composition and concentration of ions and molecules in a bacterium's environment not only influence its nutrition, but also the overall stability of its cells. A medium with inadequate **electrolytes** may represent a hypotonic environment that will cause cells to swell up and burst. Conversely, a hypertonic medium with an excessively high concentration of solutes

Tiny Earth
studentsourcing antibiotic discovery

may cause cells to lose water, shrivel, and die. Similarly, many bacteria cannot survive outside a relatively narrow pH range.

Growth on a plate indicates that the bacteria are living within an acceptable range of conditions that allows them to survive and proliferate. It does not mean that all of their needs are met. Like all living things, bacteria are hard-wired to respond to stimuli in their environments. Cellular processes, such as gene expression, are mediated by factors and complex pathways that scientists do not fully understand and cannot account for in the laboratory. For example, many scientists are trying to stimulate the expression of **silent genes** encoding production of potentially novel secondary metabolites in various species of the genus *Streptomyces*.

Finding the right combination of conditions and stimuli that promote the growth of certain bacteria or induce the expression of certain genes is perhaps the biggest obstacle to unraveling the biodiversity and biosynthetic potential of microbes. Increasingly, research shows that many bacteria are dependent on microbial communities where they exchange signals, genetic material, nutrients, and other stimuli that trigger specific responses in cells. There are more variables than any experiment can test, but the more ways we isolate and grow bacteria, the more we can learn about the organisms in a sample. Use your imagination.

References

Bauman, R. (2003) *Microbiology* (1st ed.) San Francisco: Benjamin Cummings.

Mukhopadhyaya, P. N., Deb, C., Lahiri, C., & Roy, P. (2000). A *soxA* gene, encoding a diheme cytochrome C, and a *sox* locus, essential for sulfur oxidation in a new sulfur lithotrophic bacterium. J Bacteriol, 182:4278-4287.

Slonczewski, J., & Foster, J. W. (2011). *Microbiology: An Evolving Science* (2nd ed.). New York: W.W. Norton & Co.

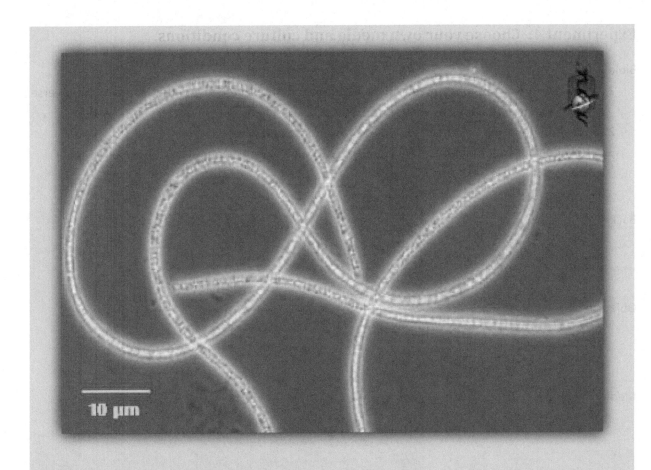

Living on a Bacterial Planet

The long chains (filaments) of the sulfur-oxidizing bacterium *Beggiatoa*, seen under the microscope under high magnification (notice the scale in the picture). This microorganism is an example of a lithotroph, which derives its nutrition from inorganic molecules, such as reduced inorganic compounds and minerals typically found in rocks, hence the name, "rock eaters." Lithotrophs, composed of both bacteria and archaea, live in extreme environments ranging from bedrock to deep hydrothermal vents. The sulfur-oxidizing bacterium *Beggiatoa* was the first example of a lithotrophic bacterium discovered in microbial mats near hydrothermal vents and sulfur-rich environments in the ocean bottom. *Beggiatoa* oxidizes sulfur compounds such as sulfide (S^{2-}) as their energy source and carbon dioxide (CO_2) as a carbon source (Mukhopadhyaya, Deb, Lahiri, & Roy, 2000)

Photo source: https://alchetron.com/Acidophile

Tiny Earth
studentsourcing antibiotic discovery

Experiment 4: Choose your own media and culture conditions

Biological Questions:

1. How can we optimize media and culture conditions to favor the growth of diverse microorganisms in your soil sample?
2. What medium and culture conditions do you choose and why?
3. How do your conditions of choice compare with your isolates' natural habitat?

Background:

Objective:

Medium of choice and rationale:

Culture condition choices:

Temperature:

Oxygen level:

Other:

Hypothesis and rationale:

Experimental design and techniques used:

Control and treatments:

Data and observations:

Interpretations and conclusions:

Notes:

Section 5: Solid Versus Liquid Cultures

Colony Morphology

Since bacteria were first cultured on solid media, microbiologists have noticed that colonies differ in color, texture, shape, and margin or edges. Works like *Bergey's Manual of Systematic Bacteriology* contain exhaustive descriptions of the physical and biochemical attributes of bacteria and have helped microbiologists identify and classify bacteria for nearly a century. **Colony morphology** is one of the first characteristics used to distinguish a particular organism from other species of bacteria. So it is important that we describe the physical characteristics of our microbes when isolated from the environment (Figure 5-1).

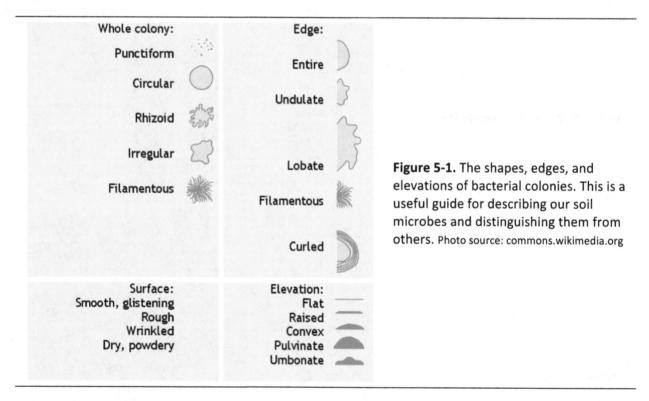

Figure 5-1. The shapes, edges, and elevations of bacterial colonies. This is a useful guide for describing our soil microbes and distinguishing them from others. Photo source: commons.wikimedia.org

Bacteria express characteristic colony morphologies. For example, *Lysobacter* and *Pseudomonas* colonies are typically slimy and irregular in shape and may fluoresce under UV light (Figure 5-2A). *Streptomyces* colonies have bold colors and develop a white fuzzy surface, which contains spores (Figure 5-2B). *Bacillus* colonies may sprawl thinly over the agar and typically show relatively dull, bland colors.

Unfortunately, in the prokaryotic world, morphology does not reliably indicate relatedness and is therefore inadequate to identify an unknown organism. Ultimately, morphology only provides us with a hint, and morphological observation is only the first step of many when attempting to identify a

bacterial isolate. To assign a family, genus, or species, we need much more information acquired through further testing. In future sections, we will explore more reliable and modern approaches to bacterial identification.

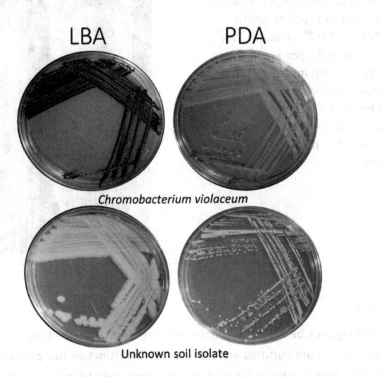

Chromobacterium violaceum

Unknown soil isolate

Figure 5-2 Bacteria display a variety of colony colors and morphologies on different media. Top: *Chromobacterium violaceum* produces smooth colonies with a dark violet metallic sheen (due to violacein production) on Luria-Bertani agar (LBA) and pale violet colonies on potato dextrose agar (PDA). Bottom: Unknown soil isolate producing non-pigmented irregular colonies on LBA and colonies with smooth margins on PDA. Photo source: Manuel Fernando Garavito Diago

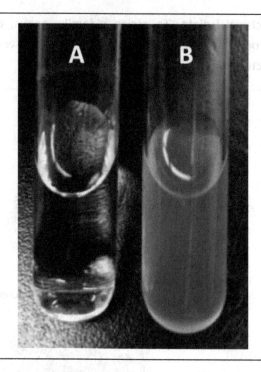

Figure 5-3 [Right]. Two test tubes each containing the bacterial growth medium 1/10th-strength Tryptic Soy Broth (TSA). (A) 1/10th-strength TSA typically looks transparent and colorless in the absence of bacterial growth. (B) Inoculating the medium with a colony of *Lysobacter antibioticus* produces a pink culture after 24–36 hours of growth at 28°C. This microorganism retains its distinctive characteristic—the pigment—in both liquid and solid culture.

Growth Phases

Solid cultures are advantageous because culturable cells proliferate where they were deposited, giving us the opportunity to isolate pure cultures and observe their distinctive morphologies. The opposite is true for liquid media. The fluid nature of liquid cultures allows cells to move randomly throughout the medium. Therefore, to effectively study bacteria in liquid culture, we typically inoculate the medium from a known pure culture, such as a single colony on a solid medium. By doing so, we are assured that the liquid culture remains a pure culture as long as appropriate aseptic technique has been practiced.

Liquid cultures are particularly suitable for studying bacterial growth, or **growth kinetics**, and biochemistry at different growth phases (Slonczewski & Foster, 2011, p. 126). Unlike a solid culture in which cells are normally in direct contact with one another and/or their substrate, cells in liquid culture are in a **planktonic,** or free-floating, state. This allows them to move throughout the medium and, if properly shaken during growth, form uniformly mixed cultures. Many bacteria require their liquid environment to be continually aerated and mixed. Therefore, liquid cultures are often grown with the assistance of shaker platforms. Caution must be exercised, however— although good for bacteria that can thrive in a planktonic state, shaking is not advisable for organisms that prefer a solid substrate. Many soil bacteria are not suited for planktonic growth and therefore when transferred from solid to liquid culture, there is a decline in the number of viable cells.

Bacterial growth can be approximated by measuring how much light of a particular wavelength (600 nm) is absorbed by a liquid culture over time. This is done with an instrument called a **spectrophotometer**, which measures absorption as **optical density units (ODs)**. As cell concentration increases, the liquid culture becomes more cloudy or turbid. As the **turbidity** of the culture increases, the OD value reported

by the spectrophotometer will also increase. The mathematical relationship between OD and cell concentration can be used to determine rates of bacterial growth over time. When OD is plotted versus incubation time, we obtain a **standard growth curve** (Figure 5-4), which is a useful model for keeping track of how a population of cells in liquid culture changes over time or predicting future behavior of the same isolate. The model shows that bacteria undergo various phases of growth in liquid culture. Growth phases are indicative of what their cells are doing physiologically and metabolically.

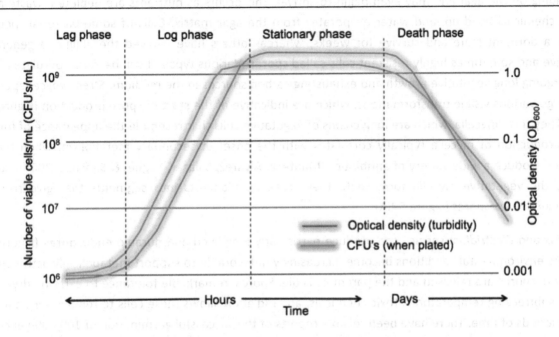

Figure 5-4. Standard bacterial growth curve and growth phases of *E. coli* in liquid culture. Graph adapted from Wessner, Dupont, & Charles (2013)

When cells are first transferred into a new medium, they will enter a period known as the **lag phase** during which very little growth occurs. During this period, the cells taking cues from the environment and making metabolic adjustments, altering patterns of gene expression to accommodate the new conditions. Once this process has completed, the cells will begin to divide rapidly. Microbiologists typically work with bacteria in the **logarithmic ("log") phase**, where cells are found reproducing exponentially. Bacteria in this phase are highly metabolically active, consuming nutrients in the medium and synthesizing macromolecules to make new cells.

Secondary metabolites, such as pigments and antibiotics, are normally produced toward the end of the log phase as cell concentration peaks and nutrients become depleted. Bacteria in the genus *Streptomyces* have been found to enter into secondary metabolism after they cease to produce essential cellular components, such as DNA (Bibb, 1996). Therefore, for this microorganism, antibiotic production occurs in a growth-phase-dependent manner, which is in turn influenced by nutrient availability in the medium. As nutrients are depleted and waste products accumulate, growth slows such that the number of cells dividing is approximately equal to those dying. This is called **stationary phase**, which can last hours to days depending on the cells' response to a lack of nutrients and an increasingly

toxic environment. Eventually, the number of dying cells surpasses the number of living and reproducing cells, and the culture enters the **death phase.**

Spores

Many markers of bacterial growth phases are also visible in solid culture. Over time, colonies stop spreading on the agar and may even begin to shrivel. This occurs as nutrients are depleted, waste and toxic chemicals build up, and water evaporates from the agar matrix. Cells of some bacterial species enter a dormant state and survive for weeks, whereas others have evolved the ability to generate inactive and sometimes highly resistant cells called **spores.** Various types of soil bacteria sporulate after undergoing long vegetative growth and exhausting carbon sources in the medium. *Streptomyces* species undergo various visible transformations, which are indicative of the start of spore production (Figure 5-2B). They form mycelia, which are long chains of vegetative cells that resemble the appearance of fungi. The production of mycelia typically correlates with the onset of secondary metabolism, when these species produce a wide variety of antibiotics (Manteca, Alvarez, Salazar, Yague, & Sanchez, 2008). Soon after, the vegetative mycelia form septa that break up filaments into segments that give rise to reproductive exospores (Figure 5-5A).

Bacillus and *Clostridium* species can produce particularly long-lived and durable **endospores** (Figure 5-5B). As environmental conditions become increasingly unfavorable to support metabolically active cells, the endospores are released and the parent cells die. Spores' remarkable tolerance to extreme dryness, heat, subfreezing temperatures, toxic chemicals, and radiation allows these cells to remain dormant for long periods of time. There have been reliable reports of the successful germination of 100,000-year-old endospores, and even (somewhat controversial) reports of 25-40 million-year-old spore germination (Nicholson et al., 2000). Avoiding contamination with long-lived endospores is the primary reason that lab supplies must be autoclaved in order to achieve sterilization. Autoclaving involves exposure to pressurized steam at 15 PSI and 121°C for a suitable period of time. (15 minutes is appropriate for small volumes.)

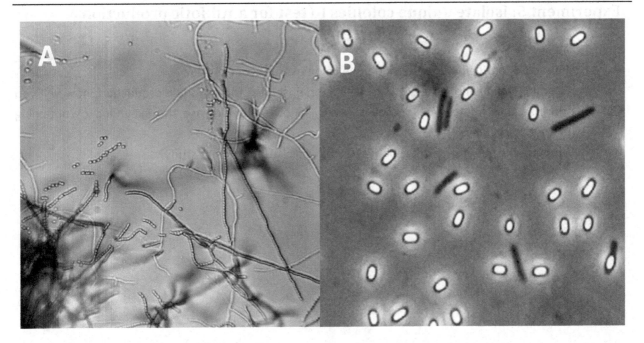

Figure 5-5. Two types of bacterial spores observed under phase contrast at 400X [left] and 1000X [right] magnification. Left: *Streptomyces* sp. mycelial filaments and long chains of exospores. Right: *Bacillus* sp. endospores appear as bright, dense structures under the microscope. Photo sources: [Left] commons.wikimedia.org (credit to CDC Public Health Image Library); [Right] commons.wikimedia.org

References

Bergey's Manual of Systematic Bacteriology (2nd ed.) 2005. New York: Springer.

Bibb, M. (1996). The regulation of antibiotic production in *Streptomyces coelicolor* A3(2). Microbiology 142:1335–1344.

Manteca, A., Alvarez, R., Salazar, N., Yague, P., & Sanchez, J. (2008). Mycelium differentiation and antibiotic production in submerged cultures of *Streptomyces coelicolor*. Appl Environ Microbiol 74:3877–3886. doi: 10.1128/AEM.02715-07.

Nicholson, W. L., Munakata, N., Horneck, G., Melosh, H. J., & Setlow, P. (2000). Resistance of Bacillus endospores to extreme terrestrial and extraterrestrial environments. Microbiol Mol Biol Rev 64:548–572.

Slonczewski, J., & Foster, J. W. (2011). *Microbiology: An Evolving Science* (2nd ed.). New York: W.W. Norton.

Wessner, D. R., Dupont, C., & Charles, T. (2013). *Microbiology* New York: Wiley Pub.

Experiment 5: Isolate unique colonies to test for antibiotic production

Biological Questions:

1. What criteria will you use to pick unique colonies from your plates?
2. Assuming you cannot test ALL of your bacterial isolates for antibiotic production, how will you prioritize the isolates you choose to study in order to increase the likelihood of obtaining antibiotic producers?
3. What are the qualities of the isolates you have picked for further study?

Background:

Objective:

Hypothesis and rationale:

Protocol:

Results:

    Number of isolates picked:

    Characteristics of isolates:

Interpretations and conclusions:

Notes:

Tiny Earth
studentsourcing antibiotic discovery

Section 6: Meet the ESKAPE Pathogens

Understanding Infectious Disease

Since ancient times, many diseases, including cholera and the bubonic plague, were attributed to miasmas, or "bad air." People believed that pests and parasites associated with plagues, decay, and spoilage could arise from inanimate, or nonliving, matter. This idea – known as **spontaneous generation** – along with the miasma theory greatly hindered preindustrial society from making the connection between microbes and disease and prevented development of effective strategies for prevention and control of disease outbreaks.

In the mid-1800s, **John Snow** helped dispel some of these misconceptions by describing the mode of transmission of cholera. He discovered the source of a particular cholera outbreak in London – a communal water pump in a dirty, densely populated neighborhood. The water source had been contaminated by sewage runoff from a house inhabited by cholera victims. The outbreak killed hundreds of people who drank water from the pump. Snow's detailed epidemiological data led to the disabling of the pump and increased awareness of water quality, public hygiene, and sanitation.

During the same time period, **Louis Pasteur**, a French chemist and microbiologist, helped disprove the theory of spontaneous generation. In an elegant experiment, he showed that sterilized broth, similar to the growth medium we use in the lab, does not spontaneously generate microorganisms from nonliving components. Instead, microbial growth originates as contamination introduced from the surrounding air. This finding was particularly important in an era when food spoilage was common, leading to great losses in disease-ridden industrial cities where food was already scarce. Pasteur realized that the key to preservation was to reduce the number of bacteria present in foods and beverages by applying heat in a process that came to be known as **pasteurization**.

Pasteur's revolutionary work supported the **germ theory of disease**, which states that microorganisms like bacteria are the cause of infectious disease. At the same time, scientists were also becoming aware that microorganisms were virtually everywhere and had useful applications as well. Yeast were shown to be responsible for the fermentation of grape juice to produce wine, and bacterial fermentation was found to convert milk to yogurt.

Work by the German physician **Robert Koch** provided the means to identify **pathogens**, or disease-causing microorganisms. While performing experiments to identify the agents responsible for tuberculosis and anthrax, Koch established a series of criteria, or "postulates," that could be applied to identify pathogens responsible for other infectious diseases as well:

1. The microbe is always present in diseased individuals but not healthy individuals.
2. The microbe is isolated from the infected individual and grown in a pure culture.
3. When the microbe in pure culture is introduced into a healthy individual, the same disease symptoms occur.
4. The microbe reisolated in pure culture from the diseased individual has the same characteristics as the original.

This process might seem second nature to us today, but in the late 1800s, it was revolutionary. Koch successfully identified *Bacillus anthracis* and *Mycobacterium tuberculosis* as the causative agents of anthrax and tuberculosis, respectively, and was awarded the Nobel Prize in Physiology or Medicine in 1905. Koch's simple and logical criteria continue to help modern clinical microbiologists identify pathogens. Today, the link between microbes and disease is well understood; this knowledge has enabled development of effective measures to prevent and treat infectious disease around the world. Nevertheless, humanity remains at risk from diseases caused by microorganisms.

Pathogens that were once believed to have been conquered during the golden age of antibiotics (see Section 7) are now reemerging in drug-resistant forms, and they are doing so at an accelerating rate. Consequently, we are effectively running out of treatment options. Hospitals have become havens for multi-drug resistant "superbugs," and the widespread misuse of antibiotics in households and in agricultural practices around the world means that drug-resistant pathogens are emerging as a threat in our homes and environment. The process by which pathogens acquire resistance is only partially understood and is an important area of ongoing research (see Section 10), but the trends we see today point to a grim future if we do not find effective solutions based on drug deployment, hygiene, or other practices.

Choosing Test Organisms

*   *Since antibiotics do not affect all bacteria equally, how will you decide which organism to test your soil microbe against?*

As we isolate individual microbes, we hope that some will produce antibiotics at detectable levels. Initially, for practical reasons, researchers assay these microbes for the ability to inhibit the growth of only a single or small number of test organisms. Microbes that show activity may later be screened against a broader panel of test organisms.

*   *Does the ability to inhibit the growth of one test organism indicate that the antibiotic will inhibit all bacteria?*

Because prokaryotes differ in their anatomical and physiological traits, different organisms may be more or less susceptible to the effects of any particular antibiotic. Some antibiotics are **broad spectrum**, meaning that they affect a wide range of bacteria. Other antibiotics have a **narrow spectrum** of activity. One anatomical feature that plays a significant role in the susceptibility of a microbe to a particular antibiotic is its cell wall composition (discussed in Section 8).

- *How can we detect production of antibiotics? How do we distinguish the producers from the nonproducers?*

In Section 7, we will conduct experiments to screen our isolates for their ability to produce antibiotics. But first, we must decide which microbe to test our isolates against.

The ESKAPE Pathogens

When choosing a test organism, a logical choice is an organism that is clinically relevant – i.e., a human pathogen. There are six organisms that are today considered to be major threats, not because they cause the most devastating illnesses but because they comprise the majority of antibiotic-resistant infections seen in health care settings. They are *Enterococcus faecium*, *Staphylococcus aureus*, *Klebsiella pneumoniae*, *Acinetobacter baumannii*, *Pseudomonas aeruginosa*, and several species of *Enterobacter* (**ESKAPE**).

The leading author of a 2009 report on Clinical Infectious Diseases, Helen Boucher, MD, stated:

> *These [ESKAPE pathogens] are among the biggest threats infectious disease physicians face today… We desperately need new drugs to fight them. But we also need cooperation among industry, academia, and government to create a sustainable R&D [research and development] infrastructure that will fill the pipeline to meet today's needs and keep it filled with drugs that tackle tomorrow's infectious diseases threats.*

ESKAPE Pathogen	Safe Relative
Enterococcus faecium	*Enterococcus raffinosus*
Staphylococcus aureus	*Staphylococcus epidermidis*
Klebsiella pneumoniae	*Escherichia coli*
Acinetobacter baumannii	*Acinetobacter baylyi*
Pseudomonas aeruginosa	*Pseudomonas putida*
Enterobacter species	*Enterobacter aerogenes*

Table 6-1. The ESKAPE pathogens and their safe relatives, used as tester organisms by **Tiny Earth**

Although it would be ideal to test the ability of our isolates to inhibit the growth of all or at least a subset of these organisms, it is not possible to do so in a teaching laboratory due to their potential to cause human disease. However, we can take advantage of evolution and test our isolates against closely related organisms that do not pose a health risk. These "safe relatives" have many of the same anatomical and physiological features as their respective ESKAPE counterparts, yet they are safe enough to be studied in teaching laboratories as long as basic biosafety protocols are followed. In addition to

Tiny Earth
studentsourcing antibiotic discovery

the six safe relatives listed above, students often test their soil isolates against *Mycobacterium smegmatis,* which is a safe relative of the causal agent of tuberculosis, *Mycobacterium tuberculosis.*

Not All Bacteria Are Harmful

Although pathogenic bacteria get most of the attention (for good reason), it's important to recognize that humans are constantly associated with bacteria in our bodies, in the foods we eat, and in the environment. If you were to examine every cell in and on your body, you would find that the majority of them are not actually human! <u>The members of the **human microbiome**, the microbes that reside in and on our bodies, outnumber our own cells 2:1 (Sender et al., 2016)</u>. Research has shown that our cells are "constantly bathed" in bacterial metabolites (Slonczewski & Foster, 2011). Therefore, there can be no doubt that microbes intimately and substantially influence our lives and our health.

The human gut, which houses 100 billion bacteria per cm^3, teems with bacterial activity that is responsible for 15–20 percent of our caloric intake (Slonczewski & Foster, 2011, p. 868). This **consortium** of microorganisms is composed of organisms such as *Bacteroides, Clostridium,* and *Escherichia* species, among many others. Disruption of the gut microbiota can cause many different metabolic and physiological disorders.

Various Gram-positive bacteria, such as *Staphylococcus* and *Bacillus,* colonize our skin and are also part of the normal human microbiome. They are not simply passive bystanders, but are an important part of our first-defenses against infection and are active inducers of proper immune function. In an experiment by Belkaid et al., mice with *Staphylococcus epidermidis* on their skin were found to have a better immune response than germ-free mice (Naik et al., 2012).

Probiotics, microbes that are consumed to improve health, are found in many fermented products, including yogurt. Pharmacologist John Cryan carried out experiments to test the neurological effects of administering doses of probiotics to mice. He found that certain probiotics had impressive effects on mouse stress and anxiety levels. Mice treated with probiotics were more willing to walk out into the open and take action to protect themselves from a perceived threat of drowning, behaviors suggestive of "happy" mice with lower anxiety levels (Bravo et al., 2011). Other research has suggested that residents of the mammalian gastrointestinal tract influence asthma, autism, colitis, cancer, obesity, and diabetes. These findings are revolutionizing the way we think about microbes and could have exciting applications in humans.

Biotechnology is the application of organisms and their products to address human needs. We have used yeast and bacteria to ferment foods and beverages and improve crop health for millennia. Bacterial products are now found in household items and cosmetics and used in medical procedures. We use bacterial lipases and proteases as detergent additives and toxins like the botulinum toxin (known commercially as Botox) to reduce wrinkles and treat certain diseases. Furthermore, we use microbes as basic tools in bioengineering and chemical manufacturing. Human genes cloned into bacteria and yeast serve as pharmaceutical factories that produce valuable proteins, such as insulin (Slonczewski & Foster, 2011, p. 35). Bacteria can be used to break down pollutants and detoxify contaminated environments, a

process known as bioremediation. In 2010, in the Gulf of Mexico, hydrocarbon-consuming microbes helped to degrade much of the Deepwater Horizon oil spill (Biello, 2010). Microbes can even help recycle elements trapped in landfill garbage and return them to the biosphere.

While a subset of microbes are pathogenic to humans, animals, or plants, the benefit we realize from the vast majority of microbes seems almost endless. In the following sections, we will learn about microbial compounds with pharmaceutical activity and the roles they may play in Nature.

References

Biello, D. (2010) Meet the microbes eating the gulf oil spill. Scientific American August 18, 2010. <http://www.scientificamerican.com/article.cfm?id=gulf-oil-eating-microbes-slide-show>

Boucher, H. W., Talbot, G. H., Bradley, J. S., Edwards, J. E., Gilbert, D., Rice, L. B., Scheld, M., Spellberg, B., & Bartlett, J. (2009) Bad bugs, no drugs: no ESKAPE! An update from the Infectious Diseases Society of America. Clin Infect Dis 48:1–12.

Bravo, J. A., Forsythe, P., Chew, M. V., Escaravage, E., Savignac, H. M., Dinan, T. G., Bienenstock, J., & Cryan, J. F. (2011) Ingestion of *Lactobacillus* strain regulates emotional behavior and central GABA receptor expression in a mouse via the vagus nerve. Proc Natl Acad Sci U S A 108:16050–16055. doi: 10.1073/pnas.1102999108.

Naik, S., Bouladoux, N., Wilhelm, C., Molloy, M. J., Salcedo, R., Kastenmuller, W., Deming, C., Quinones, M., Koo, L., Conlan, S., Spencer, S., Hall, J. A., Dzutsey, A., Kong, H., Campbell, D. J., Trinchieri, G., & Segre, J. A., Belkaid, Y. (2012) Compartmentalized control of skin immunity by resident commensals. Science 337:1115–1119. doi: 10.1126/science.1225152

Sender, R., Fuchs, S., Milo, R. (2016) Revised estimates for the number of human and bacteria cells in the body. PLoS Biol 14(8): e1002533. https://doi.org/10.1371/journal.pbio.1002533

Slonczewski, J., & Foster, J. W. (2011) *Microbiology: An Evolving Science* (2nd ed.). New York: W.W. Norton.

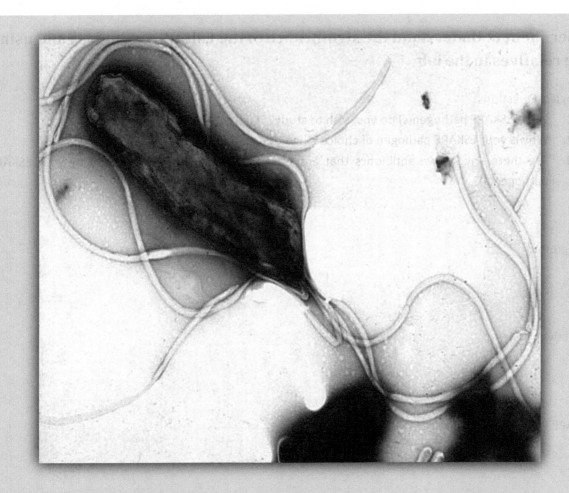

Figure 6-1. This electron micrograph shows *Helicobacter pylori*, a resident of the stomach, with multiple flagella that the bacterium uses to move in the mucous layer of the stomach lining. Photo source: commons.wikimedia.org

Milestones in Microbiology

The Australian scientist Barry Marshall discovered that peptic ulcers and gastritis are caused by bacteria living in the stomach, which was generally believed to be too acidic for bacteria to survive. His inability to isolate and culture the bacterium, *Helicobacter pylori*, damaged his credibility in the scientific community and sustained commonly held myths about the stomach and ulcers. In a courageous effort to validate his findings, Marshall drank a culture of the infectious bacterium and developed symptoms of gastritis after a few days. An endoscopy and biopsy demonstrated that the bacterium was in fact present on the stomach lining, which was inflamed. After antibiotic treatment, the symptoms subsided, providing compelling evidence that the *H. pylori* was, in fact, the cause of ulcers. Marshall conducted the experiment in the 1980s and received the 2005 Nobel Prize for his work, which revolutionized views about the extreme conditions in which bacteria can grow, the assumption that all bacteria can be cultured, and the standard treatment for ulcers.

Experiment 6: Understand the significance of the ESKAPE pathogens and using safe relatives in the lab

Biological Questions:
1. What ESKAPE pathogen(s) do you wish to study?
2. Why is your ESKAPE pathogen of choice a health concern?
3. Are there any known antibiotics that are used to treat an infection caused by your ESKAPE pathogen(s)?

Background:

Objective:

ESKAPE Pathogen(s) of Choice:

Reasons for Choosing ESKAPE Pathogen:

General Cellular and Morphological Characteristics of the Organism:

Clinical Importance and Prevalence:

Infection (How does the infection occur and where is it localized?):

Pathology (What disease is caused? What are the symptoms?):

Ineffective Antibiotics (Antibiotics to which the organism has acquired resistance):

Effective Antibiotics (Antibiotics known to inhibit the organism):

Corresponding Safe Relative:

Notes:

Section 7: Antibiotic Discovery, Structure, & Targets

The Father of Antibiotics

Alexander Fleming is famous as the "accidental" discoverer of **penicillin** – the first antibiotic, which revolutionized the world of medicine. But how "accidental" was his discovery really? Was Fleming really the first to observe this type of amazing microbial activity? In reality, this bacteriologist made his discovery because he already knew what he was looking for. Years of practice in his field had provided him with keen skills of observation and inquiry, enabling him to turn a small observation into a find with monumental implications.

Throughout the 1800s, highly corrosive **antiseptics** were being used to treat severe infections, especially those suffered by soldiers wounded in wars. These antiseptics were damaging to human tissue as well as to the human immune system. Most casualties of war actually resulted from the infections and treatments given after the battles. This situation was referred to by scientists and medical professionals as the **antiseptic dilemma**.

During the early 1900s, Fleming began his quest for an alternative to antiseptics – a chemical that could selectively kill bacteria without harming host cells. This idea resonated with Paul Ehrlich's **magic bullet** hypothesis, which stated that if certain chemicals, such as dyes, could selectively bind to specific bacteria, then there should be compounds that selectively inhibit growth as well. Ehrlich went on to develop the first human-made antimicrobial, salvarsan, in 1909. Salvarsan was effective in syphilis treatment but was later found to be too toxic for human use (Amyes, 2001), making it a great example of the antiseptic dilemma.

It was not until 1928 that Fleming came across his rather famous messy stack of plates awaiting disposal. As Fleming examined the plates, he noticed that one was contaminated. Moldy plates were not uncommon in the lab; however, there was something unique about this plate: *Staphylococcus* cells were not growing along the perimeter of the mold, forming a **zone of inhibition** (Fleming, 2001)! Fleming was intrigued by this observation and eventually showed that the zone of inhibition was caused by a compound that he named penicillin after the fungus that produces it, *Penicillium notatum*.

Characteristics of antibiotics:

- Therapeutic agents
- Selectively toxic toward microbes
- Generally antibacterial
- Small molecules (secondary metabolites)
- Originally referred to compounds produced by microorganisms, but today the term is used also for synthetic antimicrobials

---

To test the effectiveness of penicillin, Fleming performed various activity assays against common pathogens. Penicillin inhibited the growth of Gram-positive bacteria associated with scarlet fever, pneumonia, gonorrhea, meningitis, and strep throat, while leaving eukaryotic cells unharmed (Brown, 2005). It exhibited the qualities of the miracle drug Fleming had been pursuing for years. However, he was unable to purify the compound in an active and stable form, making it impossible to test *in vivo*. He could not test penicillin on humans at concentrations that would reach and have impact at the site of infection without exposing test subjects to extraneous compounds also present in the mold culture.

Work on penicillin lay dormant for ten years until pharmacologist Howard Florey and biochemist Ernst Chain came across Fleming's paper. Their combined knowledge of chemistry allowed them to purify the active compound and test it on infectious bacteria *in vivo*, proving its therapeutic ability in humans (Amyes, 2001). Their work, coupled with the extraordinarily high-producing strain discovered by Mary Hunt and Kenneth Raper, enabled penicillin to be mass produced and administered to patients orally. Penicillin was commercialized in time to reach wounded soldiers on the battlefields of World War II and significantly contributed to the Allied victory and making World War II the first war in America's history in which more soldiers died of the direct effects of bullets and bombs than of infections. The collaborative development of the first natural product antibiotic won Fleming, Florey, and Chain the Nobel Prize in Physiology or Medicine in 1945.

Tiny Earth
studentsourcing antibiotic discovery

From a Spoiled Cantaloupe in Peoria ...
the test of 100,000 strains of Penicillium

Milestones in Microbiology

The development of penicillin led to a worldwide search for a strain of the *Penicillium* mold that would produce copious amounts of the antibiotic and grow in liquid culture. Mary Hunt (popularly known as Moldy Mary), a technician at the USDA lab in Peoria, Illinois run by Dr. Kenneth Raper, scoured produce in local markets in search of the strain and came across a cantaloupe carrying a mold that produced the highest concentrations of penicillin ever observed in a strain of *Penicillium*. The strain was improved and grown in deep-vat, submerged conditions, enabling the antibiotic to be mass-produced and sent to the battlefront of World War II.

Photo source: http://www.peoriahistoricalsociety.org/!/Exhibits-PenicillinMoldyMary

Tiny Earth
studentsourcing antibiotic discovery

Milestones in Microbiology

It is worth noting that Fleming was not the first one to make these observations. Texts from Ancient Egypt describe the use of moldy bread to treat pustular eruptions on the scalp (Böttcher, 1959), while the Bible mentions the curative value of hyssop. It was on this plant (photo above) that the Swedish naturalist Westling found *Penicillium notatum* thousands of years later (Brown, 2005). Although Fleming himself coined the term "penicillin," an inscription on a therapeutic ointment with the word "PENICILLE," found in an Ancient Roman site, perplexed archeologists many years later after this drug became a common household name (Böttcher). Yet, through all these years, people had exploited these molds for their curative value without understanding the chemistry and biology underpinning the effects. Many scientists attempted to uncover its inhibitory properties in the 1800s after Louis Pasteur discovered the role of bacteria in infection. Joseph Lister noticed that the *Penicillium* mold inhibited the reproduction of bacteria ten years before Fleming was born and, ten years after, another scientist attributed this inhibition to "the secretion of a specific substance," with no further clarification as to what was secreting it or what the substance was. French scientist Ernest Duchesne even injected the culture broth into mice infected with typhoid, and they were cured soon after. Nevertheless, none of these scientists identified the chemical or pursued the research to a solid conclusion.

This story is quite revealing about the importance of record keeping, serendipity, and persistence in discovery!

Photo source: commons.wikimedia.org

Antibiotic Structure

Penicillin was special due to its ability to kill bacteria without the toxic side effects of antiseptics, which lacked selectivity and harmed human and bacterial cells alike. In 1942, Selman Waksman coined the term "antibiotic" to describe any small molecule produced by a microbe that kills or inhibits the growth of other microbes (Clardy, Fischbach, & Currie, 2009). "Small molecules" refers to the fact that antibiotics are smaller than the macromolecules that constitute a cell. Antibiotics vary in their structures (Figure 7-1), falling into several chemical groups, or **classes**, of antibiotics. Entirely new classes of antibiotics are even more challenging to discover than new antibiotics themselves. A common class of antibiotic is the β-lactams, which share a four-member ring structure, which is the core of β-lactams like penicillin, that enables them to inhibit bacterial cell wall synthesis (more on targets below) (Figure 7-1). One of the most recent classes of antibiotics was discovered in 2004, nearly 300 meters below the surface in the Sea of Japan. The antibiotic class was aptly named "abyssomicins" after the abyss of the deep ocean. These are polycyclic antibiotics produced by marine bacteria in the genus *Verrucosispora*. Abyssomicin C inhibits the growth of vancomycin- and methicillin-resistant strains of *Staphylococcus aureus* by blocking their ability to produce folic acid (Nicolaou, Harrison, & Chen, 2009).

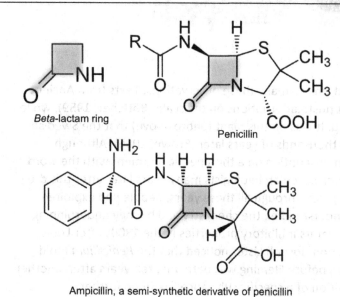

Beta-lactam ring

Penicillin

Ampicillin, a semi-synthetic derivative of penicillin

Figure 7-1. Members of the β-lactam class of antibiotics, such as penicillin and ampicillin, all share a common core structure: a four-member β-lactam ring. This structure makes β-lactam antibiotics able to inhibit bacterial cell wall synthesis.

Strictly speaking, true antibiotics are antimicrobial compounds produced by microorganisms. This category of antimicrobials includes common drugs, such as penicillin, streptomycin, and chloramphenicol, which were originally isolated from living microorganisms. Microbial products make up 60-80% of all antimicrobials; the rest are generally synthetically derived from known chemical scaffolds and developed by chemists. Today, "antibiotic" is used to refer to compounds produced by both microbes and human chemists.

Tiny Earth
studentsourcing antibiotic discovery

Antibiotic Biosynthesis

Bacteria in the genus *Streptomyces* are the most prolific antibiotic **producers** known, as they produce 60% of all antibiotics in clinical use today. Members of this genus illustrate the virtuosic biosynthetic abilities of bacteria that have changed the course of human history. They are also a perfect example of the potential for future drug discovery from bacteria. Genome sequencing has revealed that many *Streptomyces* species contain dozens of "silent" pathways for antibiotic biosynthesis (Omura et al., 2001). These silent pathways comprise genes that are not expressed under lab conditions. By analyzing the sequences of silent pathways, scientists have been able to predict the compound they would produce if expressed. Many researchers are now trying to unlock these pathways to enable the carriers of these gene clusters to produce novel antibiotics. Some estimates suggest that humans have only discovered 0.1-10% of the natural products of bacteria, which is why **Tiny Earth** is so exciting—this is the treasure trove we aim to discover!

Antibiotic structures and modes of synthesis are linked in interesting ways. Unlike many proteins, which are translated from messenger RNA to produce the final product, antibiotics are not directly encoded in DNA. Antibiotics are produced by complex **biosynthesis pathways**, stepwise chemical reactions catalyzed by enzymes within the cell. They may result from enzyme-catalyzed assembly and modification of amino acids, fatty acids, and sugars. For example, penicillin, a β-lactam antibiotic, is the product of three amino acids – cysteine, valine, and an amino acid intermediate: α-aminoadipate (Figure 7-2) (Clardy et al., 2009). Additionally, some of the enzymes involved in tetracycline (a polyketide antibiotic) and streptomycin (an aminoglycoside) biosynthesis are related to enzymes involved in fatty acid and polysaccharide synthesis, respectively (Clardy et al., 2009; Walsh, 2004). The degree to which these organic substituents are assembled and modified to form an antibiotic helps us group them based on shared chemical characteristics.

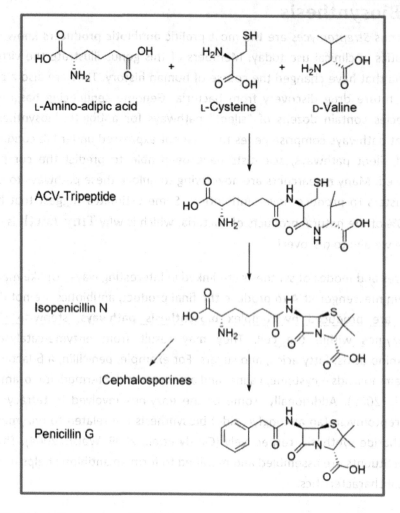

Figure 7-2. Penicillin biosynthesis. Penicillin is the product of three amino acids modified and assembled in an enzyme-catalyzed reaction. Photo source: commons.wikipedia.org

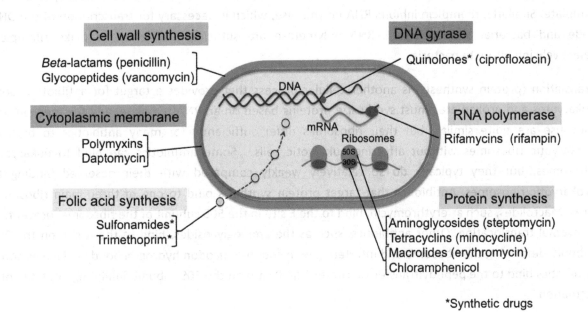

Figure 7-3. Examples of antibiotic cellular targets (modes of action).

Why Antibiotics Kill Bacteria (and not us)

Antibiotics with the same cellular or molecular target are also typically subdivided by their **mechanism or mode of action**. This refers to the specific biochemical interaction that allows the antibiotic to have an inhibitory effect. The fact that antibiotics are selectively toxic to bacteria implies that either they selectively enter bacterial cells or do not recognize a molecular target in eukaryotic cells.

One cellular component unique to bacteria is the cell wall, which is composed of a polysaccharide-peptide (a macromolecule containing amino acids and a complex sugar) called **peptidoglycan**. This tough material protects bacteria from forces in the environment, such as changes in osmotic potential and mechanical force. The wall provides bacteria with structural support and gives them their characteristic shapes. **Gram-positive** bacteria have a thick peptidoglycan layer exposed to the environment, whereas **Gram-negative** bacteria have only a thin layer of peptidoglycan positioned between the cytoplasmic membrane and the outer membrane, which is composed of phospholipids and lipopolysaccharides. Some common antibiotics, such as penicillin and vancomycin, inhibit cell wall synthesis by blocking the enzymes responsible for forming the peptide cross-links between peptidoglycan subunits. Bacterial growth requires constant maintenance and remodeling of the cell wall. When antibiotics interfere with cell wall maintenance, the growing cells will eventually burst (or lyse).

DNA metabolism has properties unique to bacteria. The enzyme DNA gyrase has a similar structure in prokaryotes and eukaryotes, but antibiotics like ciprofloxacin take advantage of small differences in affinity to molecules. DNA gyrase aids in DNA replication by keeping the DNA molecule from

overwinding and forming supercoils that block the DNA replication machinery from moving across the template. Similarly, rifampicin inhibits RNA polymerase, which is necessary for transcription of the DNA code and bacterial and eukaryotic RNA polymerase are sufficiently different to make rifampicin selectively inhibitory to bacteria.

Translation (protein synthesis) is another cellular process that provides a target for antibiotics. Both eukaryotes and prokaryotes must synthesize proteins based on an RNA template, and the mechanisms they use are quite similar, but their ribosomes differ sufficiently for many antibiotics to bind to prokaryotic ribosomes without affecting eukaryotic cells. Some antibiotics can bind to eukaryotic ribosomes, but they typically do so relatively weakly compared with their observed binding to prokaryotic ribosomes. Antibiotics that target protein synthesis bind to one of three main ribosomal sites. Macrolides, such as erythromycin, bind to the E site in the 50S subunit of the ribosome, preventing ribosomal translocation. Other antibiotics, such as the aminoglycosides, bind to the A site on the 30S subunit, deforming the ribosome and interfering with codon-anticodon hydrogen bonding. Finally, some antibiotics bind to the peptidyltransferase center (the P site) on the 50S subunit, inhibiting peptide bond formation.

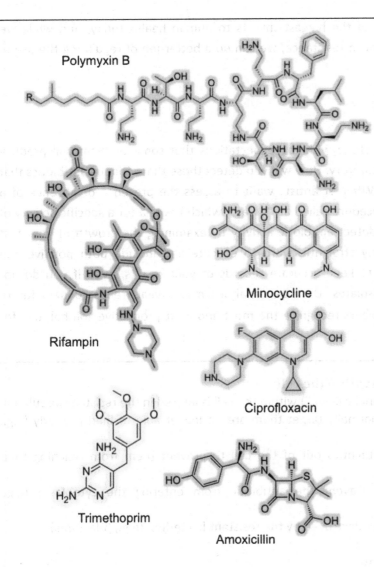

Polymyxin B

Rifampin

Minocycline

Ciprofloxacin

Trimethoprim

Amoxicillin

Figure 7-4. Structures of common antibiotics that target various cellular and molecular components. The colors highlighting the chemical structures match the coloring scheme used in Figure 7-3. Red = cytoplasmic membrane, purple = RNA polymerase, yellow = folic acid synthesis, green = protein synthesis, magenta = DNA gyrase, and blue = cell wall synthesis.

Antibiotic Resistance

Antibiotics are effective because they exploit the cellular and molecular differences between bacteria and eukaryotes, targeting necessary functions in bacterial cells, but many bacteria have evolved mechanisms to resist the effects of these compounds. There are two broad mechanisms by which bacteria can acquire resistance to an antibiotic:

1. Bacteria may acquire resistance through a random mutation in a normal gene, or
2. Bacteria may acquire a preexisting resistance gene from another bacterium, most commonly through conjugation.

TinyEarth
studentsourcing antibiotic discovery

73

The rise of antibiotic resistance is one of the biggest threats to human health today, and while we cannot entirely prevent the development of resistance, we can do a better job of regulating the use of antibiotics while developing new drugs.

Antibiotic Production Assay

You have isolated a diversity of soil bacteria with the expectations that some of them will produce antibiotics at detectable levels in the laboratory. How will you detect those that produce antibiotics that inhibit growth of your test organism? When scientists want to assess the presence or absence of a particular component, they design a procedure called an "assay," which is a test for a specific activity of interest. You will conduct an assay to detect antibiotic activity by examining the growth of your test organism. The best assays are relatively straightforward to execute and include both positive and negative controls. It is also important to keep accurate records of your results, even if you do not observe antibiotic activity from your isolates. Database analyses may reveal trends to help future generations of **Tiny Earth** team members recognize the most and least productive soil habitats for antibiotic discovery.

Mechanisms of antibiotic resistance within the cell:
1. Molecular target (e.g., the bacterial cell wall) within the cell is altered in the resistant population so that antibiotics that would normally target them are no longer able to bind properly (e.g., vancomycin).
2. Resistant bacteria transport antibiotics out of the cell to prevent them from reaching their targets (e.g., tetracyclines).
3. The resistant bacterium may prevent the antibiotic from entering the cytoplasm (e.g., lantibiotics).
4. The antibiotic may be modified or destroyed by the resistant bacterium (e.g., β-lactams).

More on antibiotic resistance in Section 10.

References

Amyes, S. G. B. (2001) *Magic Bullets, Lost Horizons: The Rise and Fall of Antibiotics*. New York: Taylor & Francis.

Böttcher, H. H. (1959) *Miracle Drugs*. London: Heinemann.

Brown, K. (2005) *Penicillin Man: Alexander Fleming and the Antibiotic Revolution*. Stroud, Gloucestershire: Sutton.

Clardy, J., Fischbach, M. A., & Currie, C. R. (2009) The natural history of antibiotics. Curr Biol 19:R437–R441. doi: 10.1016/j.cub.2009.04.001.

Nicolaou, K. C., Harrison, S. T., & Chen, J. S. (2009) Discoveries from the abyss: The abyssomicins and their total synthesis. Synthesis (Stuttg) 2009:33–42. doi: 10.1055/s-0028-1083259

TinyEarth
studentsourcing antibiotic discovery

Omura, S., Ikeda, H., Ishikawa, J., Hanamoto, A., Takahashi, C., Shinose, M., Takahashi, Y., Horikawa, H., Nakazawa, H., Osonoe, T., Kikuchi, H., Shiba, T., Sakaki, Y., & Hattori, M. (2001) Genome sequence of an industrial microorganism *Streptomyces avermitilis*: Deducing the ability of producing secondary metabolites. Proc Natl Acad Sci U S A 98:12215–12220. doi: 10.1073/pnas.211433198

Walsh, C. T. (2004) Polyketide and nonribosomal peptide antibiotics: Modularity and versatility. Science 303:1805–1810. doi: 10.1126/science.1094318

Other sources:

Butler, M. S., & Buss, A. D. (2006). Natural products — the future scaffolds for novel antibiotics? Biochem Pharmacol 71:919–929. doi: http://dx.doi.org/10.1016/j.bcp.2005.10.012

D'Costa, V. M., Griffiths, E., & Wright, G. D. (2007) Expanding the soil antibiotic resistome: Exploring environmental diversity. Curr Opin Microbiol 10:481-489. doi:10.1016/j.mib.2007.08.009

Harvey, A. (2000). Strategies for discovering drugs from previously unexplored natural products. Drug Discov Today 5:294–300.

Linares, J. F., Gustafsson, I., Baquero, F., & Martinez, J. L. (2006) Antibiotics as intermicrobial signaling agents instead of weapons. Proc Natl Acad Sci U S A 103:19484–19489. doi: 10.1073/pnas.0608949103

Watve, M. G., Tickoo, R., Jog, M. M., & Bhole, B. D. (2001) How many antibiotics are produced by the genus *Streptomyces*? Arch Microbiol 176:386–390. doi: 10.1007/s002030100345

Experiment 7: Design a method to screen for antibiotic producers

Biological Questions:

1. How will you determine whether your soil isolates produce antibiotics?
2. What positive and negative controls will you use in your assays?
3. What factors influence antibiotic production in a microorganism?
4. Can we increase the antibiotic yield of our isolates?

Background:

Objective:

Hypothesis and rationale:

Experimental design and protocols used:

Controls and treatments:

Data and observations:

Interpretations and conclusions:

Notes:

Tiny Earth
studentsourcing antibiotic discovery

Assignment: Calculating Frequency of Antibiotic Producers

Objective:

Tester organism:

Tester organism media:

Results:

Culture Media	Number of patches tested	Isolates producing antibiotics (number)	Isolates producing antibiotics (%)
	Total:	Total:	

Calculations:

Comments:

Notes:

Section 8: Getting to Know Your Isolates

As we experience the thrill of isolating microbes that produce antibiotic compounds, it is an appropriate time to reflect on our accomplishments thus far and to consider the future direction of our research. Starting with soil samples containing a high density of bacteria, we have isolated microbes capable of inhibiting bacteria related to known pathogens. Furthermore, we have demonstrated that the antibiotic producers are capable of growing in isolation (away from the community of microbes inhabiting the soil) and under laboratory conditions – important traits required for mass production of an antibiotic. But what's next?

We must emphasize that it is a long journey from initial discovery to mass market. There are many criteria that must be met for a new antibiotic to be successful commercially. A few important considerations for clinically useful antibiotics include: Vast amounts of compound are required; toxicity to humans must be minimal at an effective treatment dose; and compounds that remain active after oral ingestion (i.e., in pill form) are more desirable than compounds requiring intravenous administration. A first step in addressing these issues requires isolation of the active compound in pure form. We learned from Fleming's work that this can be a challenge. Separation of the active compound from all of the other compounds produced by the organism requires expensive equipment and often takes months or years of work for even experienced chemists. For this reason, scientists place high value on steps that help to identify, early on, whether the active compound is likely to be new or is a previously identified molecule. We will discuss the purification and structural identification process in Section 9 and Future Directions.

Concurrent with chemical purification and characterization, another approach that lends insight into the potential identity of the unknown molecule is characterization of the producing microbe. For example, *Acremonium chrysogenum* is known to produce cephalosporin C (a β-lactam). If an active soil isolate can be classified as *Acremonium* or a close relative, a priority would be to determine whether the active compound exhibits chemical properties of the cephalosporins. If the antibiotic-producing isolate is a species or genus not shown previously to produce antibiotics, it is of greater interest because the antibiotic has a greater likelihood of being new.

Classifying Microbes

Taxonomy is the field of biology concerned with naming and organizing living organisms into meaningful groups based on similar characteristics. Groups with shared physical features often (but not always) share an evolutionary history. Historically, scientists classified microbes by observing morphological features under the microscope and through biochemical (metabolic) assays that determine the presence of specific enzymes. In the late 20th century, the development of technologies for comparing DNA sequences provided biologists with an approach to classification that also indicates evolutionary

relationships and thus gained widespread appeal. Nucleotide sequence similarity provides a way to assess evolutionary relatedness. After all, mutations (heritable changes in the DNA sequence) are the underlying molecular basis for Darwin's "descent with modification." Although whole-genome comparisons are now possible, a bacterial genome may consist of several million base pairs—far too many for quick, routine comparisons. For this reason, scientists typically compare sequences of established "marker genes," those that are present in all microbes and for which function has been conserved. By far, the most commonly used marker gene encodes a small ribosomal subunit (SSU) RNA, the 16S rRNA gene (18S rRNA gene in eukaryotes). 16S rRNA gene comparisons are performed routinely today, but they still do not entirely replace morphological and biochemical analysis. It is important to remember that the strongest taxonomic identifications involve a wide range of techniques, so the results from one method can validate another method. We discuss morphological and molecular taxonomic classification methods in this section and biochemical classification in Section 11.

Molecular Phylogeny

The 16S rRNA gene was first proposed as a tool for comparing microbes by Carl Woese and George Fox in 1977 (Woese and Fox, 1977). At that time, classification of multicellular organisms relied on readily observable morphological features, a system that is not easily applied to microbes because they have far fewer distinguishing anatomical features than biochemical properties. Woese was also interested in evolutionary relationships. Frustrated by the challenges in determining evolutionary relationships among organisms with unimpressive fossil records with few distinguishing visible differences, Woese and Fox searched for a new metric. The idea of using DNA sequences was revolutionary. One feature that makes DNA sequence comparison so valuable is that all living creatures use DNA as their heritable material. Furthermore, all organisms share homologous versions of the SSU genes and these genes evolve very slowly, producing a steady and measurable evolutionary record. For the first time, scientists had a single marker with which to compare the relationships among all living creatures. This resulted in a dramatic rearrangement of what we call the universal tree of life. Comparing 16S and 18S rRNA gene sequences revealed that life is organized in three domains—Archaea, Bacteria, and Eukarya. The discovery that Archaea, although morphologically similar to Bacteria, were as different from Bacteria as are Eukaryotes, along with the prevalence and diversity of microbes revealed by molecular phylogeny, stunned the scientific world. It's sobering to note that all of the Bacteria and Archaea and most of the Eukaryotes (the exceptions are plants, animals, and fungi) are microscopic. We truly live on a microbial planet.

Phylogenetic trees are hypotheses regarding the evolutionary relationships between taxonomic groups; some trees are constructed using SSU sequence data only while others take all available data into consideration. For this reason, trees for the same taxonomic groups may differ (although usually only slightly) depending on the criteria used for constructing the tree. The universal tree of life is based on what we call **molecular phylogeny**, meaning that the relationships presented are based on comparison of molecular features, usually DNA sequence, rather than morphological traits. Increasingly, DNA sequences are used in the construction of trees, but morphological data can still contribute to the complete puzzle when making predictions about evolutionary relationships.

Other genes can serve as markers for comparison, but the 16S rRNA gene remains the gold standard for initial classification. There are many features that make the SSU gene a good yardstick, including its effectively universal presence and convenient size of about 1500 nucleotides; however, its most important advantage over other similar genes is that it contains regions of relatively high variability interspersed among other highly conserved regions. Comparison of the hypervariable regions is useful for identification since these regions typically contain nucleotide sequences that are unique to a particular species.

Phylogenetic Tree of Life

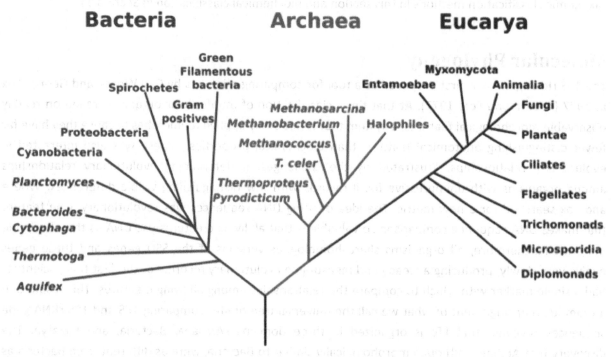

Figure 8-1. The universal tree of life. Photo source: commons.wikimedia.org

Therefore, while SSU sequence comparisons were initially used to create phylogenetic trees for understanding the evolutionary history of life, 16S rRNA gene analysis is now routinely used to develop preliminary hypotheses about the identity of unknown bacterial isolates. This is possible because of the vast collection of known 16S rRNA gene sequences in a publicly available database called GenBank. Search algorithms, such as BLAST, compare an input sequence to millions of known sequences in the database. Once closely matching sequences are found in the database, we can make a preliminary assumption that the unknown falls within the same taxonomic group as the known organisms with highly similar sequences (assuming that the highly similar sequences were themselves reliably identified). More definitive taxonomic assignment can be obtained from observing multiple molecular markers and morphological traits. We will use 16S rRNA gene sequence analysis to make a preliminary

identification of our unknown organisms and to make predictions about whether their active molecules are novel.

Obtaining 16S rRNA Gene Sequence Data

DNA sequencing technology has advanced significantly in the past decade; there are now several methods to obtain a DNA sequence for a particular gene or genome. Common to all methods, however, is the requirement for many copies of the DNA destined for sequence analysis (the template). Polymerase chain reaction (PCR) is the technique most commonly employed to amplify (make copies of) the region to be sequenced. We can design PCR primers that are complementary to highly conserved regions of the 16S rRNA gene, thus allowing the same primers to bind to the DNA of a broad range of organisms. Because the amplification products will include the hypervariable regions located between these conserved sites, species-specific sequence data can be obtained for identification and classification purposes.

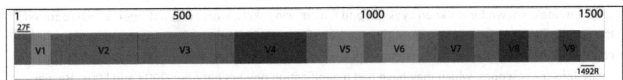

Figure 8-2. 16S rRNA gene illustrating the variable and conserved regions. "V" indicates Variable Regions. Variable regions can be used in group or species-specific applications. Gray boxes are the conserved regions. Conserved regions are used in nonspecific applications. Primers for PCR and sequencing (27F and 1492R) bind to conserved regions to amplify and read all variable regions between the primer set as a template for sequencing.

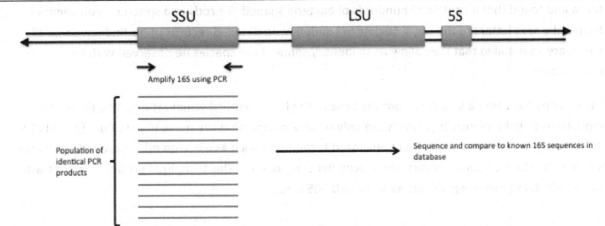

Figure 8-3. Diagrammatic representation of 16S rRNA gene amplification from the prokaryotic chromosome. The small subunit of the bacterial ribosome is encoded by the 16S rRNA gene (SSU), whereas the large subunit is encoded by the 23S rRNA gene (LSU) and the 5S rRNA gene (5S). Schematic adapted from Woese and Fox, 1977.

Morphological Characterization of Isolates

As mentioned, 16S rRNA gene sequence data are exceptionally useful for assigning preliminary taxonomic placement of an organism, but the tentative molecular identification is strengthened through use of several methods. Below, we introduce microscopy as a method to identify key morphological features. Biochemical (metabolic) tests also make up a facet of the identification tools available and will be discussed in Section 11.

Microbes Under the Microscope

The pioneers of microscopy in the late 17th century were also pioneers in the field of biology. Their development of powerful lenses allowed them to delve deeper into the microscopic world of unicellular organisms. Robert Hooke, a renowned Englishman who specialized in the sciences and architecture, is credited with the invention of the compound microscope with which he made detailed observations that are compiled in the book, *Micrographia*, published in 1665, which became a scientific bestseller. The book is famous for its detailed drawings of a fly's eye and the plant cells in a slice of cork. Hooke coined the term "cell" as the cork cell walls reminded him of the cells in monasteries.

Hooke's work inspired a Dutchman who is often called "the father of microbiology," Antonie van Leeuwenhoek, known for his keen eyesight and lens-making skills, worked as a draper, which required the use of magnifying glasses to count the number of threads in fabrics. After reading *Micrographia* and combining his knowledge of lens-making with Hooke's techniques, Leeuwenhoek devised powerful single-lens microscopes, which may have had magnification powers between 200× and 500×. He was very secretive about his techniques and fewer than ten of his microscopes remain. He was such an advanced inventor that it took more than 150 years for scientists to develop microscopes as powerful as Leeuwenhoek's! He was the first to observe and document unicellular organisms, such as bacteria and protists, which he described as "wee animalcules." He famously observed the plaque between his own teeth and found that it contained hundreds of bacteria shaped like rods and spheres. Leeuwenhoek frequently sent letters to the Royal Society in London, with detailed records of his findings some of which are so detailed that they allow us to identify some of the species he observed with his microscopes.

Microscopy has come a long way from the time of the first microbial visualizations. Yet, there are limitations to light microscopy, which can only resolve objects that are more than 0.2 µm (a µm is 1×10^{-6} meter, or a micron) apart. More advanced techniques, such as electron microscopy, discern even smaller structures, such as viruses and subcellular components. This technique produces images with incredible detail, resolving objects as small as 0.005 µm.

Staining the Bacterial Cell Wall

Staining enhances our ability to see the shapes of bacterial cells. Bacteria can be of many different shapes, but the most commonly observed are spherical—called cocci (plural) or coccus (singular)—and rod-shaped—called bacilli (plural) or bacillus (singular). Stains bind to cellular components that would

otherwise be transparent under the light microscope. Bacterial cell walls are composed of an organized mesh of carbohydrates, lipids, and proteins. The structural component is a highly cross-linked polymer of sugar and amino acids called peptidoglycan. The peptidoglycan layer protects bacteria and gives them their characteristic shapes. One of the most famous classical staining methods, Gram staining, was developed in the late 1800s to help visualize bacteria in biopsies and has since become crucial for the classification and identification of bacteria by helping distinguish between the two main patterns of bacterial cell wall architecture.

Gram staining employs two stains, crystal violet and safranin, which are purple and pink, respectively. In Gram-positive bacteria, the peptidoglycan layer is very thick (>20 nm, or nanometers) and serves as the outermost wall component. Gram-positive cells retain large amounts of crystal violet in this layer. Once the crystal violet is complexed with iodine, the stains are better able to resist alcohol-acetone decolorization than in Gram-negative bacteria. As a result, Gram-positive cells are left with a purple appearance even after counterstaining with safranin. Conversely, in Gram-negative bacteria, the peptidoglycan layer is thin (normally <10 nm) and covered by an outer membrane. Because the peptidoglycan is so thin, Gram-negative walls are more susceptible to alcohol-acetone decolorization and are rendered colorless when washed with the alcohol-acetone solution. The decolorized cells will thus be left appearing pink once the safranin counterstain has been applied. By discriminating between Gram-positive and Gram-negative cells on a microscope slide, clinical personnel and microbiologists can deduce much information about an isolate's physiology. Furthermore, Gram staining provides an initial broad division that can be used to help classify bacteria. Gram-positives and Gram-negatives make up the two major groups of bacteria, which are generally representative of their evolutionary lineages. Therefore, Gram staining, although a classical method, is still widely used in both clinical and research microbiology to differentiate bacteria and serves as a preliminary method of characterization.

References

Woese, C. R., & Fox, G. E. (1977) Phylogenetic structure of the prokaryotic domain: The primary kingdoms. Proc Natl Acad Sci U S A 74:5088–5090.

Milestones in Microbiology

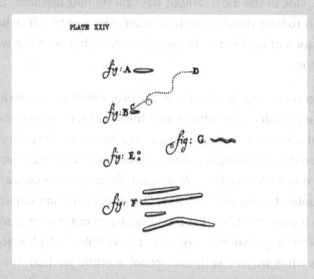

Leeuwenhoek's first representation of the "wee animalcules" he observed under the microscope. This is believed to be the first drawing of a bacterium. Source: University of California Museum of Paleontology – website: http://www.ucmp.berkeley.edu/history/leeuwenhoek.html

Painting of Antonie van Leeuwenhoek by Jan Verkolje. Photo source: https://en.wikipedia.org/wiki/Antonie_van_Leeuwenhoek

Experiment 8: Initial identification of antibiotic-producing isolates

Biological Questions:

1. What do you wish to know about your antibiotic producers?
2. Can we identify bacteria based on their macroscopic morphologies? Why or why not?
3. What cellular and molecular components in our isolates can give us the most information about their identities?
4. How do we confirm what we learn about our isolates?

Background:

Objective:

Results:

Isolate name	Tentative genus	Closest relative (% identity)	Size of query sequence (nt)	Date of BLAST analysis	Gram stain	Cell shape	Antibiotic production	Other

Based on morphological and/or molecular data, indicate the number of distinct antibiotic producers:

Literature search:

- Morphology: Do your observations match information in the literature?

- Antibiotic production: Do your observations match information in the literature?

Interpretations and conclusions:

Notes:

Tiny Earth
studentsourcing antibiotic discovery

89

Section 9: It All Comes Down to Chemistry

Section below adapted from Clayden, J., Greeves, N., Warren, S., Wothers, P. *Organic Chemistry*. Oxford University Press, 2007.

Extraction of Secondary Metabolites or Natural Products

A pure microbial culture produces a vast number of different metabolites, so a first step in the study of a potentially new antibiotic is to separate the active compound from other chemical "contaminants." The purification process usually entails a series of separation steps in which the desirable compound is separated from other molecules in the mix according to its chemical and physical properties. For example, many methods separate compounds based on their relative polarity as indicated by the degree of interaction with various solvents. Contaminants that are chemically similar to the active compound will be the most difficult to separate. Some of the most difficult cases involve enantiomers – molecules that share the same chemical formula and the same chemical bonding pattern, but differ in stereochemistry—they are mirror images of each other. Only one molecule is active; yet it shares most of the same chemical properties as its enantiomeric form, creating difficulties in the purification process.

What Are Organic Molecules?

Organic chemistry started as the chemistry of life, when that was thought to be different from the chemistry in the laboratory. (There was an early theory called "vitalism" that invoked a mysterious force in living organisms.) Organic chemistry then became the chemistry of carbon compounds, and is one of the foundational sciences of biology and the pharmaceutical, perfumery, flavor and dyestuff, and materials industries.

Organic compounds available to us today are those that are present in living things, those produced for over millions of years by petroleum formation, and those synthesized from simple building blocks by synthetic chemists. In earlier times, many of the organic compounds known from nature were those found in "essential oils" that could be distilled from plants or extracted from crushed plant material with acid. Three fine examples are menthol – a flavor extracted from spearmint; *cis*-jasmone – a perfume from jasmine flowers; and quinine – one of the active compounds (against malaria) from the bark of the cinchona tree. Most organic molecules are colorless, but some are known as pigments, which are colored compounds such as indigo, which makes denim blue, and carotene which gives carrots their characteristic color.

Tiny Earth
studentsourcing antibiotic discovery

Penicillin

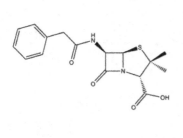

Kanamcyin

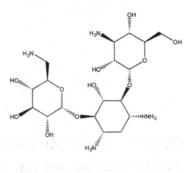

Erythromycin

Figure 9-1. [From Left] Chemical structures of penicillin, erythromycin, and kanamycin. Image source: drawn by Nam Kim.

Organic molecules can be crystalline solids, oils, waxes, liquids, or gases. Familiar examples include white crystalline sugar – a natural compound isolated from plants as hard white crystals when pure – and petroleum – a mixture of colorless, volatile, and highly flammable hydrocarbons that include what is commonly known as gasoline, and isooctane, which lends its name to the octane rating of gasoline. In the figure above, isooctane is shown in both a long-hand nomenclature, where all the carbons are shown (lower structure), and the shorthand (upper structure) used by organic chemists to show organic molecules.

What Are Secondary Metabolites?

The macromolecules that are common to all living things (i.e., nucleic acids, proteins, lipids, and carbohydrates) are the products of chemical reactions common to life. These are known as primary metabolic processes. More specialized chemical reactions and molecules are more restricted in their distribution to one or a few species. These molecules are not essential for life, but they are presumed to be important to the organisms in which they are produced, although many have unknown roles. These molecules are often called secondary metabolites, and we have already met quite a few examples in our tour through antibiotics. The majority of known antibiotics are produced as secondary metabolites as the microbial culture reaches the end of exponential growth (refer to the growth curve in Section 5).

Secondary metabolites can range from relatively small molecules that you have already seen, such as penicillin G, up to very large polyethers, including brevetoxin, which is a molecule produced by algae in "red tides" that can kill fish and those who eat the fish.

Milestones in Microbiology

Dorothy Crowfoot Hodgkin, a British chemist, advanced the technique of X-ray crystallography, a critical method to determine the 3D structures of biomolecules. She solved the structure of penicillin and demonstrated that it contains a β-lactam ring. Hodgkin also solved the structure of vitamin B_{12}, which led to the Nobel Prize in Chemistry in 1964. Britain's Royal Society celebrated their 350th anniversary with a set of commemorative stamps, one of which was of Hodgkin and her vitamin B_{12} molecule. Source: http://www.paleophilatelie.eu/description/stamps/uk_2010.html

How Do We Isolate or Extract Secondary Metabolites?

To isolate the compound responsible for antibiotic activity observed in the patch plates, we need to employ separation techniques that are based on characteristics such as size, polarity, solubility, or affinity. There are many useful separation techniques; some are cheap and easy and can be done on a large scale while others require expensive equipment and are time consuming. Each characterization step usually affects the choice of the next one as more is learned about the molecule of interest. For a first step in purification, it is a good idea to try a very general method that has been shown to isolate many secondary metabolites while removing common media compounds and primary metabolites.

End of section adapted from Clayden, J., Greeves, N., Warren, S., Wothers, P. *Organic Chemistry* Oxford University Press, 2007

Solubility of Common Compounds

Dissolves well in water	Do not dissolve well in water
Na⁺Cl⁻ **table salt**	**hexane** $CH_3\text{-}CH_2\text{-}CH_2\text{-}CH_2\text{-}CH_2\text{-}CH_3$
glucose (blood sugar)	**cholesterol**
choline (neurotransmitter)	**short chain diglyceride**
glycerol (antifreeze)	**benzopyrene**
triethylammonium chloride (an organic salt)	**triethyl amine**

Source: Gillian Phillips.

Extracting with Organic Solvents

While the process of chemical separation to isolate compounds may seem new, similar phenomena surround us. For example, salad dressings demonstrate that oil and vinegar do not mix and form separate layers with different densities and chemical properties. These two liquids also feel very different to our skin. Oil sticks while vinegar and other water-based solutions wash off easily. These familiar interactions are the result of a chemical property known as **polarity**.

Polarity defines the distribution of electron density and charge in a molecule. It results from the tendency of certain atoms to hold onto their shared electrons more closely than other atoms in a bond due to differences in electronegativity. These differences cause some molecules to have "poles" with partially opposing charges; we call these molecules "polar." Water (H_2O) is a great example. Each water molecule has a partial negative charge on the oxygen and partial positive charges on the hydrogen atoms. Atoms in molecules that exhibit this separation of electron density, like other water molecules and water-soluble compounds, will be attracted to other atoms of opposite charges in other polar molecules. These bonds are weak compared with covalent bonds but are strong enough to pull and solubilize polar molecules in a sample. Less polar molecules, such as **ethyl acetate** ($CH_3\text{-}COO\text{-}CH_2\text{-}CH_3$ or

Tiny Earth
studentsourcing antibiotic discovery

EtOAc) separate from water due to the differences in polarity (similar to oil and water). Even though EtOAc has a "pole" with the carbonyl group (C=O) within its structure, it is not strong enough to associate with water due to the methyl (CH₃) and ethyl (CH₃CH₂) groups. We focus on interaction with water in biology because it is such an important component of biological systems. Triglycerides, such as the vegetable oils used in salad dressing and the oils on our skin, also share this characteristic. Other molecules, such as the surfactant in detergents have hybrid (amphipathic) properties, containing polar or **hydrophilic** ("water-loving") heads and long nonpolar or **hydrophobic** ("water-fearing") tails. This enables them to mix well with both types of molecules, which makes it easier, for example, to remove grease or fat from our dishes with water.

Compounds produced by bacteria cover the full spectrum of polarity — some will be amphipathic while others will be either strongly hydrophilic or hydrophobic. However, most primary metabolites, such as sugars, amino acids, and peptides, have hydrophilic properties because cells are filled with water. Water acts as the "universal solvent" in cells, keeping metabolites and ionic species in solution for reactions within the cell. Therefore, the first step we use in isolating an active compound from a sample is removing most of the constituents of cells and seeing if activity is retained in the sample. Many small molecules, including antibiotics, will have hydrophobic and hydrophilic moieties. Therefore, if we can extract the target molecule in a less polar solvent, such as EtOAc, it will be separated from other molecules found within the cell as well as from the water-soluble nutrients found in the medium. Other solvents, such as **methanol** (CH₃-OH or MeOH), the simplest alcohol, extract a greater spectrum of compounds due to their ability to solubilize polar and nonpolar compounds, including many water-soluble compounds that complicate the isolation of the active one.

EtOAc and MeOH are just two of a wide range of solvents used in extraction protocols as well as in many household products, including glues, nail polish removers, and paint products. Because different solvents solubilize different types of compounds, solubility can suggest the properties of a compound, therefore serving as a useful first step in purification of a compound.

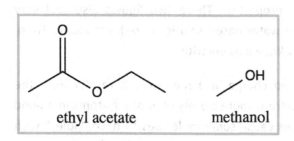

ethyl acetate   methanol

Figure 9-1. Left: Molecular structure of ethyl acetate. This organic compound is nonpolar and serves as a common solvent for other organic, nonpolar compounds. **Right:** Molecular structure of methanol. This compound contains a polar alcohol functional group (-OH), giving it hydrophilic properties. However, its methyl (-CH₃) group, which is slightly hydrophobic, allows it to solubilize both polar and nonpolar compounds to various degrees.

Future Directions

Although the complete purification and analysis of active compounds is likely beyond the scope of your work, it is worth a quick look at the process used to determine the chemical identity of a new molecule.

Tiny Earth
studentsourcing antibiotic discovery

From Bacterial Isolate to Molecules

Crude extracts such as those created by the extraction process described above are typically complex mixtures of chemicals. This mixture needs to be reduced to a single compound for structural analysis. Therefore, three things are required to isolate to a biologically active molecule through a process called bioassay-guided isolation. It requires a biological assay for activity, purification techniques, and methods to determine the chemical structure.

First, a biological assay is required so the activity can be followed as the purification techniques are used to isolate the active molecule away from other components. Once a pure molecule is obtained, techniques that can identify the molecule due to unique characteristics are used to determine its chemical structure.

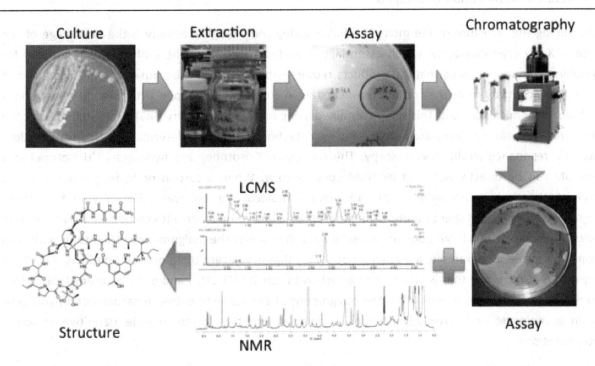

Figure 9-2. Bioassay-guided isolation of thiostrepton from a *Streptomyces* sp. by undergraduate student Kira Garry.

Bioassay-guided isolation is usually time intensive and often leads to known compounds. So before an extract is subjected to the process, it needs to go through a de-replication procedure to determine whether it contains commonly re-isolated compounds, thereby enabling the researcher to prioritize extracts containing novel compounds. Liquid chromatography/mass spectrometry (LC/MS) along with statistical analysis and biological assays that give mode of action information can be used to do this. Once an extract has been prioritized for further work, it will undergo bioassay-guided isolation. A simple example of this is shown in Figure 12-1 where thiostrepton was isolated from a *Streptomyces* sp. by student Kira Garry at Yale University.

1. Biological Assay

A biological assay is required before purification starts so the activity can be followed at each step.

2. Purification Techniques

The purification of crude extracts is done using various techniques that can be described as liquid chromatography (LC). Highly automated and easy-to-use LC systems are now common in chemistry research laboratories that allow for fast and relatively cheap purification of mixtures. HPLC (high performance LC) systems are also available in cases in which the purification to a single compound is difficult.

3. Structure Determination Techniques

Determining the structure of the molecule that is giving the biological activity is the next stage of the process. X-ray crystallography, which essentially provides a picture of the molecule, can be used for crystalline compounds. Most natural products require other techniques because they are produced at very low concentrations or they do not form crystals. A common first step in structure determination is to obtain a chemical formula. This can be obtained using mass spectrometry (MS) where the mass of the compound is measured very accurately. The main technique used to determine structure is nuclear magnetic resonance (NMR) spectroscopy. The carbons (^{13}C isotope) and hydrogens (^{1}H isotope) in a molecule can be directly detected by NMR spectroscopy. When a carbon or hydrogen atom is in a different chemical environment within an organic molecule, it behaves differently in the strong magnetic field of a NMR spectrometer. The differences allow comparison with carbons and hydrogens in known molecules and a large body of historical data that allows the assignment of the atoms within an organic molecule. For example, a methyl group (CH_3^-) that is adjacent to an oxygen (methoxy; CH_3-O-) is very different from one that is attached to a carbon (methyl; $CH3$-CH_2-) and behaves predictably. More sophisticated NMR experiments allow the assignment of connectivity between carbons and hydrogens within a molecule and have advanced to a point where they often provide definitive structure determinations.

If the compound is known in the literature, this procedure of structure determination can be relatively fast and may take days or weeks. If the compound is new and the structure is similar but not identical to molecules already in the literature, then the process may take weeks to months depending on the complexity of the molecule. In complicated cases, where the carbon backbone has not been observed before, the structure of the novel compound may take months to unravel, particularly if issues of stereochemistry are involved. The mode of action is a key area of interest when novel compounds are isolated. If novel molecules can be identified with new modes of action, this work could have great impact on drug discovery and treatment of infectious disease.

References

Clayden, J., Greeves, N., Warren, S., & Wothers, P. (2007). *Organic Chemistry,* New York: Oxford University Press.

Experiment 9: Test an organic extract of your isolate for antibiotic activity

Biological Questions:

1. Can we isolate an antibiotic from a bacterial isolate? How?
2. What does the choice of solvent for extraction assume about the chemical properties of the antibiotic?
3. How can we assess whether the antibiotic is present in the extract?
4. What else do we need to learn about the observed antibiotic activity?
5. How will you proceed to study your antibiotic extract?

Background:

Objective:

Hypothesis and rationale:

Experimental design and protocols used:

Solvents used:

Solvent pros and cons:

Controls and treatments:

Data and observations:

Interpretations and conclusions:

Future directions:

Notes:

Tiny Earth
studentsourcing antibiotic discovery

Section 10: Resisting Antibiotics

The antibiotic crisis stems from the increasing prevalence of infectious organisms that fail to respond to treatment with conventional antibiotics, requiring clinicians to prescribe other antibiotics. Occasionally, clinicians have to resort to administering "last resort" antibiotics, which are reserved for the most recalcitrant infections. By the time these antibiotics are deployed, the infection may have spread and made the patient extremely ill and at risk of death. In the worst cases, the infectious organism is resistant to every antibiotic administered. The main reason that the ESKAPE pathogens are such a health threat is not that they, on their own, are particularly virulent; rather, these organisms represent the vast majority of antibiotic-resistant isolates that confound physicians in affected patients. In today's world, it is the acquisition of antibiotic resistance that renders treatment of bacterial infections challenging.

How Does Antibiotic Resistance Arise?

To understand antibiotic resistance, it is helpful to refer back to the mechanism of action of antibiotics and the molecular interactions that occur in cells. An antibiotic is a molecule that enters a cell and interacts with a target molecule; for example, antibiotics that bind to the prokaryotic ribosome have an inhibitory effect on protein synthesis. Any cellular change that prevents the antibiotic from reaching or binding to its target confers resistance to the organism.

There are two main mechanisms through which resistance is acquired. One involves mutations and the other involves acquisition of fragments of DNA harboring genes that confer resistance. Bacteria can acquire DNA from other bacteria, from the environment (released from lysed cells for example), or from viruses through a process called **horizontal gene transfer** (**HGT**). We use the term "horizontal" to distinguish this from the traditional "vertical" transfer of DNA that occurs when a bacterial cell undergoes fission and passes its genes on to a daughter cell. Examples of resistance genes acquired through HGT are genes that code for pumps that expel antibiotics from the cell or enzymes that chemically modify antibiotics thereby inactivating them (i.e., they are no longer reach or bind to their targets).

Mutations that arise through errors in DNA replication can also lead to resistance if: (a) the mutation alters the structure of an antibiotic target such that the binding affinity of the antibiotic is decreased and (b) the function of the target is retained. Remember that antibiotics target structures or functions that are essential for the life of the organism although it may be less effective than the original; only certain mutations meet these criteria.

Antibiotic Resistance in the Environment

When there is selective pressure to maintain the change to the genome, regardless of the mechanism by which the change arose, a resistant population of cells can arise. This can occur in microbes proliferating within patients taking antibiotics to fight infections; from there, resistant bacteria present in feces and bodily fluids can contaminate household or hospital surfaces. Antibiotic-resistant bacteria can spread in

the environment through waste disposal, and the use of antibiotics in livestock feed provides further selection pressure for survival of resistant organisms. More than half of antibiotics sold in the United States, for example, are used in livestock production, which has become a topic of contentious debate because most of this use is to promote growth of pigs, cattle, and poultry, not to treat disease (Figure 10-1).

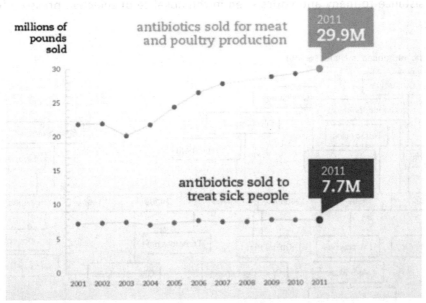

Figure 10-1. U.S. sales of antibiotics, 2001–2011. Photo source: Pew Charitable Trusts
http://www.pewhealth.org/other-resource/record-high-antibiotic-sales-for-meat-and-poultry-production-85899449119

Antibiotic use by humans is relatively recent in the history of evolution of life, but antibiotics have been produced by microbes in their natural environments for millennia. The natural role of these compounds is currently unknown, but we can be certain the intended function is not to cure humans of infectious disease. Antibiotics may be one of the most ancient forms of biological warfare. Perhaps secretion of antibiotics is a mechanism employed by microbes to compete with neighboring microbes for limited resources. And as usually occurs in nature, those neighbors that survived the onslaught of antimicrobial compounds proliferated, thus passing on their resistance determinants to subsequent populations of cells either through vertical or horizontal transmission. However, there are only a few examples that have been studied sufficiently to provide strong support for this notion. Alternatively, resistance genes have been speculated to protect microbes from toxins secreted by plants and insects, and antibiotics have been proposed to play a role in cell-cell signaling. The natural role of most antibiotics remains unknown and the subject of active research.

What we do know is that resistant microbes are frequently detected soon after the introduction of an antibiotic for clinical use (Figure 2). Surprisingly, this trend proves true even for compounds created by chemists and synthesized in the lab, for which there has not been selection pressure for resistance in evolutionary history. This highlights the need for more prudent antibiotic use and for the ongoing discovery of new compounds.

Tiny Earth
studentsourcing antibiotic discovery

In the context of our own research, we might ask whether those microbes that produce antibiotics are likely to harbor antibiotic-resistance determinants. It may seem logical that a microbe would be resistant to an antibiotic that it produces. But how likely is it to be resistant to other antibiotics? And how prevalent is resistance in the environment in the absence of known selective pressure? One important feature in the rapid spread of antibiotic resistance is the fact that antibiotic-resistance genes tend to cluster within the same region of the bacterial chromosome, such that HGT often results in acquisition of resistance to many antibiotics even in the absence of selective pressure for many of the resistance genes.

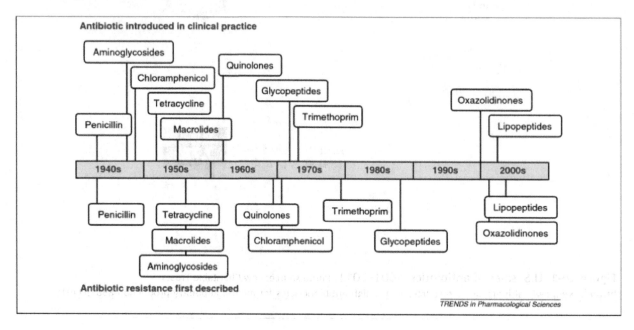

Figure 10-2. Timeline of introduction and appearance of resistance to various antibiotics. Photo source: Högberg, D. L., Heddini, A., Cars, O. (2010) The global need for effective antibiotics: challenges and recent advances. Trends Pharmacol Sci, 31:509–515

Fighting Antibiotic Resistance

The prevalence of antibiotic resistance has called for discovery of new antibiotics and also for the modification of existing antibiotics. At the time of its discovery, penicillin could easily treat a *Staphylococcus aureus* skin infection. As the bacterium acquired resistance, alternatives needed to be developed. In 1959, methicillin was introduced as an alternative to penicillin. Methicillin is a penicillin derivative, which is insensitive to enzymes that would normally break down ß-lactams (*beta*-lactamases). Yet within years of its introduction, resistance was observed. The number of reported cases of methicillin-resistant *S. aureus* (MRSA) has been growing rapidly over the last two decades (Figure 10-3). The last resort antibiotic, vancomycin, has come into common use to treat infections by multidrug-resistant bacteria, and the synthetic antibiotic zylox is now used to treat even more serious infections that are no longer sensitive to vancomycin (Figure 10-4).

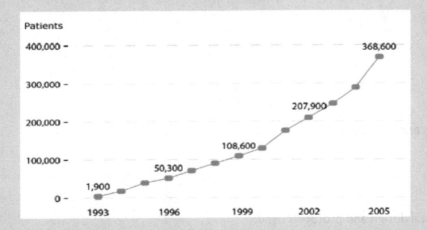

Figure 10-3. Cases of methicillin-resistant *Staphylococcus aureus* (MRSA) annually in the United States. Adapted from "Hospital stays with MRSA infections 1993-2005." Source: AHRQ, Center for Delivery, Organization and Markets, Healthcare Cost and Utilization Project, Nationwide Inpatient Sample, 1993-2005.

References

Allen, H. K., Donato, J., Wang, H. H., Cloud-Hansen, K. A., Davies, J., & Handelsman, J. (2010) Call of the wild: Antibiotic resistance genes in natural environments. Nat Rev Microbiol 8:251–259.

Davies, J., & Davies, D. (2010) Origins and evolution of antibiotic resistance. Microbiol Mol Biol Rev 74:417–433. doi: 10.1128/Mmbr.00016-10

Rice, L. B. (2010) Progress and challenges in implementing the research on ESKAPE pathogens. Infect Control Hosp Epidemiol 31: S7–S10.

Experiment 10: Testing an isolate's resistance to common antibiotics

Biological Questions:

1. Are the antibiotic-producing isolates sensitive to known antibiotics?
2. If so, what does this tell us about the isolates? How might this relate to the antibiotics they produce?

Background:

Objective:

Hypothesis and rationale:

Experimental design and protocols used:

Controls and treatments:

Data and observations:

Isolate ID	Antibiotic tested	Mechanism of action of antibiotic	Resistance observed (Y/N)	Test organisms inhibited	Real world example of bacterial resistance

Isolates tested	Resistant (%)	Producers tested (number)	Producers resistant (%)

Interpretations and conclusions:

Notes:

Tiny Earth
studentsourcing antibiotic discovery

Section 11: "Classic" versus "Modern" Classification

Biological Classification

Humans make sense of themselves and the world around them by classifying things based on shared characteristics, whether it is by their physical appearance, function, or origin. For example, classification provides a shorthand for differentiating plants with medicinal value from those that are poisonous, and differentiating animals that walk on their toes from those that walk on their knuckles. Carl Linnaeus, the father of taxonomy, pioneered the classification of organisms based on shared physical characteristics. He meticulously grouped organisms into taxonomic ranks and set the foundation for naming them, using a binomial containing the genus and species designation. Charles Darwin, on the other hand, championed the principles of common descent and paved the way for the classification of organisms based on their evolutionary relatedness. Whether it is looking at morphology or genetic similarity, each system of classification reflects different patterns of evolution and adaptation to environments, distribution in time and space, or utility to humans.

Whatever classification system we employ, it is important to know the criteria used to differentiate things. The use of molecular phylogeny has become the standard for classifying bacteria based on their genetic relatedness, but this is usually supported by morphological and biochemical characterization techniques as discussed in Section 8. To classify and identify bacteria, microbiologists assess many features such as the structure or function of key biomolecules; the shape, size, or staining pattern of the cells; the type of metabolism; or DNA sequence composition.

In this section, we will describe some of the most common biochemical characterization methods used in clinical diagnostic labs to identify bacterial pathogens isolated from patients. They are also applied in research labs to establish taxonomic and phylogenetic relationships, providing a better understanding of shared characteristics, evolution, and adaptation to natural environments than could be obtained with any single method.

The Diagnostics Lab

When it comes to diagnosing and treating patients, pathogen identification must be fast, reliable, and low cost, whenever possible. Classical methods of identification are based on fundamental microbiological principles about how bacteria respond to certain changes to their environment. For example, changing the chemical or nutrient composition of a growth medium affects how bacteria grow or what chemicals they produce. To exploit these changes, two types of specialized media are used — **selective media**, which support the growth of some species and not others, and **differential media**, which differentiate species by visible characteristics.

In hospitals, the use of selective media is a widespread method of identifying human pathogens. Bacteria may be isolated from bodily fluids (e.g., urine or blood), abscesses, or other areas of infection in the patient's body. These samples are streaked out on specialized media that accomplish different objectives. To identify methicillin-resistant bacteria present in a sample, we can formulate a selective medium containing methicillin, which will inhibit the growth of all susceptible bacteria but not the resistant ones – a simple process of elimination. Selective media may also lack an essential amino acid, which would inhibit bacteria unable to synthesize that nutrient. Differential media, on the other hand, will help distinguish groups of bacteria through changes in appearance of the organism or the medium itself, usually in response to differences in biochemical pathways. Researchers and clinical personnel use these visual cues to assign phenotypes and chemical reactions associated with known bacteria, pathogenic or not.

Specialized Media and Enzymology

As described in Section 8, Gram staining allows us to assign bacteria to one of two large groups of classification: Gram-negative or Gram-positive. Other tests do this while conveying even more information about the microbe's biochemistry. MacConkey agar is a specialized medium that differentiates between Gram-negative bacteria, especially those that colonize the human gastrointestinal (GI) tract. This medium inhibits the growth of Gram-positive bacteria by disrupting their cell walls with crystal violet and bile salts infused in the medium. Many Gram-negative bacteria, such as *Escherichia coli*, thrive in the GI tract as part of our natural gut flora along with many specialized Gram-positive bacteria. Other Gram-negative bacteria, such as *Salmonella* and *Shigella*, are notorious pathogens that can cause food poisoning and even death. To differentiate between these bacteria, MacConkey agar allows us to deduce information about their ability to ferment carbohydrates. A pH indicator in the medium changes the appearance of cells producing acid, a by-product of fermentation, from their original color to pink/red. *E. coli* ferments the lactose present in the medium and releases acid, making colonies and the surrounding agar appear red in the presence of a pH indicator. Conversely, *Salmonella* and *Shigella* do not ferment lactose and maintain a neutral pH, making colonies display their typical white or tan color (Wessner, et al., p. 176). MacConkey agar is therefore both selective and differential, revealing information about the cell wall composition and ability to ferment lactose.

Another method to differentiate enteric bacteria based on their ability to metabolize different compounds is the triple sugar iron (TSI) test. TSI medium, which consists of solidified agar in a slanted test tube, supports classification of bacteria based on their ability to ferment different carbohydrates (glucose, sucrose, and lactose), to produce H_2S (hydrogen sulfide, a by-product of bacterial anaerobic digestion), and to grow in the presence or absence of oxygen (ASM Microbe Library). In this method, bacteria are stabbed into the agar, where they begin to metabolize sugars under aerobic conditions at the surface of the agar or anaerobic conditions at the butt of the tube. A pH indicator turns the medium from red to yellow in response to acid as a by-product of fermentation. For example, a lactose fermenter like *Escherichia* or *Klebsiella* will continue to lower the pH long after glucose and sucrose have been depleted in the medium. Since they are both facultative anaerobes, they will ferment sugar both in the presence and absence of oxygen, making the whole tube appear yellow. In contrast, *Citrobacter* and *Salmonella* will only ferment carbohydrates under anaerobic conditions and release H_2S. Therefore, only

the butt of the tube will appear yellow, and black precipitate will form from the reaction of H_2S with ferric ions in the medium (Wessner et al., p. 175).

Similarly, the starch agar test differentiates between bacteria that hydrolyze starch, a branched polymer of glucose units, and bacteria that do not. For this method, bacteria are grown on starch agar. When colonies become visible, the plate is flooded with iodine, which is normally red but turns blue when it complexes with starch, serving as an effective indicator for the presence or absence of starch molecules. A starch hydrolyzer like *Bacillus subtilis* will secrete amylase, which breaks down the surrounding starch to glucose. Upon flooding the colonies, the medium surrounding the colonies appears red in the absence of starch, which has been broken down by the amylase-positive bacteria. The rest of the plate will appear a dark shade of blue where the starch is still present. *Streptococcus* and *Staphylococcus* are both starch negative and can be used as controls.

By testing a bacterium's ability to metabolize different compounds, we are indirectly screening for the presence of key enzymes that are unique to certain taxonomic groups of bacteria. Bacteria are equipped to survive in distinct environments where different carbon and energy sources are available. They are also equipped to deal with a variety of mechanical, chemical, and environmental conditions that threaten their existence. For example, hydrogen peroxide (H_2O_2) is a strong oxidizing agent that rapidly kills susceptible cells and is employed by many organisms to protect against infectious bacteria. H_2O_2 is also used as an antiseptic applied on cuts or wounds on the skin. Nevertheless, many bacteria have evolved a mechanism to counteract H_2O_2 with the enzyme catalase. *Staphylococcus* bacteria, like those that colonize our skin, and *Bacillus*, which is commonly found in the soil, both test positive for the presence of this enzyme. Testing positive for catalase is made evident by exposing target bacteria to a 3% H_2O_2 solution and observing for effervescence. When catalase acts upon H_2O_2, it produces water and oxygen gas.

$$2H_2O_2 + catalase \rightarrow 2H_2O + O_2$$

When dealing with common or well-studied bacteria, these classical biochemistry-based tests can give us great information about our bacterium to narrow down its possible identity. Diagnostic labs with well-developed identification keys can use these methods to type pathogens down to one or several genera and figure out a line of treatment for patients. However, to identify a bacterium down to the species level, or when dealing with a poorly studied bacterium, sequencing technology is normally necessary.

Classic or Modern Approach

Over the past two decades, sequencing technologies have become faster, more reliable, and cheaper, leading to the exponential increase of sequenced genomes available in online repositories like GenBank and other databases. 16S rRNA gene sequencing has therefore become a useful method for identifying bacteria down to the genus level, and more specific primers can help us identify their species or particular strain. Knowing that a bacterium's 16S rRNA gene sequence has a 97% or higher identity to a known species provides us information about an organism of interest and what phenotypes to expect. As we indicated in Section 8, researchers usually combine morphological, biochemical, and molecular

TinyEarth
studentsourcing antibiotic discovery

analyses to provide a complete picture of the identity of an unknown organism. Results may bring to light discrepancies that may indicate we are dealing with a new strain or a variant of a known species. Whatever the case, coupling knowledge of a bacterium's phylogenetic background with morphology and biochemical information acquired through classical biochemistry-based methods allows us to draw a comprehensive picture of our isolates and acquire new insight into their cellular and molecular processes.

References

ASM Microbe Library. *Laboratory Protocols*. <http://microbelibrary.org/about/51> Date accessed: 3 September 2013.

Fox, A. Culture and Identification of Infectious Agents. Bacteriol Microbiol Immunol, On-Line: University of South Carolina School of Medicine <http://pathmicro.med.sc.edu/fox/culture.htm> Date accessed: 3 September 2013.

Wessner, D. R., Dupont, C., & Charles, T. (2013) *Microbiology* New York: Wiley & Sons.

Experiment 11: Biochemical characterization of isolates

Biological Questions:
1. Now that you know the genus of your isolate, what else do you want to know about it?
2. Is your biochemical characterization information consistent with previous characterization of this genus?

- Note: Reproduce the following prompts for every biochemical test done. -

Background:

Objective:

Biochemical test:

Procedure:

Results:

Interpretation:

Is this consistent with what you know about your isolate(s)?

Conclusions:

Notes:

Section 12: Bacteria in Context

"Good" versus "Bad" Bacteria

The popular belief that all bacteria are "germs," which the Merriam-Webster's Dictionary defines as "microorganisms causing disease," has led to great efforts to eradicate bacteria from our lives with stringent sanitary and hygienic measures. Conversely, the food industry has marketed "good bacteria," or probiotics in fermented products such as the "live and active culture" label on yogurts. This dichotomy has led to the notion that, in general, bacteria cannot be trusted, but can have beneficial effects if consumed from the right packages. However, the notion of discretely "good" and "bad" bacteria is misleading. The truth is that most bacteria are harmless and essential components of the Earth's ecosystems and host organisms. From birth, bacteria colonize our skin and guts, enhance our immune systems, and enrich our diets with nutrients that would otherwise be inaccessible to us as humans. Recent research indicates that gut bacteria play roles in protecting us from diseases as diverse as autism, asthma, diabetes, depression, and obesity. The interdependence between bacteria and other organisms is not coincidental, but is the product of a long history of coevolution and interspecies interactions.

Symbiotic Relationships

Relationships define the way we, humans, interact with each other. They define how we communicate, the way we feel toward one another, the agreements and commitment we make, and the norms that dictate those interactions. They can last a short time or a lifetime, and they often lay a foundation for those same relationships in future generations. As social beings, and as living things, we are fundamentally interconnected and interdependent.

Symbiosis is a long-term, intimate relationship between two or more species (Wessner et al., p. 563). Like all relationships, symbioses may serve various purposes for each of its participating members, whether it is receiving essential nutrients, providing shelter and protection, or disseminating progeny. These relationships often fall in a continuum between beneficial and harmful for one species versus the other. On one end of the spectrum, a **mutualistic** relationship defines an interaction in which both species benefit. For example, herbivores rely on their gut bacteria to break down cellulose, and the gut bacteria in return are provided a habitat and a steady food supply. At the other end of the spectrum, a **parasitic** relationship defines an interaction where one species benefits and the other is harmed. Bacteria that have observable or measureable effects on their hosts may be mutualistic, parasitic, or fall anywhere in between.

Residing On or Inside Another Organism

Symbioses are not only defined by their effects (beneficial versus harmful) on the host, but also by their location in relationship to the host. The species involved in a symbiotic relationship are known as **symbionts**. **Ectosymbionts** reside on the surface of their hosts, while **endosymbionts** reside in the tissues or within the cells of their host (Wessner et al., p. 563).

Most scientists now agree that eukaryotic cells are the product of a form of endosymbiosis. When biologist Lynn Margulis published a paper supporting the **endosymbiotic theory**, many scientists were quick to reject the idea that mitochondria and chloroplasts were once "free-living prokaryotic cells" engulfed by early eukaryotic cells (Sagan, 1967). Today, molecular and genetic evidence supported by 16S rRNA sequencing of mitochondrial and chloroplast DNA indicates that these organelles may have originated from α-Proteobacteria and cyanobacteria, respectively. The process of symbiosis was perhaps the single most important event in the evolution of complex organisms.

Figure 12-1. A mealybug feeding on sap. Photo source: http://schaechter.asmblog.org/schaechter/2011/09/a-bug-in-a-bug-in-a-bug.html

Figure 12-2. A leaf-cutting worker ant covered by the ectosymbiont *Streptomyces*. Leaf-cutting ants rely on the antibiotics produced by *Streptomyces* species to keep their "fungus farms" parasite-free. Photo source: http://scienceblogs.com/notrocketscience/leafcutter-ants-rely-on-bacteria-to-fertilise-their-fungus-g/> (accessed 17 July 2014)

In the long term, some symbiotic relationships irreversibly alter host physiology, biochemistry, and genetics. The human genome with 21,000 protein-coding genes and the *E. coli* genome with just over 4,000 are both enormous in comparison with certain bacteria that rely on other members of a three-way symbiosis. The bacterium *Candidatus Tremblaya princeps* contains only 120 protein-coding genes, an unprecedented low number for any living organism. *Tremblaya*, an endosymbiont of the mealybug, synthesizes vitamins and amino acids from the sap consumed by its host in a mutually beneficial relationship. Yet, *Tremblaya* is itself dependent on its own endosymbiont, the γ-Proteobacterium *Moranella*, whose genome is significantly larger, to synthesize proteins that are not encoded in *Tremblayas*'s minimalist genome (Husnik et al., 2013). The interdependence displayed in this three-way symbiosis has meticulously divided labor among these organisms, all in the safety and steady food supply of the mealybug host (Figure 12-1).

Tiny Earth
studentsourcing antibiotic discovery

Streptomyces, which have some of the largest bacterial genomes and produce most commercially and clinically used antibiotics, are also involved in symbiotic relationships thanks to their bioactivity against pathogens. Leaf-cutting ants rely on antibiotic producers like *Streptomyces* to protect their food from microbial infection (Scott et al., 2008). These so-called farming ants cultivate the fungus *Leucoagaricus* for food, which is prone to infection by yet another fungus called *Escovopsis* (Currie et al., 1999; Seipke et al., 2011; Haeder, Wirth, Herz, & Spiteller, 2009). *Streptomyces* lives on the ants' exoskeletons as an ectosymbiont and produce antibiotics that specifically inhibit *Escovopsis* (Seipke et al., 2011). This protects the ants' cultivar fungus as their source of sustenance and provides shelter for the antibiotic producers living on them (Figure 12-2).

Plants and Microbes

Anywhere you look on the planet, plants interact with microbes in the soil, on their surfaces, and even living within their tissues. A few of these interactions are parasitic and are the cause for great loss in agriculture. Like the *Escovopsis* fungus threatening the crops of leaf-cutting ants, species of the eukaryotic microorganism *Pythium* attack the root tips of plants. Almost all plants are susceptible to *Pythium*, which, under the right conditions and with no competition, can spread very quickly and ravage fields with root rot (Moorman, 2013). The use of biological control agents, such as bacteria that enhance crop growth or inhibit plant disease, has been purposely applied in agriculture to restore the balance. Thus, our dependence on bacteria for our food source is tightly intertwined with the practices of modern agriculture.

Bacteria have been used for millennia to enhance crop nutrition. Nitrogen gas (N_2) constitutes roughly 80% of the Earth's atmosphere. Nitrogen is an essential component of amino acids and nucleotides, but N_2 gas is inaccessible to the vast majority of organisms because of the ultra-stable triple bond between the N atoms. Genes encoding nitrogenase, the enzyme that converts N_2 from the atmosphere to NH_4^+ (ammonium), have only been found in Bacteria and Archaea (Wessner et al., p. 474). The conversion of nitrogen gas into ammonium is known as **nitrogen fixation**, an essential part of the nitrogen cycle. Ammonium and its deprotonated form, ammonia (NH_3), can then be assimilated by many organisms, like plants, into essential biological molecules (Figure 12-3).

Leguminous plants (e.g., beans, peanuts, and peas) are protein rich and therefore have a high demand for nitrogen, which is an abundant element in protein. To obtain their nitrogen, legumes have evolved living quarters for nitrogen-fixing bacteria. Bacteria that live in the soil with a plant host and fix nitrogen are collectively known as **rhizobia**. In response to contact with rhizobia, legumes form **root nodules**, tumor-like organs that house the rhizobia in a perfect partnership. The plant secretes a chemical signal that invites *Rhizobium* to its root hairs (elongated cells on the surface of the root), and once the microbe-plant contact occurs, the root hair curls around the bacteria, enveloping them inside the root cell (Needham, 2000). The rhizobia spread into the root cortex through a plant structure called an infection thread, and in the cortex, the bacteria lose their cell walls as they make their home within plant cells and become nitrogen-fixing bacteroids. The root nodule provides an anaerobic environment for nitrogenase activity. In order to provide oxygen (O_2) for other reactions without interfering with nitrogen fixation, plants produce the heme protein leghemoglobin, which carries oxygen to the cells

while simultaneously sequestering it away from nitrogenase (Wessner et al., p. 566). This interdependence between legumes and rhizobia demonstrates a shared evolutionary history.

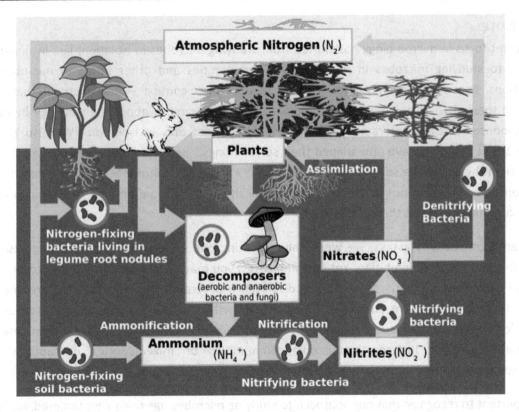

Figure 12-3. Schematic of nitrogen cycle. Bacteria play an essential role in the nitrogen cycle by "fixing" nitrogen (converting N_2 gas to ammonia) and making it usable for plants. Photo source: commons.wikimedia.org

Microbes and Us

Microbes not only make up most of the cells and DNA inside and on our bodies, but also play important roles in our digestive system, immunity, and probably even behavior. Whether we acquire them from things we touch, from yogurt or other fermented products, or from each other or other species, categorizing them as either "good" or "bad" is not straightforward. The Human Microbiome Project, an initiative launched by the U.S. National Institutes of Health, seeks to characterize all the entities that make up the **human microbiome**, or collection of microorganisms in our bodies. Articles challenging traditional views of microbes and urging us to "tend" our microbial flora with "good" bacteria-promoting diets and even microbiota transplants (Zimmer, 2012) permeate the media. Nevertheless, bacteria that can enrich our nutrition and prevent pathogenic bacteria from colonizing the gut epithelium can be closely related to the bacteria that cause food poisoning and lead to massive product recalls. That is because bacteria, like all organisms, exist in their current state in context. Microbes in a **consortium**, or a collection of symbiotic species in a microbial community, are kept in check by neighboring organisms but display different phenotypes in isolation. This creates a challenge when

115

Tiny Earth

studying microbes outside of their context, whether that is a set of abiotic conditions or the inside of mealybug.

Final Note

The current focus in microbiology has shifted from studying microbes in isolation, i.e., in single-species cultures, to studying microbes in mixed-species communities and other forms of microbe-microbe associations. As we have seen, microbes are shaped by their context — the microbes that surround them and their physical environment — and we can learn far more about their biology by observing their responses to these interactions than by studying them only in isolation. (We also know from Section 1 that microbes have also shaped their surroundings.) Bacteria grow and look very different in the lab than they do in the soil, and most of them (~99%) are not culturable under standard laboratory conditions; we simply do not understand the complexity of their requirements well enough to design culture conditions that suit them.

In our antibiotic activity assays, we were only expecting one type of interaction: antagonism, which results in a clear zone of inhibition. Yet, in some cases, you may have noticed that your tester strain or bacterial isolate grew slightly differently or displayed a different morphology in the presence of the other. Maybe one organism enhances the other's growth or cooperates to access resources. These interactions could be the focus of a whole other course in microbiology research or someone's entire life's work in research. Just search "microbial communities" or "mixed-species" or "biofilms" on your search engine, and the wealth of up-and-coming research you find will be tremendous!

It is important to recognize that our approach to studying microbes has been very targeted, and that just as microbes are abundant and diverse, so are the possibilities of research. As you go on to pursue the chemical structure of your antibiotic or study its spectrum and mechanism of action in more detail, keep in mind that each bacterium contains a wealth of information, which grows as you study it in the context of other organisms or other variables. You have already gained a strong foundation to talk about your microbes, learn more about them in the literature, and design some final experiments. The insights you have gathered about them are the product of your interactions with the organism, and in many ways, *you* have become their context. This is the nature of research. Our experiences leave an indelible mark in the world, and with this research, you have left yours.

References

Currie, C.R., Scott, J.A., Summerbell, R.C., Malloch, D. (1999) Fungus-growing ants use antibiotic-producing bacteria to control garden parasites. Nature 398:701-704.

Haeder, S., Wirth, R., Herz, H., & Spiteller, D. (2009) Candicidin-producing *Streptomyces* support leaf-cutting ants to protect their fungus garden against the pathogenic fungus *Escovopsis*. Proc Natl Acad Sci U S A 106:4742–4746.

Husnik, F., Nikoh, N., Koga, R., Ross, L., Duncan, R. P., Fujie, M., Tanaka, M., Satoh, N., Bachtrog, D., Wilson, A. C., von Dohlen, D. D., Fukatsu, T., & McCutcheon, J. P. (2013) Horizontal gene transfer from diverse

bacteria to an insect genome enables a tripartite nested mealybug symbiosis. Cell 153:1567–1578. doi: 10.1016/j.cell.2013.05.040

Moorman, G. W. (2013) Plants & Pests: *Pythium*. Penn State College of Agricultural Sciences. http://extension.psu.edu/pests/plant-diseases/all-fact-sheets/pythium

Needham, C. (2000) *Intimate Strangers : Unseen Life on Earth*. Washington, DC: ASM Press.

Sagan, L. (1967). On the origin of mitosing cells. J Theor Biol 14:255–274.

Scott, J.J., Oh, D.C., Yuceer, M.C., Klepzig, K.D., Clardy, J., Currie, C.R. (2008) Bacterial protection of beetle-fungus mutualism. Science 322:63.

Seipke, R. F., Barke, J., Brearley, C., Hill, L., Yu, D. W., Goss, R. J. M., & Hutchings, M. I. (2011). A single *Streptomyces* symbiont makes multiple antifungals to support the fungus farming ant *Acromyrmex octospinosus*. PLoS ONE 6(8):e22028. doi: 10.1371/journal.pone.0022028

Wessner, D. R., Dupont, C., & Charles, T. (2013) *Microbiology* New York: Wiley & Sons.

Zimmer, C. Tending the Body's Microbial Garden. The New York Times. June 18, 2012. http://www.nytimes.com/2012/06/19/science/studies-of-human-microbiome-yield-new-insights.html?_r=0

Experiment 12: Assess activity against eukaryotes, potential use in biological control, and ecological relationships with other organisms

Biological Questions:

1. Could we use the antibiotics produced by our isolates to treat bacterial infections in humans? Why or why not?
2. How do our antibiotic-producing isolates interact with plants and other organisms?
3. Could we use the antibiotic-producing organism as a biological control agent in our crops? Against what disease?

Isolate's interactions with plants:

Hypothesis and rationale:

Experimental design and protocols used:

Controls and treatments:

Observations:

Interpretations and conclusions:

Isolate's effect on plant pathogens, e.g., *Pythium*:

Hypothesis and rationale:

Experimental design and protocols used:

Controls and treatments:

Observations:

Interpretations and conclusions:

Design experiment to assess other ecological relationships:

Concluding Remarks

Think about how far you have come in only a few weeks. You have learned about the global antibiotic crisis, you have learned that soil is not just "dirt," you have isolated bacteria from your own soil samples, and you have applied the scientific method to investigate these samples. Throughout this time, you have learned how to communicate with your peers in your classroom and around the world and you have shared your experimental results with them. You are on your way to becoming an active partner in the educational mission of your campus and a lifelong learner.

Furthermore, you have played an important role in addressing what the United Nations has called "the greatest and most urgent global risk." While local, national, and global actions are required to solve the antibiotic crisis, individuals can have an impact. Going forward, consider simple things you can do to stop the misuse of antibiotics and reduce the spread of infections, including washing your hands, supporting companies that adopt safe antibiotic-use policies, getting vaccinated, and not demanding antibiotics when you have a viral infection like a cold or flu. Remember, in the United States, consumer demand led to nine of the largest food chains adopting new sourcing policies that require antibiotic-free meat, which have prompted changes in agricultural practices. It is important for you to understand your power as an individual and a consumer.

While we are running out of time to deal with the public health emergency of antibiotic resistance, it is not too late if we respond effectively with global collaboration. Through your research, you have already been part of a global initiative to crowdsource antibiotic discovery through the efforts of thousands of student researchers conducting mass-scale fundamental biological discovery.

Even though antimicrobial resistance has significant global consequences, humans have the ingenuity to solve this problem...if we act. We hope that everyone who is part of **Tiny Earth** recognizes that, together, we can make a difference.

PART II:
Research Protocols

Tiny Earth
studentsourcing antibiotic discovery

Contents

Agarose Gel Electrophoresis

Agarose gel electrophoresis is a common technique in molecular biology and microbiology that separates DNA fragments based on three features: (1) charge (positive versus negative), (2) size in base pairs (bp), and (3) conformation (linear versus circular). Scientists use agarose gel electrophoresis to follow up on DNA extraction and amplification protocols, such as polymerase chain reaction (PCR), which generate millions of DNA fragments. Running a DNA solution or reaction through an agarose gel separates millions of DNA fragments into discrete bands that indicate size, quantity, and uniformity.

An agarose gel is a jellylike material made up of agarose, a polysaccharide extracted from seaweed, and a buffer solution. Agarose forms a porous matrix that allows molecules to pass through with some impedance determined by the concentration of the agarose and size of the molecules. When the gel is placed in an electric field in buffer solution, charged molecules migrate through the gel toward the opposite charge. One such molecule is DNA, which has a partial negative charge on the phosphate group of the DNA backbone. DNA molecules loaded into a gel migrate toward the positive electrode. Since the gel matrix impedes flow, smaller molecules will travel rapidly, easily slipping through pores in the matrix, whereas larger molecules will be slowed down as they bump into the gel matrix; this process spreads the DNA molecules through the gel based on their size.

A PCR product, which contains millions of copies of one specific stretch of DNA, will appear as one discrete band on a gel. A solution containing a mixture of DNA fragments of different sizes will generate either multiple discrete bands or a smear of randomly sized fragments. To estimate the size of the fragment in each band, a molecular-weight size marker or DNA ladder, which contains DNA fragments of known sizes, is run in its own lane on the same gel with the

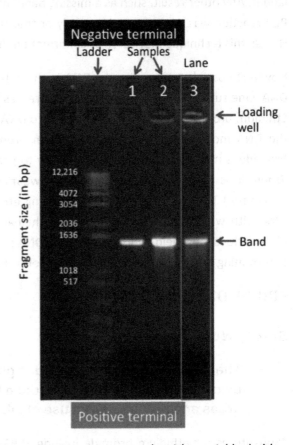

Figure 1. An agarose gel with a 1-kb ladder reference. A 1-kb ladder consists of fragments of DNA that differ in size by 1000-bp (1-kb) increments. It is used as a standard for comparison with unknown samples. In this gel, the 1-kb ladder is in the left-most lane and the other three lanes contain samples with discrete bands that represent DNA molecules that are approximately 1500 bp. DNA migrates through the gel in a buffer solution from the negative terminal to the positive terminal when an electric field is applied.

unknown samples. This way, scientists can use gels to analyze mixed samples or PCR products, given that they have a basic understanding of the DNA sample or product at hand. Amplifying regions of bacterial DNA, such as the 16S rRNA gene, with PCR will generate fragments of approximately 1500 bp or smaller. Therefore, we would expect to see one band that has traveled the same distance as a 1500-bp band on the ladder. Any other result, such as a missing band, multiple bands, or a smear, may indicate that the original PCR reaction was not executed properly or that the template DNA did not contain the desired template. Hence, this technique may serve as confirmation that the predicted product was synthesized.

How is it possible to visualize the DNA in the gel? Various fluorescent tags emit light when they bind to DNA. One such tag, ethidium bromide, fluoresces with an orange color when exposed to ultraviolet light. Ethidium bromide molecules intercalate into DNA, or insert between adjacent base pairs, which disrupts the DNA molecule. In living cells ethidium bromide can produce mutations. (Note: Use of ethidium bromide is minimized because of its ability to produce mutations, which can lead to cancer in animals. When it is used precautions including wearing proper personal protective [PPE] equipment are necessary.) The brightness of the fluorescing ethidium bromide is indicative of the relative quantity of DNA with which it is associated — a bright band contains more DNA than a dim band. While these observations only yield approximations of DNA size and concentration, they serve as a useful first step in determining the outcome of a reaction or confirming the presence of a specific product.

PROTOCOL

Safety Notes:

- **The protocol used here provides guidelines for agarose gel electrophoresis using ethidium bromide.* Ethidium bromide should be handled only in designated areas and requires strict use of lab coats, gloves, and goggles.**

*Substitutes for ethidium bromide include SYBR safe and GelRed, which is more sensitive and stable than either ethidium bromide or SYBR safe.

Note: Different tags and stains may require different viewing trays and safety precautions. Chamber and gel tray sizes may also vary depending on the equipment available at your facility and the number of samples to be analyzed.

MATERIALS
- Agarose
- 1× TBE (TRIS-borate-EDTA) buffer
- 1-kb ladder
- Ethidium bromide (1% solution in deionized [DI] water)
- Erlenmeyer flask
- Microwave oven
- 6× loading dye
- Gel tray, comb, chamber, and power pack for electrophoresis
- UV chamber or lamp

Tiny Earth
studentsourcing antibiotic discovery

PROTOCOL

1. Weigh 1 g of agarose and mix with 100 mL 1× TBE buffer in an Erlenmeyer flask – this will make a 1% agarose gel
2. Microwave contents of Erlenmeyer flask (1-2 min) until the mixture boils or becomes transparent.
3. Allow mixture to cool (10–15 min)
4. Carefully add 2–3 µL of ethidium bromide to cool agarose mixture. Pour mixture into gel tray with appropriate comb and allow 20 minutes to solidify.
5. Carefully remove comb from gel. Place gel tray into gel electrophoresis chamber, submerged in 1× TBE buffer, and start loading wells:
   a. Load 1-kb ladder into first well.
   b. Mix 5 µL of PCR product with 1 µL 6× loading dye and dispense into wells.
6. Plug electrodes into appropriate terminals of the chamber (positive with positive, negative with negative), ensuring that DNA is loaded on the negative end of the gel. What will happen if you plug in the electrodes backward?
7. Allow gel to run for 40–60 minutes (at 100 mA/V or constant voltage at approximately 180 V, depending on the equipment).
8. Finally, carefully remove gel from tray and place in UV chamber to photograph it (expect to see band at about 1.5 kb for full-length 16S rRNA gene).

Antibiotic Resistance Test

Note alternative method at the end of this protocol.

Soon after the introduction of antibiotics into clinical practice, resistant microorganisms were detected. Surprisingly, resistance to synthetic antibiotics (created by chemists rather than found in Nature) appeared as rapidly as resistance to antibiotics found in Nature, proving incorrect predictions that because the synthetic antibiotics didn't come from Nature, resistance hadn't yet evolved. Antibiotics that take tremendous resources to develop for clinical use can become ineffective within months or years of their introduction – often due to drug misuse or overuse. The tendency of antibiotics to stop working has deterred pharmaceutical companies from pursuing new antibiotics even though the demand continues to rise. So, how does antibiotic resistance come about? We have noticed that, generally, low- and long-term exposure to antibiotics provide a selective pressure for microorganisms with favorable genotypes – those carrying resistance genes or with spontaneous mutations – to increase in frequency in the population (more on antibiotic resistance in Section 10). Selection pressure can result in proliferation of resistant bacteria at the expense of sensitive ones of the same species, and the resistance genes can even be transferred to other species through horizontal gene transfer. This evolutionary phenomenon has existed for as long as antibiotics have existed in Nature; however, the incredibly fast rate at which antibiotic resistance spreads is associated with mass production and widespread use of antibiotics and is problematic.

Resistance varies in distribution and mechanism. Soil bacteria are resistant to their own antibiotics, often because of genes that confer resistance only to the antibiotic produced. Other resistance genes provide resistance to several antibiotics, and some bacteria contain many antibiotic resistance genes, making them resistant to many antibiotics. The soil antibiotic resistome is the collection of resistance genes from microorganisms in the soil. While humans have vastly increased the frequency of resistance genes in the bacterial world, resistant bacteria were present before antibiotic use by humans, and resistance genes can be found even in the most remote environments on the planet.

In this protocol, we will test bacterial isolates for the presence of resistance genes against common antibiotics. ***For more information on antibiotic resistance, please refer to Section 10.***

MATERIALS
- Antibiotic-containing media plates (see preparation for instructor below)
- Sterile inoculating loops or toothpicks
- Streak plates of isolate to be tested or original master plate

Preparation of Antibiotic-Containing Media (for instructor)
1. Prepare LBA or isolate's original medium. Make enough media for each student to have one plate with medium of choice per antibiotic.
2. Place aliquots of media into separate capped bottles that will each be mixed with an aliquot of antibiotic solution. Placing the media into the bottles prior to autoclaving will decrease the

Tiny Earth
studentsourcing antibiotic discovery

chance of contamination. Alternatively, use aseptic technique to distribute the media after autoclaving.

3. After autoclaving media, allow to cool down (comfortably warm to the touch). Be sure to work quickly to keep the media from solidifying, or keep it warm in a water bath.

4. Follow antibiotic specifications in the table below for the following steps.

5. Determine the volume to antibiotic stock solution to be added to the batch of media.

6. Add x volume of antibiotic solution to batch of media, cap bottle, and mix gently by swirling to distribute antibiotic solution.

7. Pour plates and label appropriately. Keep plate containing light-sensitive antibiotics wrapped in foil or in the dark. After solidifying, store plates until lab session.

Antibiotic Specifications

Antibiotic	Solvent	Stock solution and storage temperature	Working solution (final concentration)	Light sensitive?***	Antibiotic mode of action?
Penicillin	DI* water	10 mg/mL (−20°C)	10 µg/mL media	No	
Gramicidin	Methanol	10 mg/mL (−20°C)	10 µg/mL media	No	
Trimethoprim	DMSO**	5 mg/mL (−20°C)	5 µg/mL media	No	
Rifampicin	DMSO	10 mg/mL (−20°C)	1 µg/mL media	Yes	
Tetracycline	70% ethanol	10 mg/mL (−20°C)	1 µg/mL media	Yes	

*Deionized

**Dimethyl sulfoxide

***Media with light-sensitive antibiotics must be wrapped in foil or stored in the dark. Plates must also be wrapped in foil or stored in the dark.

Tiny Earth
studentsourcing antibiotic discovery

PROTOCOL

Safety Notes:

- **Must wear gloves and goggles, and practice aseptic technique throughout this protocol.**

- **Handle all solvents in a chemical fume hood.**

- **Ensure proper glove choice with use of DMSO since it can be absorbed directly into the skin.**

- **Label all secondary containers of chemicals and do not allow DMSO to enter drains.**

- **Dispose of chemical waste according to your institution's policies.**

Obtain streak plates of your isolates (recommended), or original master plate.

1. Obtain antibiotic-containing media plate(s) of interest. Media plates will contain standard media (LB, PDA, TSA, etc.) with the following antibiotic concentrations:

   a. Penicillin: 10 µg/mL
   b. Gramicidin: 10 µg/mL
   c. Trimethoprim: 5 µg/mL
   d. Rifampicin: 1 µg/mL
   e. Tetracycline: 1 µg/mL

2. Review Table 1 with antibiotic specifications. Ensure that antibiotic-containing media plate is labeled appropriately with antibiotic, concentration, and isolate(s) to be tested.

3. Using sterile inoculating loop or toothpick, pick isolate(s) from streak plate(s) or master plate and patch onto antibiotic plate. Make sure patch is labeled on the back of the plate with isolate name.

4. Incubate plate at isolate's designated growth conditions for 1–2 days, or until dense patch forms. If necessary, ensure plates are refrigerated at 4°C until next lab session to prevent overgrowth of patch (if next lab session is more than 2 days later).

5. After incubation period, observe plates for growth. Does the isolate appear to be susceptible or resistant to the antibiotic? Develop a hypothesis that explains the result based on your observations and what you know about your isolate. Record observations.

NOTE ON PROTOCOL ALTERNATIVE: Instructor may use the Kirby-Bauer Disk Diffusion Susceptibility test as an alternative to this protocol. This technique may be of interest to aspiring microbiologists. For more details on the Kirby-Bauer protocol, and to see the procedure, please the ASM Microbe Library's Laboratory Protocols at https://www.microbelibrary.org/.

Catalase Test

Adapted from: Karen Reiner – Microbe Library http://microbelibrary.org/index.php/library/laboratory-test/3226-catalase-test-protocol

Hydrogen peroxide (H_2O_2) is a strong oxidizing agent that rapidly kills susceptible cells and is employed by many organisms to protect themselves against infectious bacteria. H_2O_2 is also used as an antiseptic applied on cuts or wounds on the skin; you will typically find it next to rubbing alcohol and first-aid kits at the store. Many bacteria have evolved defense mechanisms that allow them to counteract H_2O_2 activity in order to survive. This is facilitated by catalase, an enzyme that breaks down H_2O_2 into water and oxygen gas.

$$2H_2O_2 + catalase \rightarrow 2H_2O + O_2$$

Bacteria containing catalase will effervesce, or form bubbles of oxygen, when they come in contact with H_2O_2. This serves as a simple test for the presence of catalase. For this reason, it is one of the bacterial enzymes described and used to classify bacteria (Gagnon et al., 1959; McLeod et al., 1923). A 3% H_2O_2 solution is typically used to test bacteria for catalase activity. Other applications, especially in diagnostics, include the identification of anaerobes using 15% H_2O_2 solution, as anaerobes typically lack the enzyme (Bartelt, 2000).

The catalase test is essential for differentiating catalase-positive *Micrococcus* and *Staphylococcus* from catalase-negative *Streptococcus*. While it is primarily useful in differentiating among genera, the test is also valuable in speciation of certain Gram positive bacteria such as *Aerococcus urinae* (positive) from *Aerococcus viridans* (negative) and Gram-negative organisms such as *Campylobacter fetus*, *Campylobacter jejuni*, and *Campylobacter coli* (all positive) from other *Campylobacter* species (MacFaddin, 2000; Mahon et al., 2011). Some microbiologists use the amount of activity in the catalase test to differentiate among certain members of the *Enterobacteriaceae* family (Taylor and Achanzar, 1972). The catalase test is also valuable in differentiating aerobic and obligate anaerobic bacteria, as anaerobes are generally known to lack the enzyme (Mahon et al., 2011; McLeod et al., 1923). In this context, the catalase test is valuable in differentiating aerotolerant strains of *Clostridium*, which are catalase negative, from other members of the same phylum, such as *Bacillus*, which are catalase positive (Mahon et al., 2011).

MATERIALS
- 3% H_2O_2
- glass microscope slides or petri dishes
- inoculating loop or toothpicks
- streak plates of isolates
- streak plates of positive and negative controls (from safe ESKAPE relatives: Positive: *P. putida*; Negative: *S. epidermidis*

PROTOCOL

1. Obtain the streak plate of your bacterial isolate with fresh (1–3 day old), fully grown colonies.
2. Obtain a microscope slide or piece of parafilm. Optional: place microscope slide/parafilm piece inside a Petri dish and cover with lid to limit catalase aerosols during the test.
3. Using a sterile inoculating loop, stick, or toothpick, pick a single colony from the streak plate. A small yet visible cell mass will suffice. Note: Be careful not to pick any agar, especially if the isolate was grown on agar containing red blood cells, as these may result in a false-positive reaction.
4. Gently apply the cells with a back-and-forth motion until there is a small, visible smear in the center of the slide/film. To conserve materials, smear up to three isolates in separate smears on a single slide.
5. Using dropper or pipette, place 1 drop of 3% H_2O_2 solution onto the smear on the slide. Do not mix. Note: carrying out steps 5 and 6 on a dark background will enhance the visibility of bubbles.
6. Observe for the production of oxygen bubbles – this will happen rapidly and vigorously in a positive reaction. A weak reaction or no reaction may indicate a negative. Optional: For weak catalase-positive microorganisms, examine slides under a dissecting microscope or using 4x or 10x magnification on a light microscope.
7. Perform a control reaction using organisms known to be positive and negative for catalase.

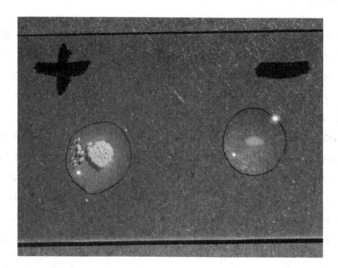

Figure 2. Catalase test. *Bacillus subtilis* is catalase positive (left) and *Enterococcus raffinosus* is catalase negative (right). Photo source: Manuel Fernando Garavito Diago

REFERENCES

Gagnon, M., Hunting, W., & Esselen, W. B. (1959) A new method for catalase determination. Anal Chem 31:144.

MacFaddin, J. F. (2000) *Biochemical Tests for Identification of Medical Bacteria* (3rd ed.). Philadelphia, PA: Lippincott Williams & Wilkins.

Mahon, C. R., Lehman, D. C., & Manuselis, G. (2011) *Textbook of Diagnostic Microbiology* (4th ed.). Philadelphia, PA: W. B Saunders Co.

McLeod, J. W., & Gordon, J. (1923) Catalase production and sensitiveness to hydrogen peroxide amongst bacteria: With a scheme for classification based on these properties. J Pathol Bacteriol 26:326–331.

Taylor, W. I., & Achanzar, D. (1972) Catalase test as an aid to the identification of Enterobacteriaceae. J Appl Microbiol 24: 58–61.

Adapted from:
Reiner, K. (2010) "Catalase Test Protocol". *Laboratory Protocols*. **Microbe Library**. American Society for Microbiology. Accessed 13 October 2013. http://microbelibrary.org/index.php/library/laboratory-test/3226-catalase-test-protocol

Chemical Extraction of Antibiotics

Separations have been a central theme in our research course: we have separated microbes from their natural habitat in our sample collections, we have separated individual cells in spread-and-streak plates, and now, our goal is to separate their bioactive compounds to be studied in isolation. This reductionist approach enables us to study cells, reactions, and metabolites under conditions that reduce confounding variables (other cells or molecules). Separating a bioactive compound from other molecules present in a culture is the first step in determining that compound's physical and chemical properties, mode of action, and activity spectrum. Just the way we use many household products to remove stains on fabrics and surfaces, we can apply specific solvents to cultures to extract compounds with similar properties. These compounds are typically classified based on their **polarity**, a chemical property discussed in Section 9. Polar or water-soluble compounds are at one end of the polarity spectrum while nonpolar or fat-soluble compounds lie at the opposite end. Chemists typically like to use solvents that have intermediate polarity to extract a compound of interest without getting all the "junk" at the extremes, such as water-soluble nutrients and long-chain fatty acids. In this protocol, we will use one of two common solvents, ethyl acetate or methanol, to attempt to separate the bioactive compound from most cell components and nutrients in our cultures. Whether the bioactivity is retained in water and/or ethyl acetate indicates the polarity of the active molecule and suggests ways that the compound or compounds can be manipulated in future experiments. ***For more information on chemical extractions, please refer to Section 9.

SESSION 1 – PREPARING PLATES

MATERIALS
- One medium plate per isolate (same as isolate's original medium)
- Sterile plastic inoculating loop or sterile swab– 1 per isolate
- Streak plates of isolates (or original master plate)

PROTOCOL

Safety Notes:

- **Must wear gloves, lab coat, and goggles. Use sterile technique in every step of Session 1 Protocol.**

1. Select isolates to be cultured for chemical extraction (1 or 2 per student)
2. Obtain streak plate of isolates, or original master plate if streak plates are missing.
3. Using the large end of the sterile loop, collect enough single colonies of isolate to spread on the entire surface of a media plate (fill about half of the loop). Or use a sterile swap to pick up a few colonies of isolate to spread across the surface of a media plate.
4. Gently inoculate entire surface of the fresh media plate by rubbing the loop or swab with colonies back and forth until the entire area is covered.

5. Ensure the plate is evenly coated with inoculum. If needed, turn the plate 90° and continue to rub the loop/swab back and forth. This will grow into a **lawn** of your isolate.

6. Incubate plates at 28°C, or temperatures and conditions specific to isolate. Incubate until next lab session, or 2-3 days, and up to a week.

SESSION 2 – CHOPPING UP PLATE

MATERIALS
- 100-250-mL glass bottles (with cap) – 1 per isolate
- Microspatula or cutting device
- Freezing compartment*

*Options include a freezer (−20°C or −80°C) or a dry ice/ethanol bath

PROTOCOL

Safety Notes:

- **Must wear gloves, lab coat, and goggles. No need to keep lawn sterile with a Bunsen burner or flame in Session 2 Protocol.**

1. Obtain inoculated media plates from previous session. Ensure your isolates have grown into a dense lawn.

2. Using a microspatula, cut the media plate with fully grown isolate into small pieces, about 1 cm^2 each (no need to make precise cuts).

3. Scoop all the pieces with microspatula into a 100-250-mL glass bottle and label with isolate name. Push all the pieces to the bottom of bottle with microspatula.

4. Freeze bottle in freezing compartments. Follow specific instructions for freezer compartment of choice below:

   FOR FREEZER, place bottle in freezer until next lab session (CONTINUE ON TO **SESSION 3-A** IN THE SUBSEQUENT LAB PERIOD)

   FOR DRY ICE/ETHANOL BATH, place bottle into bath for 20–30 minutes (Caution: ethanol with dry ice is supercooled to temperatures that can cause frostbite upon contact with skin. Do not splash ethanol. Place bottles into bath gently to keep glass from shattering!) (CONTINUE TO **SESSION 3-A** IN THE SAME LAB PERIOD)

Question: What is the purpose of freezing the pieces of agar?

SESSION 3-A – ORGANIC EXTRACTION PART 1

MATERIALS
- Ethyl acetate or methanol
- Deionized water (not recommended for methanol extraction)

- Pasteur pipettes (glass) and bulbs
- 20-mL scintillation vial or other glass container* – 2 per isolate (1 per isolate for methonal)
- Analytical scale (optional)
- Fume hood
- Recommended: drying-system or vacuum

PROTOCOL

Safety Notes:

- As a general precaution, always use glassware instead of plastic when working with solvents.

- Must wear gloves, lab coat, and goggles. Must handle solvents inside fume hood.

- Inhalation of organic solvents can cause adverse health effects, drowsiness, and loss of consciousness.

- Keep away from Bunsen burner or flame when working with open bottles or beakers with flammable solvents, such as ethyl acetate and methanol.

Note: All steps on this protocol apply to both ethyl acetate and methanol, unless otherwise noted. Ethyl acetate-specific instructions are underlined. Methanol-specific instructions are bold and in red. Pay close attention to differences in the text.

Note: No need to keep things sterile with Bunsen burner or flame in Session 3 Protocol.

1. Remove bottles from freezer OR dry ice/ethanol bath. Bottle may be thawed or kept frozen for next step.
2. FOR ETHYL ACETATE EXTRACTION: Add 15 mL of ethyl acetate and 10 mL of water to bottle. You may notice two layers will start to form. The top layer is the ethyl acetate phase, and the bottom layer is the aqueous phase.
What does the placement of layer say about the density of ethyl acetate?
Place capped bottle on shaker at room temperature until next lab session.

    OR

    FOR METHANOL EXTRACTION: Add 15 mL of methanol (DO NOT ADD WATER) to bottle and place capped bottle on shaker at room temperature until next lab session.

    Note: Methanol and water are miscible, which means they can mix together. Mixing methanol with water will dilute our extract and will make it difficult and time-consuming to dry the extract.

While shaking at room temperature, bottle will thaw and organic solvent will extract soluble components in the lawn and agar.

SESSION 3-B – ORGANIC EXTRACTION PART 2

1. Using a Pasteur pipette and bulb, gently transfer all the liquid from the bottle to a labeled scintillation vial or other glass container. Once all liquid is transferred, let sit for 2–3 minutes to allow any debris to settle (e.g., small chunks of agar).

    FOR ETHYL ACETATE, organic (top) and aqueous (bottom) layers will start to separate. Depending on the color of your extract, both layers may appear clear. Carefully identify the interface between them. Note: Emulsion (a cloudy third layer) may form between the top and bottom layers. Try not to disrupt the emulsion.

    FOR METHANOL, note that separate layers will not form. If pre-weighing vial, only one vial is needed and should be weighed prior to transfer step.

2. Optional*: Pre-weigh second set of scintillation vials or other glass container with appropriate labels (isolate name, etc.) on analytical scale. Record weights.

3. Using a Pasteur pipette and bulb, transfer solvent from vials or containers in step 3 to preweighed vial or container. Follow specific instructions for solvent of choice below:

    FOR ETHYL ACETATE, transfer organic layer (top) – ethyl acetate with soluble components of the lawn and the agar – into pre-weighed vial or container. Carefully collect as much of the organic layer as possible. Avoid collecting emulsion (if present) and aqueous layer. It is better to leave some solvent than collect water. Once organic layer is removed, keep vial or container uncapped in fume hood to evaporate remaining ethyl acetate.

    FOR METHANOL, all 15 ml transferred to vial should be placed uncapped in fume hood to evaporate solvent.

    After that, store aqueous phase at 4°C or freeze at −20°C if intention to assay aqueous phase for activity (refer to note at the end of Session 4 Protocol).

4. Allow extract to dry down by evaporation. Vials or containers with extracts may be left uncapped inside fume hood until next lab session, or until completely dried down.* Alternatively, extracts may be dried using drying system or applied vacuum, which may reduce the drying-down period to several minutes or hours.

*Pre-weighing empty vials and containers prior to transferring extracts, and then re-weighing with dried extract, makes it possible to calculate how much extract is recovered from cultures. This facilitates preparing extracts at the same concentration, which makes it possible to compare the potency of different samples by assaying their activity based on a known

concentration. Knowing the concentration of material facilitates using appropriate amounts of material in subsequent chemical analyses *via* Liquid Chromatography Mass Spectrometry or Thin Layer Chromatography (TLC). An analytical balance is highly recommended because the weight of extracted material can range from milligrams to submilligrams (less than 10^{-3} grams). It is advisable to keep the same vial and lid together since lid weights can vary substantially and a lid from different extract can contaminate a sample.

SESSION 4 – ASSAY EXTRACT FOR ANTIBIOTIC ACTIVITY

Note: All dried extracts will be redissolved in methanol, regardless of the solvent used in the extraction – Session 3.

MATERIALS

- Dried-down extract in scintillation vial or other glass container
- Media plates (because we are testing cell-free extract, does not need to be the same as isolate's original medium)
- Overnight culture of safe ESKAPE relative (your tester strain)
- Methanol
- Sterile 15-mL conical tube or test tube
- Micropipettor and tips (P20 and P200)
- LB with 1/2x (0.75%) agar (if using top agar method)

PROTOCOL

Safety Notes:

- **Must wear gloves, lab coat, and goggles, and use sterile technique.**

1. Your extracts are now dried down in a vial/container.
   Optional (if vials/containers were pre-weighed): re-weigh vial/container on the same analytical balance, calculate mass of dried extract, and record in your notes.
2. IF MASS NOT CALCULATED: Resuspend dried-extract in 80 µL methanol

   OR

   IF MASS CALCULATED: Resuspend pre-weighed dried-extract methanol – adjust volume of solvent to attain desired concentration (recommended concentration: 5–10 µg/µL).

Spread-Spot Method

1. Spread some of an overnight liquid culture of safe ESKAPE relative (tester strain) using sterile loop or sterile swab on media that best supports tester strain growth (generally LBA or 1/10 TSA). Allow spread tester strain to soak into media so plate is dry for next step. Initially you should use the same tester strain(s) your isolate had activity against.

2. Prepare to spot dried extract on a spread plate of safe ESKAPE relative (tester strain):

Indicate on your media plate where extract and control will be spotted by drawing a dot on the back of the plate (one circle for each extract and one for the control).

Note: Properly label back of media plate with safe ESKAPE relative name, isolate name, and extracts and controls to be spotted into the circles.

Question: What will the control(s) be in the extract activity assay?

1. Using a P20 micropipettor, spot 10 µL of resuspended extract on the appropriate pre-drawn dot. Allow the solvent to evaporate – the spot should appear dry. Repeat for methanol control.
2. Load another 10 µL on same spot and let dry (OR volume determined for specific concentration). Repeat for the control.
3. Repeat step 5 one more time until 30 µL total volume is loaded onto the appropriate pre-drawn dot.

Top Agar Method

***Note: Top agar (LB with 1/2x (0.75%) agar) must be liquefied in microwave or water bath and allowed to cool down (warm to the touch) prior to Step 8 below. If cooled for too much, it will solidify.

3b. Skip step 3 above, but continue with steps 4-7, spotting extract and control on sterile media plate. Because we are using top agar (which supports growth of tester strain) and cell-free extracts the type of media is not as critical here.

While the spots are drying, obtain an overnight liquid culture of your tester strain and an empty, sterile conical tube or test tube. Set P200 micropipette to 100 µL.

***Following steps must be done carefully but quickly to keep liquefied top agar from solidifying in the tube. Following steps will not be used for Spread-Spot method. ***

1. Using sterile technique, transfer ~7 mL of liquefied top agar to the sterile tube.
2. Inoculate liquefied top agar in tube with 100 µL of tester strain overnight liquid culture. Gently mix by rolling tube back and forth in hands.
3. Quickly and carefully pour inoculated top agar onto spotted media plate. Gently tilt the plate to spread top agar evenly over the entire plate. After covering entire surface, keep plate upright until top agar solidifies (i.e., becoming translucent and appearing more rigid).
4. Incubate at 28°C, or temperatures and conditions specific to tester strain. Plate may be incubated upside-down after top agar solidifies. Incubate overnight or until tester strain grows into a lawn, and keep refrigerated at 4°C to avoid overgrowth until next lab session.

AQUEOUS PHASE NOTE: Session 4 Protocol may be repeated using aqueous phase. Note that aqueous spots will take significantly longer than those in organic solvents to evaporate in the fume hood and may not fully dry in one lab session. Alternatively, we recommend using a lyophilizer to dry down the frozen aqueous phase and then proceeding through Session 4 Protocol.

SESSION 5 – SCREEN ZONES OF INHIBITION

MATERIALS
- Plates from previous session

PROTOCOL

Safety Notes:

- **Must wear gloves, lab coat, and goggles, and use sterile technique.**

Observe plates for zones of inhibitions. Ensure that methanol control worked properly. Measure zones of inhibition and record observations. Did your organic extracts retain antibiotic activity? How do the zones of inhibition compare with observations made in previous assays?

Alternatives: EXTRACTION WITH OTHER SOLVENTS

2-Butanol:
Although 2-butanol is immiscible with water, the organic and aqueous fractions are typically not as distinct as when ethyl acetate is used. The cloudy region in between these layers can be eliminated using centrifugation. Transfer the liquid to a conical tube and centrifuge for 5 minutes at 10,000 rpm. The organic layer can then be easily pipetted to a scintillation vial for drying.

Hexane:
Hexane is easy to use for extractions because it evaporates very quickly. However, when hexane is spotted onto agar, it spreads across the plate quite far from the point where it was originally spotted. Therefore, if hexane is used as the extraction solvent, the bioassay procedure must be altered. Rather than spotting 10 µL of re-suspended extract 3 times (as described in "Day 4"), spot 5 µL of re-suspended hexane extract 6 times.

Colony Morphology Description

Since bacteria were first cultured on solid media, microbiologists have noticed that colonies display differences in physical appearance at the macroscopic level. Reference books such as *Bergey's Manual of Systematic Bacteriology* contain extensive descriptions of bacterial physical and functional attributes, which have enabled microbiologists to identify and classify bacteria for nearly a century. Colony morphology is one of the first things we observe about bacteria at the macroscale and use to distinguish them from other microbes and distantly related bacteria. The main descriptors used by microbiologists are: (1) color, (2) surface texture and elevation, (3) shape, and (4) margin. We use specific terms to describe morphological characteristics, such the ones described in Figure 3. However, bacteria come in a many forms; therefore, there is much room for creativity when describing colony morphology.

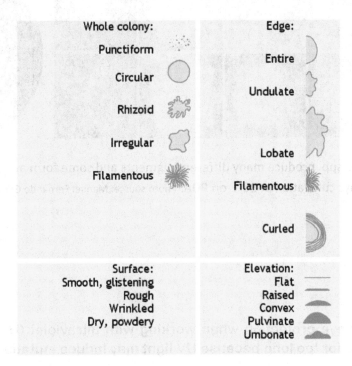

Figure 3. Descriptors of colony morphology. Photo from commons.wikimedia.org

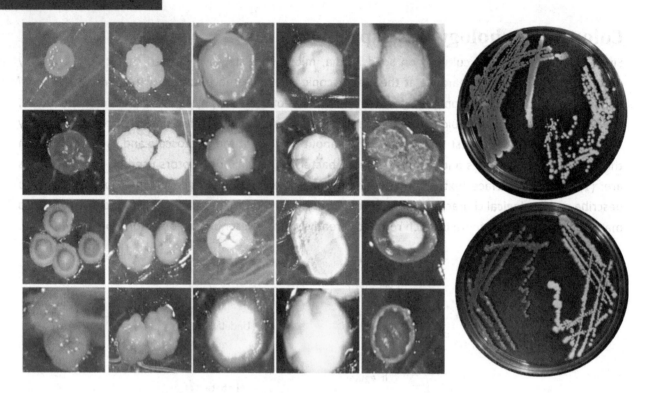

Figure 4. *Streptomyces* spp. produce many different pigments and some form aerial mycelia. Soil isolates are shown after 10 days cultivation at 28°C on PDA. Photo source: Manuel Fernando Garavito Diago

PROTOCOL

Safety Notes:

- **Use proper eye protection when working with ultraviolet (UV) light, and do not expose cells for too long because UV light may induce mutations.**

1. Many classrooms will use colony morphology differences as the first level of selection from dilution plates to identify different isolates for further testing. Observe colonies from soil dilution series. Alternatively, allow streak plate of bacterial isolates or master plate to grow for 2-4 days under optimal growth conditions. **Note:** Even if colonies are visible after a one-day incubation period, give the cells more time to produce pigments and other morphological identifiers that may not be as evident during logarithmic growth phase.

2. Once the cells are in the stationary phase of growth, start observing and describing their physical characteristics. **Note:** Keep the plate covered whenever possible, and keep it covered and sealed with parafilm at all times when working with unknown isolates in a BSL-1 lab. **Optional:** Use a dissecting microscope for better observations.

Tiny Earth
studentsourcing antibiotic discovery

3. Start by describing colony color, or pigmentation. Differentiate between colony pigments and pigments secreted into the agar surrounding the colony. If an ultraviolet lamp is available, shine the light on the colonies for few seconds to see if they glow in the dark.

4. Record an estimate of colony size; if possible, use a clear ruler to measure the diameter.

5. Pay close attention to the way colonies are shaped and scattered. Make sure you base your observations on single colonies. If colonies are too close together or packed together as a lawn or in slime, be sure to specify that in your notes. Note: You are not limited to using the terms in Figure 3.

6. Describe the margin, or edges, and elevation of the colonies. Although colony shape and margin influence one another, do not assume they are the same thing. **Note**: Carefully tilt the plate when observing colony elevation but do not bring it too close to your face.

7. Describe colony texture; this is where you will probably have to be most creative.

8. If possible, take pictures of your isolates using a lab camera. If your instructor allows personal devices in lab for picture taking, make sure it is protected in a plastic ziploc bag or wrapped in parafilm. Refer to Best Practice guidelines at the beginning of this book for more details.

Combining 16S rRNA Gene Sequences into a Single Contig

To determine an isolate's genus and closest matches in public databases, students can use PCR sequencing of the 16S rRNA gene and NIH's Basic Local Alignment Search Tool (BLAST) or the Ribosomal Database Project. Some classes may choose to sequence the full length (~1500 bases) of the 16S rRNA gene, which requires aligning the sequences from several PCR and sequencing reactions.

To obtain a preliminary identification of isolates, a single forward sequence can be used following the "DNA Sequence Analysis with BLAST and RDP" protocol. First, follow one of the "PCR Analysis" protocols, lysing cells and amplifying the 16S rRNA gene, verify product by gel electrophoresis and either purify the PCR product or pay for the sequencing facility to do the clean-up for you. We recommend sequencing using the forward (27F) primer. The 5' end of the gene tends to be more variable and is more reliable in identifying the genus than using the reverse primer (1492R or 1391R). Alternatively, one can use a reverse primer from the middle of the gene (519R or 769R). Your preliminary analysis will usually provide you with between 500-750 bp of coverage of the 16S rRNA. However, you may want to obtain full-length sequencing coverage of the gene to better confirm the identity of an isolate. To do so additional regions of the 16S rRNA gene, both in the forward and reverse direction, should be performed. To do this, use the remainder of your initial product from the "Colony PCR" or repeat the procedure for 16S rRNA PCR amplification. At the sequencing step, prepare a sample for each primer to be used covering different regions of the gene. Some good options to start with are 27F, 515F, 769R, 1492R. Please visit www.tinyearth.wisc.edu to access the "PCR and Sequencing Troubleshooting Guide" for help in addressing common reasons for unsuccessful PCR, sequences for additional primers mentioned above, and suggestions for accurate interpretation of sequencing results.

After sending these samples to a sequencing facility and obtaining the results, trim the sequences as described above. You can then use several online tools to align these sequences into a single contig.

First, in order for the forward and reverse sequences to align, enter each of the three reverse sequences into the revseq tool (http://emboss.bioinformatics.nl/cgi-bin/emboss/revseq), selecting "Yes" for both the "Reverse sequence?" and "Complement sequence?" options. The results should be an inversion of the original sequence and each base from the original sequence should be replaced by its complement (G becomes C, C becomes G, etc.).

You can align sequences to create a consensus sequence. For this process, several programs can be used (see https://www.ebi.ac.uk/Tools/msa/). In addition, BLAST permits alignment of two sequences by selecting "Align two or more sequences" in the top box below where one inputs the query sequence. The results page will show an alignment of the sequences, which can be saved as a consensus file. Repeat this process for the three reverse sequences, which should provide two consensus sequences, one for the forward direction and one for the reverse direction. These can be combined into one final consensus sequence using the same procedure described above. You will likely find that the forward and reverse sequences have a large region of nearly perfect consensus in the middle and that the forward has additional bases at the beginning of the sequence, while the reverse has additional bases at the end of the sequence. To combine these two sequences, simply copy the extra bases present at the beginning of the forward sequence and paste them at the beginning of the reverse sequence.

Submit this final consensus sequence to BLAST using the above procedure. If the sequence is at least 97% identical to a species in the database, then you have identified the genus and species of your isolate. If your consensus sequence is less than 97% identical to the first BLAST result, then it is possible that your isolate is of a previously undiscovered species.

Culturing from Soil Sample

We will use a culture-dependent approach to study bacteria, which relies on the ability of some bacteria to grow in the lab. Microbiologists have used this approach for over a century, and while the premise has not changed, our increased understanding of bacterial nutrition and growth has enabled development of media and lab conditions to more closely meet bacterial requirements for survival. This has also increased the reproducibility of natural phenomena from lab to lab, enabling microbiologists to repeat each others' experiments and confirm observations, thereby advancing the field. While we are far from attaining perfection in culturing bacteria and accurately replicating their natural habitats, we have the tools of observation, inquiry, and ingenuity to come a step closer. In addition, the more we learn about environments like the soil, the more we realize that this is truly an inexhaustible source of bacteria from which we still have much to learn.

After you collect a soil sample, the first step is to suspend the bacteria in liquid so that they can be transferred to another medium (e.g., a nutrient plate), leaving behind plant material, soil animals, and minerals from the soil. It is important to take into consideration the kind of vegetation the soil supported and select appropriate media accordingly. The soil contains a wide range of bacteria, so it is likely to yield growth in almost any standard bacteriological medium.

MATERIALS
- 3 LB plates/group
- Conical tube
- Soil sample
- Spread beads
- Sterile water

PROTOCOL
1. Weigh 1 g of soil sample, and place into conical tube.
2. Determine 3 different ways to plate this sample to visualize microbes.
3. Record all three procedures in lab notebook.

DNA Sequence Analysis with BLAST and RDP

Genomes contain large amounts of information – the human genome is over 3 billion base pairs long and bacterial genomes like that of *Escherichia coli* contain nearly 5 million base pairs. Making sense of all this information requires biological knowledge of how genes work and what they encode and powerful computational tools to sort through large amounts of information and find patterns. Sequenced genomes are submitted into large databases like GenBank that are impossible to navigate without search tools, just as Google Search helps find specific information in the whole of the World Wide Web.

The Basic Local Alignment Search Tool (BLAST) (Altschul et al., 1990) is a bio-informatics tool that allows us to navigate through huge databases and compare an amino acid or nucleotide sequence with a library of sequences. BLAST comparisons of DNA sequences can find closely related genes or regions of DNA in the database. These closely related genes whose functions or organism of origin have been determined previously provide information about the likely function of a newly discovered gene's product or the identity of the organism from which it originated.

MATERIALS
- 16S rRNA gene* sequence and chromatogram
- BLAST website

*For more information on the 16S rRNA gene, please refer to Section 8.

PROTOCOL
1. Go to the BLAST website: http://www.ncbi.nlm.nih.gov/BLAST/
2. Choose BLAST program to run a "nucleotide blast"
3. Enter your sequence* into the "Enter query sequence" field and enter appropriate nucleotide range*
4. Under "Choose Search Set," select the "16S ribosomal RNA sequences (Bacteria and Archaea)" database on the drop-down menu to conduct a search.
5. Once you have submitted your sequence and set the parameters, click "BLAST" at the bottom of the page. BLAST will take a couple of seconds to compare your sequence to other sequences in the database.
6. Once the search is done, analyze your BLAST data. The "Descriptions" column lists identifiers for similar sequences in the database. These identifiers are ranked by "max ident," which is the percentage of matching nucleotides. Normally, a "max ident" of 97% or higher means that your sequence matches the specific description, which corresponds to a strain or species. The expectation value (E value) tells you how statistically significant your match is; hence, the lower the E value, the more reliable the match.**

*Before entering your sequence into the "Enter Query Field," be sure to assess the quality of your sequence. This can be done by looking at your sequence trace chromatogram, which shows the

TinyEarth

fluorescence peaks given off by each of the four nucleotides during Sanger sequencing. You can view and trim sequence chromatograms using freely available software (e.g., Finch, DNA Baser, Chromas, and 4Peaks). Peaks are considered low quality when they are not discrete or separated from one another; this usually happens at the beginning and end of the sequence. You can trim low-quality data from the beginning and end of the sequence or pick a "clean" nucleotide range in your sequence on which to conduct the BLAST analysis. After pasting your full sequence into the appropriate box, enter the appropriate region range into the "Query Subrange" fields.

**There are two numbers you should care about: Max score and E value. The higher the Max score, the better the match. The default BLAST algorithm assigns +2 for each matching nucleotide and −3 for each mismatch to give a raw score, and then adjusts that score by length and database size to calculate the "Bit score." The E value (or expected value) estimates how many times we expect to find a match of the same quality (bit score) in the database purely by chance. The lower the E value, the better. The matches with an E value above 1 can be discarded.

The Alignment - The first line with ">" gives the address (accession number) of the full entry in the database, name of entry, and length. The summary section below the name shows the bit score and raw score in parentheses, E value, and % identity. The last part is the alignment itself: the query on top and the subject (sequence from the database) on the bottom, and vertical lines for each match between them. The numbers specify nucleotide position in each sequence.

NOTE ON PROTOCOL ALTERNATIVE: Students may also input their sequences into the RDP database (http://rdp.cme.msu.edu/seqmatch/seqmatch_intro.jsp), which specifically contains curated bacterial and archaeal 16S rRNA gene sequences. Comparing the results from BLAST and RDP can be a simple way for students to confirm the identity of their sequence.

REFERENCES

Altschul, S. F., Gish, W., Miller, W., Myers, E. W., & Lipman, D. J. (1990) Basic local alignment search tool. J Mol Biol 215:403–410. doi: 10.1016/S0022-2836(05)80360-2

Fermentation Test

Adapted from: Clifford Grimsley – Gaston College

Many organic compounds can be produced through fermentation, and many microbes satisfy their energy requirements through fermentation in which carbohydrates are incompletely oxidized because oxygen is insufficient. This incomplete oxidation produces several different end products, such as acids, alcohols, aldehydes, and gases, such as methane or CO_2. Microbes ferment different substances and produce diverse end products, which are also characteristic of taxonomic groups; thus both the substrates and end products of fermentation are characteristic of taxonomic groups, making fermentation capabilities extraordinarily useful in microbe identification.

Fermentation of carbohydrates often results in the production of acid and gas. To determine whether an acid is produced, a pH indicator can be added to the growth medium. Growth media containing the pH indicator Phenol Red are normally red or pink at a pH 7, and a change to yellow indicates acid is produced. The production of gas is observed by using a Durham tube, which is an ordinary test tube that contains a small inverted vial. If gas is produced, the inverted vial will collect some of the gas and a bubble will be visible. The fermentation media are prepared by adding 0.05% of a single carbohydrate and 0.02% of a pH indicator to a nutrient broth medium. If the organism can break down the particular carbohydrate in the tube, then the various end products will be produced.

MATERIALS
- Durham fermentation tube containing lactose + phenol red
- Durham fermentation tube containing dextrose + phenol red
- Durham fermentation tube containing sucrose + phenol red
- Broth culture of controls.
- Streak plate of isolate

PROTOCOL
1. Pick bacterial isolate with a stick or inoculating loop. Inoculate the three carbohydrate broths with your isolate. Repeat for each isolate and control.
2. Be sure that each tube is labeled with the carbohydrate and the inoculated organism. Place the tubes in a beaker labeled with the initials of your group and the date.
3. Incubate all tubes at 37°C for 24–48 hours.
4. Your instructor will set up controls for you to view.
5. After incubation, compare each of the inoculated tubes with the control tube of the same media to determine whether acid or gas was produced. Record your results.

TinyEarth
studentsourcing antibiotic discovery

Fermentation Protocol Data Sheet

Sugar	Isolate 1	Isolate 2	Isolate 3	positive control	negative control
Dextrose					
Lactose					
Sucrose					

Record results as follows:

AG = Acid and gas produced
A= Acid only produced
a = Slight acidity produced
O = Carbohydrate not fermented

Glycerol Stock Preparation

When working with bacterial isolates in multiple experiments, it is important to preserve and store bacteria in an unchanging state that can be accessed for future use. Freezing allows us to keep bacteria in a dormant state for long periods of time, with one disadvantage – water forms ice crystals upon freezing, which can rupture and kill cells. To keep this from happening, we freeze bacteria in a glycerol solution, which bathes and stabilizes bacterial cells by preventing the formation of ice crystals. Bacteria or bacterial spores can be stored for years at −80°C in 20% glycerol solution and liquid medium.

MATERIALS

- 80% glycerol solution
- Fresh streak plate
- Liquid medium (same as streak plate)
- Cryogenic vials (1.5 or 1.8 mL)

PROTOCOL

Safety Notes:

- **Must wear gloves and goggles, and practice aseptic technique throughout this protocol.**

1. Streak out bacterial isoate on appropriate medium. Incubate until colonies are visible.
2. Pre-mix 80% glycerol and liquid medium in a conical tube. Adjust to a final concentration of 20% glycerol with liquid medium. (Note: if your isolate is streaked on LB agar, mix glycerol with LB broth.)
3. Dispense 1000–1200 μL of 20% glycerol mix into cryogenic vial. Label tube with isolate designation, glycerol concentration, and date. For example: SH-LB-1, 20% gly, 11/12/13. Use an alcohol-proof and waterproof marker.
4. Using a sterile inoculating loop, pick a single colony from the streak plate. Collect as much of the colony as possible without picking up agar.
5. Carefully pick the colony off the plate and quickly transfer it to the respective labeled cryogenic vial. Insert loop into the glycerol mix and gently wiggle or twist the handle to deposit the colony in the glycerol mix. ***Note: Whenever possible, keep the vial supported in a rack, and, if picked up for observation, keep below eye level and pointed away from your body.
6. Gently pipette up and down or gently vortex the cryogenic vial until the colony is uniformly mixed.
7. Freeze and store glycerol stock at −80°C.
8. Input the bacterial isolate information and location of glycerol stock in your notes and in the database.

Gram Stain Test

Gram stain employs two stains, crystal violet and safranin, which are violet and red, respectively. In Gram-positive bacteria, the peptidoglycan layer is very thick (>20 nanometers) and exposed to the outside. Gram-positive cells retain large amounts of crystal violet in this layer, and binding is fixed with a mordant, iodine, giving the cells a purple appearance under the microscope, even after washing cells with a decolorizer such as alcohol. Conversely, in Gram-negative bacteria, the peptidoglycan layer is thin (normally <10 nanometers) and covered by an outer membrane, the S-layer. It retains very little crystal violet but stains very well with the counterstain safranin, which gives the cells a pink appearance under the microscope. By discriminating between purple and pink cells on a microscope slide, clinical microbiologists can deduce much information about an isolate's physiology. Furthermore, Gram staining serves as a classification system for bacteria. Gram-positives and Gram-negatives make up two major subdivisions of bacteria, which are generally representative of different taxonomic groups. Therefore, Gram stain, as a classical method, is still widely used to differentiate bacteria, and clinical personnel and microbiologists use it as a preliminary method of characterization.

In addition, Gram stain or other staining methods provide contrast to assist in observation of the shape of the bacterial cell. Negative staining with nigrosin is also used to determine cell shape. Bacteria come in many shapes, but the most commonly observed are spherical [called cocci (plural) or coccus (singular)] and rod-shaped [called bacilli (plural) or bacillus (singular)].

Smith, A. C., & Hussey, M. A. (2005). "Gram Stain Protocols". Laboratory Protocols. **Microbe Library**. *American Society for Microbiology*. Accessed 13 October 2013. <http://microbelibrary.org/component/resource/gram-stain/2886-gram-stain-protocols>

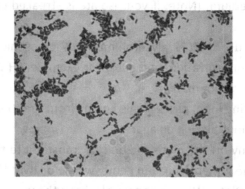

Figure 5a. *Bacillus subtilis*, a Gram-positive bacterium, stains purple with crystal violet. Photo from commons.wikimedia.org

Figure 5b. *Citrobacter freundii*, a Gram-negative bacterium, stains reddish/pink with counterstain safranin. Photo from commons.wikimedia.org

MATERIALS

- Gram stain kit
- Isolate streak plate or master plate (1- to 3-day-old culture, or fresh culture stored at 4°C)
- Positive and negative controls
- Inoculating loop, stick, or toothpick
- Microscope slide
- Forceps
- Sink or tray
- Paper towel
- Bright-field microscope and immersion oil
- Optional: Hot plate or slide warmer (alternative to Bunsen burner or flame)

PROTOCOL

1. Draw a circle on a clean, dry microscope slide and label outside with bacterial isolate designation.
2. Collect a small sample of bacterial colony with the tip of a stick/toothpick or inoculating loop.
3. Make a smear of the sample within the circle using a sterile inoculating loop or stick/toothpick. Let dry. Recommended: Smear controls side by side for comparison. A common Gram-positive control is *Staphylococcus cohnii* and a common Gram-negative control is *Escherichia coli*.
4. Using forceps, fix cells by passing slide through the Bunsen burner flame 3 or 4 times, with the smear facing up. Optional: Heat fix cells by putting slide on hot plate (set to warm or low heat) for 1–2 minutes. If the slide takes more than 2 minutes to dry, it may indicate that the smear is too thick or too watery. Once the cells are heat fixed, you may proceed to staining. Note: Heat fixing a wet sample will cause cells to boil and disrupt their cell walls and will negatively affect stain results.
5. Transfer slide to a sink or a tray where stains can be rinsed. Carefully hold one end of the slide with forceps or gloved hands. If staining multiple slides, mount the slides on a wire rack or any other surface that will allow rinsing to flow through.
6. Flood smear with crystal violet for 1 minute.

Tiny Earth
studentsourcing antibiotic discovery

7. Gently rinse slide with an indirect stream of water from the tab or a squirt bottle for about 2 seconds. Note: Slightly tilt slide and gently dispense water over the smear, not directly onto the smear. Blot the edges of the slide on paper towel – do not wipe the smear.
8. Flood smear with Gram iodine. Wait 1 minute.
9. As in step 7, gently rinse with water and blot edges of the slide on paper towel.
10. Drip 95% alcohol solution across the smear – do this for less than 15 seconds, or until the solution runs clear off the smear. Do a quick rinse with water. Quickly blot on paper towel. Note: This is a critical step in Gram staining: Too much decolorizing agent for too long will lead to erroneous results. Note: You may use 75% ethanol and 25% acetone as an alternative decolorizer.
11. Flood smear with safranin for 1 minute.
12. Gently rinse with water and blot.
13. Let slide air-dry for several minutes.
14. View slide under the microscope under bright field. Use oil immersion for greater magnification.

MacConkey Agar Test

MacConkey agar is a specialized medium utilized to differentiate among Gram-negative bacteria, especially those that inhabit the human gastrointestinal (GI) tract. This medium inhibits the growth of Gram-positive bacteria by disrupting their cell walls with crystal violet and bile salts infused in the medium. Many Gram-negative bacteria such as *Escherichia coli* thrive in the GI tract as part of our natural gut flora, as well as many specialized Gram-positive bacteria. Other Gram-negative bacteria such as *Salmonella* and *Shigella* are notorious pathogens that can cause food poisoning and even death. To differentiate among these bacteria, MacConkey agar allows us to deduce information about their ability to ferment carbohydrates. A pH indicator in the medium changes the appearance of cells producing acid, as a by-product of fermentation, from their original color to pink/red. *Escherichia coli* ferments the lactose present in the medium and releases acid, making colonies and the surrounding agar appear red in the presence of a pH indicator. Conversely, *Salmonella* and *Shigella* do not ferment lactose and maintain a neutral pH, making colonies display their typical white or tan color (Wessner, Dupont, & Charles, p. 176). MacConkey agar is therefore both selective and differential, telling us about cell wall composition and cell's ability to ferment lactose.

REFERENCES

Wessner, D. R., Dupont, C., & Charles, T. (2013) *Microbiology* New York, NY: Wiley & Sons.

Differentiating Bacteria with the MacConkey Agar Test

Adapted from: Mary E. Allen – Microbe Library

<http://microbelibrary.org/component/resource/laboratory-test/2855-macconkey-agar-plates-protocols>

MacConkey agar is a selective and differential medium used for the isolation and differentiation of nonfastidious Gram-negative rods, particularly members of the family *Enterobacteriaceae* and the genus *Pseudomonas*. The inclusion of crystal violet and bile salts in the media prevent the growth of Gram-positive bacteria and fastidious Gram-negative bacteria, such as *Neisseria* and *Pasteurella*. The tolerance of Gram-negative enteric bacteria to bile is partly a result of the relatively bile-resistant outer membrane, which hides the bile-sensitive cytoplasmic membrane.

MacCONKEY AGAR RECIPE

Peptone (Difco) or Gelysate (BBL)	17 g
Proteose peptone (Difco) or Polypeptone (BBL)	3.0 g
Lactose	10 g
NaCl	5.0 g
Crystal Violet	1.0 mg

Tiny Earth
studentsourcing antibiotic discovery

Neutral Red	30 mg
Bile Salts	1.5 g
Agar	13 g
Distilled Water	Add to make 1 L

Adjust pH to 7.1 ± 0.2. Boil to dissolve agar. Sterilize at 121°C for 15 minutes.

PROTOCOL

1. Streak a plate of MacConkey's agar with a pure or mixed culture. If using a mixed culture, use a streak plate or spread plate to achieve colony isolation. Good colony separation will ensure the best differentiation of lactose-fermenting and nonfermenting colonies of bacteria.

2. Streak plate of *Escherichia coli* and *Serratia marcescens* on MacConkey agar as controls. Both microorganisms grow on this selective medium because they are Gram-negative nonfastidious rods. Growth of *E. coli*, which ferments lactose, appears red/pink on the agar. Growth of *S. marcescens*, which does not ferment lactose, appears colorless and translucent.

Adapted from:

Allen, M. E. (2005). "MacConkey Agar Plates Protocols". Laboratory Protocols. **Microbe Library**. *American Society for Microbiology*. Accessed 13 October 2013. <http://microbelibrary.org/component/resource/laboratory-test/2855-macconkey-agar-plates-protocols>

PCR Analysis

Polymerase chain reaction (PCR) is a common technique used to **amplify** (make multiple copies of) specific regions of DNA for several applications, including sequencing and genetic analysis. PCR helps scientists overcome the problem of having too little material or an impure DNA sample to study. Developed in 1983 by the biochemist Kary Mullis, this elegant technique uses the same mechanism cells use to make copies of their genetic material during reproduction, except PCR does it without the cells themselves. PCR is carried out in a test tube containing a DNA template, primers, DNA polymerase, and reagents that stabilize the reaction in water. Each round of PCR requires three steps: (1) denaturation, (2) annealing, and (3) elongation, each of which doubles the amount of DNA template present in the reaction.

The **DNA template** can be any DNA molecule, such as a bacterial chromosome, a plasmid, or a fragment of DNA. The **primers** specify which region of DNA in the template is amplified. A primer is a short fragment of single-stranded DNA (ssDNA), which binds to (or anneals) to one strand of the DNA template and is recognized by the enzyme **DNA polymerase** as the point to start copying the DNA. In the first step of the reaction (**denaturation**), the double-stranded DNA (dsDNA) template must be "unzipped" into two separate strands. To denature dsDNA, we must disrupt the hydrogen bonds between complementary base pairs by raising the reaction temperature to 94°C. In the second step (**annealing**), the temperature is lowered to 58°C, allowing primers to bind at specific, complementary sites on the ssDNA template. There are typically two primers, one for each complementary strand. In the third step (**elongation**), DNA polymerase recognizes the primer and starts synthesizing a new complementary DNA strand in the 5' to 3' direction.

Repeating this process over multiple rounds, typically around 30, enables exponential amplification of the DNA. The conditions of the PCR reactions require a highly stable enzyme that will withstand great fluctuations in temperature without compromising its structure and function or the quality of the new DNA copies. Just as dsDNA denatures at high temperatures, so do enzymes. But unlike DNA, whose strands reassociate upon cooling, most enzymes irreversibly lose their three-dimensional structure and activity at very high temperatures. In the past, scientists needed to add new enzymes in every round of the reaction, decreasing the efficiency and the reliability of PCR by building up a massive protein concentration through successive rounds of amplification. An extreme bacterium, *Thermus aquaticus*, a thermophilic or "heat-loving" bacterium isolated from the hot springs of the Yellowstone National Park, held the answer to this problem. This microorganism survives and reproduces at near-boiling temperatures, which also indicated that its enzymes were heat-resistant as well. A team was able to purify *Thermus aquaticus*' DNA polymerase, or *Taq* polymerase for short. This enzyme has an optimal temperature of 72°C, whereas most enzymes used in molecular biology work optimally at 37°C. *Taq* polymerase has become the standard enzyme used in PCR (Saiki et al., 1988), revolutionizing our ability to amplify DNA with high fidelity.

REFERENCES

Saiki, R. K., Gelfand, D. H., Stoffel, S., Scharf, S. J., Higuchi, R., Horn, G. T., Mullis, K. B., & Erlich, H. A. (1988) Primer-directed enzymatic amplification of DNA with a thermostable DNA polymerase. Science 239:487–491.

PCR Bead Method

MATERIALS

- 27F primer (stock solution: 20 µM)*
- 1492R primer (stock solution: 20 µM)*
- llustra™ PuReTaq™ Ready-To-Go™ PCR Bead and tube
- Sterile nuclease-free deionized water (ultrapure)
- Streak plate of isolate
- Micropipettor and tips
- Optional: Heat block

*Stored at −20°C

PROTOCOL

Protocol adapted from "puRe *Taq* Ready-To-Go PCR Beads" guide

1. Obtain PCR bead tubes, which contain *Taq* polymerase (heat-resistant enzyme) and other necessary reagents. Label tubes with names of isolates or DNA samples, and if possible, primers used.
2. Dispense 23 µL of ultrapure water into the PCR bead tube. The bead will start to dissolve and slightly effervesce. Optional: Use the heat block to preheat primer stocks to 80°C for 2 minutes, and plunge in ice prior to adding to reaction mix.
3. Add 1 µL of forward primer (27F). As you dispense the primer solution, insert the micropipette tip into the mix so that the small volume goes directly into the mix.
4. Add 1 µL of reverse primer (1492R) to the mix. This will bring the volume of the reaction mix to 25 µL.
5. Using a micropipette tip, carefully touch the colony on the streak plate. A small, visible dab of cells that barely fills the very end of the pipette tip will provide enough DNA template for the reaction. Optional: resuspend cells in 100 µL of 1× phosphate-buffered saline (PBS) solution, mix thoroughly by gently vortexing, and add 5 µL of the cell suspension to the mix. This will bring the reaction mix volume to 30 µL.
6. Dip pipette tip into reaction mix and gently swirl for 5–10 seconds to dislodge cells. Cap the tubes. If necessary, gently tap for a few seconds to attain a more uniform mix and collect all of the reagents at the bottom of the tube. Avoid forming bubbles.
7. Transfer tubes to thermal cycler (PCR machine).
8. Select appropriate program† to start cycling (about 2 hours).
9. Once cycling is complete, remove tubes and incubate on ice. Follow your instructor's instructions about storage, and follow up protocols to quality test the PCR products and prepare them for sequencing.

Protocol adapted from "puRe Taq Ready-To-Go PCR Beads" guide

†PCR cycling program:

94°C for 10 minutes – breaking down cells/ denaturation

94°C for 30 seconds – denaturation

58°C 30 seconds – annealing

72°C 1 min 50 sec (1 minute per kb of DNA template) – elongation

Cycle 30 times

72°C for 10 minutes

Reagent Method

MATERIALS
- Master mix (purchased from Promega, NEB, etc) = primers, buffer, dNTPs, $MgCl_2$, H_2O, and DNA polymerase or reagents purchased separately.
  - 0.1–0.5 µM (final concentration) forward primer
  - 0.1–0.5 µM (final concentration) reverse primer
  - Polymerase buffer (1× final concentration) (may be provided with polymerase)
  - 0.2 mM each dNTP (final concentration)
  - 1.5–2.5 mM (final concentration) $MgCl_2$
  - DNA polymerase (e.g., *Taq*) (adjust concentration depending on product specifications)
- H_2O to 25–100 µL final volume
- Template DNA = small pin-head volume of bacterial cells from streak plate OR 5 µL of cell suspension.

Optional: Make a cell suspension by resuspending cells in 100 µL of phosphate-buffered saline (PBS) solution and mix thoroughly by vortexing gently.

PROTOCOL*
1. Obtain all PCR reagents (keep frozen). Thaw on ice. Label tubes with names of samples, and if possible, primers used. Place on ice.
2. Determine the volume of each reagent to add to your reaction(s) and calculate amounts for master mix if appropriate.
3. Add each reagent to master mix starting with water and ending with the DNA polymerase enzyme. Add everything but the template (bacterial cells or cell lysis) to your master mix; check off as added. Return *Taq* enzyme to freezer.
4. Dispense master mix into individual tubes.
5. Using a micropipette tip, carefully touch the colony on the streak plate. A small dab that collects a small yet visible blob of cells will provide enough DNA template for the reaction. Or add 5 µL of the cell suspension to the mix.

Tiny Earth
studentsourcing antibiotic discovery

6. Using a micropipettor, mix the contents of each tube by gently swishing the solution up and down several times. Cap the tubes. If necessary, gently flick or vortex for a few seconds to attain a more uniform mix.

7. Transfer tubes to thermal cycler (PCR machine).

8. Select appropriate program† to start cycling (about 2 hours).

9. Once cycling is complete, remove tubes and keep in ice. Follow your instructor's instructions about storage, and follow-up protocols to quality test the PCR products and prepare them for sequencing.

†PCR cycling program:

94°C for 10 minutes – breaking down cells/ denaturation

94°C for 30 seconds – denaturation

58°C 30 seconds – annealing

72°C 1 min 50 sec (1 minute per kb of DNA template) – elongation

Cycle 30 times

72°C for 10 minutes

Picking and Patching Colonies

Isolating single species of bacteria from a mixed culture containing tens or hundreds of species is a routine procedure that allows microbiologists to carefully examine an organism and its unique characteristics. Dilution plating allows us to spread individual bacteria on a plate to grow into distinct colonies. Yet colonies overgrow with time and mix with one another, cells migrate, and cultures get contaminated, so sterile conditions in your work environment and proper techniques are very important to isolating a bacterium and starting a pure culture.

The isolation approach we will use is aptly called "pick and patch" and involves precisely those things: "picking" bacteria from a mixed culture (e.g., usually a dilution plate) and "patching" them onto a fresh plate, which may be a pure culture or a "master plate" containing all your unique bacteria of interest for your study. The light touch of a colony with a sterile toothpick or a metal rod picks up thousands of bacteria that can be transferred and smeared or patched onto a fresh plate. At the end of this procedure you will have a "master plate" that will serve as a bacterial catalog for your experiments.

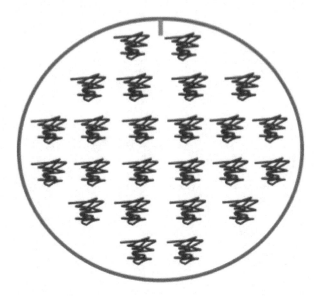

Figure 6. Master plate. This example shows how your plate should look after incubating to allow the isolates to grow. Patches (in red) were oriented on the plate using a 6×6 grid, although smaller ones can be used. Grid was aligned with point of orientation drawn on the back plate (orange vertical line at the top). Notice how patches do not touch – this is critical to prevent cross-contamination.

MATERIALS

- 2 media plates of choice
- Square grid (alternatively, draw grid on back of plates)
- Sterile toothpicks

Tiny Earth
studentsourcing antibiotic discovery

PROTOCOL

1. Obtain 2 plates containing your media of choice. Label with date, media type, student and soil sample name around the back edge of the plate, and draw a small vertical line at the edge of your plate as point of orientation.

2. Tape the plate face-up on a square grid plate. Align grid with the vertical line on the plate.

3. Using a sterile toothpick, pick a unique colony from your dilution plate (10^{-2} or 10^{-3}). Patch (gently zigzag) colony smear on toothpick onto fresh media plate within the boundaries of one square on square grid. Be careful not to puncture the agar as you smear.

4. Continue to pick and patch colonies onto media plate, each time occupying a new square. Make sure patches do not overlap or touch because this will contaminate the patch, assuming that you picked a single colony. Try to find as many morphologically unique colonies (i.e., different textures, colony margins, pigments), but do not patch more than 24 colonies per plate to avoid overcrowding.

5. This collection of colony patches will be your master plate.

Screen for Isolate Antibiotic Production #1 – Patch/Patch

Alexander Fleming is credited with having discovered the first antibiotic introduced into widespread clinical use, penicillin. In 1928, Fleming made an observation that became the basis for the way microbiologists have searched systematically for antibiotic producing microorganisms ever since. He noticed that a mold (*Penicillium notatum*) that had contaminated a *Staphylococcus* culture was inhibiting the growth of the bacterial cells around it, creating a pronounced "zone of inhibition." The mold secretes its powerful chemical weapon into its surroundings where it diffuses into the broth or agar medium. Susceptible microorganisms that come in contact with this chemical are inhibited in their ability to survive or reproduce. Areas on a plate that would normally be lush with colonies or a lawn of bacteria become clear, creating visible zones of inhibition.

Microbiologists apply these basic principles when conducting activity assays – tests that determine the presence of antimicrobial compounds in a culture. Many researchers are concerned with finding compounds that specifically target bacteria, especially for those that pose a great threat to our health. Therefore, human pathogens or related bacteria (due to the risk to the research of working with the pathogens themselves) are used as test subjects in activity assays to find compounds that are "active" against them.

REFERENCES
Bibb, M. (1996) The regulation of antibiotic production in *Streptomyces coelicolor* A3(2). Microbiology 142:1335–1344.

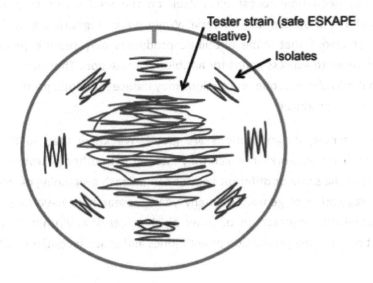

Figure 7. Patch-patch method. Candidate antibiotic producers are patched around the edge of plate, and a tester strain is patched in the middle, separated by small gap.

MATERIALS
- 2 plates containing media of choice
- Master plates (made in previous experiment) with candidate isolates to be tested

- Plate of safe ESKAPE relative as tester
- Sterile toothpicks

PROTOCOL

1. Obtain your master plate and the culture containing your safe ESKAPE relative of choice.
2. Choose a fresh medium plate to grow safe ESKAPE relative.
3. Pick isolates from your master plate and patch them around the perimeter of the plate (see diagram above)
4. Label each patch with the appropriate name on the back of the plate.
5. Patch your tester strain (safe ESKAPE pathogen) in the center of the plate near, but without touching the patches of soil isolates. Incubate at predetermined temperature for 1-3 days but no longer, to avoid overgrowth. Once patches produce dense growth, make observations or store plates at 4°C until the next lab session.

Screen for Isolate Antibiotic Production #2 – Spread/Patch

THEORY

The spread-patch protocol tests for antibiotic production by candidate isolates that are in close physical contact with the tester strain. In this protocol, the tester strain is spread on a plate, and then the isolates are patched onto the bacterial spread. If the isolate is active against the tester strain, it should theoretically have no trouble growing on the bacterial spread. Yet, this is not always the case as an antibiotic producer may need time to establish itself on the medium or may not be successful at invading a growing culture of susceptible bacteria. While we can ignore establishment times in this experiment, we cannot ignore that some antibiotic producers may require physical or biochemical contact with other microbes to express genes for antibiotic production. Therefore, this protocol is based on the assumption that microbe-microbe interactions may induce antibiotic production and will increase the chances of identifying a producer.

While this approach is simple, its implications are grand. We know that, in their natural habitats, microbes are part of intricate networks in which they interact with other microbes. Extracellular signals coming from members of the same or different species can unleash a signaling cascade within a cell that ultimately affects its regulation of genes. For many years, researchers have been attempting to find what specific microbe-microbe interactions or other biochemical or environmental cues would trigger the expression of that result in the production of antibiotics and other secondary metabolites.

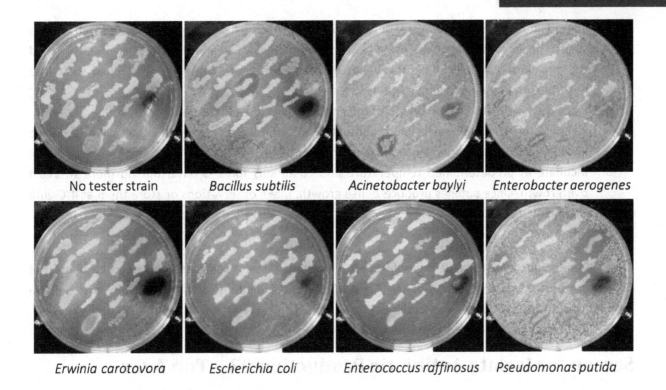

| No tester strain | Bacillus subtilis | Acinetobacter baylyi | Enterobacter aerogenes |

| Erwinia carotovora | Escherichia coli | Enterococcus raffinosus | Pseudomonas putida |

Figure 8. Spread-patch method to test isolates for antibiotic production. Tester strains were spread on PDA plates, the plates were dried, and isolates were patched onto the plate with toothpicks. Plates were incubated at 28°C for 48 h. Photo source: Manuel Fernando Garavito Diago

MATERIALS

- 2 appropriate media plates (same as master plate)
- Liquid culture of safe ESKAPE relative
- Master plates with isolates
- Spread beads or sterile swabs
- Square grid template
- Sterile toothpicks

PROTOCOL

1. Obtain appropriate media plate for your isolates to grow.
2. Label plate with respective medium, safe ESKAPE relative, and master plate used. Add vertical line as point of orientation, aligned with master plate.
3. Obtain a liquid culture of your safe ESKAPE relative.
4. Dispense 150 µL of the safe ESKAPE relative liquid culture onto the medium plate. This is the inoculation step.
4b. ***Alternatively, dip a sterile swab into ESKAPE relative and spread across plate, turning the plate 2-3 times to get even coverage of the culture on the plate.

5. Spread liquid with L-shaped spreader or add 5-10 spread beads to the plate, being careful not to splash the inoculum. If you are using beads, cover plate with lid and shake side by side to spread the inoculum. Carefully shake the beads off into appropriate container. The liquid should be absorbed into medium within minutes.

6. Place the new plate face-up on top of the grid and align line of orientation with grid.

7. Pick isolates from the master plate and patch onto the plate spread with safe ESKAPE relative arranged in the same orientation as on the master plate.

8. Incubate at predetermined temperature and conditions for 1–3 days, but no more to avoid overgrowth. Once patches produce dense growth, make observations or store them at 4°C until the next lab session.

***Depending on density of the safe ESKAPE relative tester strain you may need to dilute the culture prior to spreading onto plates. Try a 1/10 – 1/100 dilution prior to patching isolates if you find that a tester strain overgrows the isolates.

Screen for Isolate Antibiotic Production #3 – Top Agar

THEORY
Another method of screening for antibiotic production that we will be using is called top agar. In this technique, liquefied agar is mixed with the tester strain and poured over patches of the soil isolates. Since the tester strain is uniformly distributed on the overlying agar (which solidifies quickly), it could almost allow for the three-dimensional visualization of zones of inhibition.

MATERIALS
- 2 of each appropriate media plates
- Sterile glass bottle
- Liquid culture of safe ESKAPE relative
- Master plates with isolates
- Molten top agar (medium with 1/2 the amount of agar, or 0.75%, used in the typical recipe)*
- Square grid
- Sterile toothpicks

*Recommendation: Prepare top agar up to 1 day and at least 2 hours prior to lab session. Ensure medium contains a homogenous mixture of ingredients. Dispense into separate bottles (50 mL) (one per group of students working together; each student will need ~7 mL per plate) and autoclave. The agar will come out fully melted and with minimal water loss. Allow to cool (between 45°C and 55°C) until the time they will be used by the students or place in a 50-55°C water bath for use. Alternatively, microwave bottle of top agar (if made days prior or allowed to solidify) until agar melts but avoid boiling. This alternative runs the risk of water loss, resulting in higher concentrations of agar.

TinyEarth
studentsourcing antibiotic discovery

PROTOCOL

1. Patch isolates of interest onto appropriate solid medium for safe ESKAPE relative to grow. Do not use excessive inoculum and patch lightly.

2. Obtain bottle with molten top agar (0.75%) cooled down to 45–55°C, or comfortably warm to the touch. If too hot, top agar may kill cells in the next step. If too cold, top agar may solidify in the bottle.

3. In a sterile glass bottle, mix 100 μL of overnight liquid culture of your safe ESKAPE relative with 7 mL of top agar. Cap bottle and mix contents by swirling.

4. Gently pour top agar with safe ESKAPE relative over the patched plate. Pour onto one side of the plate and tip over to flood entire plate.

5. Cover the entire surface of the plate and let sit until top agar solidifies, at least 10–15 minutes. Incubate upside down (but be sure not to turn the plate until top agar is completely solid and rigid). Incubate under predetermined temperature and conditions. Incubate for 1–3 days, but no more to avoid overgrowth. Once isolates and tester strains produce dense growth, make observations or store them at 4°C until the next lab session.

Safe ESKAPE Relatives Information Sheet

ESKAPE Pathogen	Safe Relative	Culture media	Conditions*	ATCC #
Enterococcus faecium	Enterococcus raffinosus	BHI/ Sheep blood agar	30°C or 37°C	49464
	Bacillus subtilis	LB	30°C or 37°C aerobic	
Staphylococcus aureus	Staphylococcus epidermidis	BHI, TSA	30°C or 37°C aerobic	14990
Klebsiella species	Escherichia coli	NB	30°C or 37°C aerobic	11775
Acinetobacter baumannii	Acinetobacter baylyi	BHI	30°C or 37°C aerobic	33305
Pseudomonas aeruginosa	Pseudomonas putida	LB	30°C or 37°C aerobic	

Tiny Earth
studentsourcing antibiotic discovery

ESKAPE Pathogen	Safe Relative	Culture media	Conditions*	ATCC #
Enterobacter species	*Enterobacter aerogenes*	TSA	30°C or 37°C aerobic	51697
	Erwinia carotovora	LB	30°C	
A positive control for antibiotic producers	*Lysobacter antibioticus* (10TSA2)	NB/TSA	30°C aerobic or room temp	

*For liquid culture, aerobic means incubate with shaking. *E. carotovora* and *E. raffinosus* should not be shaken.

For solid culture, all strains should be grown in regular aerobic conditions.

Gray boxes indicate Handelsman Lab, University of Wisconsin-Madison, strains.

- *E. carotovora* grows fairly slowly in liquid culture. Inoculate liquid culture 2 days in advance.
- *L. antibioticus* grows slowly on a plate. Streak out culture 2–3 days in advance.
- *S. epidermidis* grows very slowly in the antibiotic assays. Some dislike using it for that reason.
- All other strains will grow overnight without any problems. For best results, use liquid cultures within 16–24 hours after inoculation.
- *A. baylyi* produces two colony morphologies – opaque and white-colored. Both colony types have been sequenced and BLAST results indicate that both types are most closely related to *A. baylyi*. Sequence and chromatogram data are available upon request.

Review of Isolates and Activities

What media did you use?

How many colonies were picked for your master plate?

How many of those grew?

What tester strain did you use the first time?

How many active isolates did you have with this tester strain?

What two tester strains did you use the second time?

How many active isolates did you have with these tester strains?

How many active isolates did you streak out?

Table of Isolate Activity Spectrum

Overall spectrum of activity. Fill in isolate name on the top row (you can fill in up to eight isolates in this table, but feel free to reproduce the table or expand it if you have more isolates). Tester strains(safe ESKAPE relatives) appear listed in the first column. For isolates showing activity (zone of inhibition) against a tester strain, write in a plus sign (+); for no activity (no zone of inhibition), write in a minus sign (−):

Isolate name								
E. carotovora								
E. coli								
E. raffinosus								
E. aerogenes								
B. subtilis								
P. putida								
A. baylyi								
S. epidermidis								

TinyEarth
studentsourcing antibiotic discovery

Serial Dilutions

Adapted from: Jackie Reynolds – Microbe Library
<http://microbelibrary.org/component/resource/laboratory-test/2884-serial-dilution-protocols>

Determining microbial counts for liquid and solid samples is a common practice in the lab to quantify the biomass of a soil sample, calculate an antibiotic's minimal inhibitory concentration (MIC), or determine the population density in a liquid culture. In most environmental samples, bacteria are numerous, ranging from the tens of thousands to the millions in as little as 1 mL of seawater or 1 g of soil. Given the size of these populations and rate of cell turnover, it would be nearly impossible to get an exact count by counting all the cells directly. Instead of counting cells one by one, microbiologists calculate cell density through colony forming units (CFUs), which give us an approximation of the number of viable cells per milliliter or gram of a sample.

To calculate CFUs, a sample must be diluted in water or a saline solution that keeps the cells in suspension alive. Diluting 1 g of soil with saline solution to a final volume of 10 mL would create a 10-fold or 1:10 dilution of our soil sample; therefore, if the cells are properly suspended in the solution, all the cells contained in 1 g of sample will be evenly distributed in 10 mL of solution. Making serial dilutions of a sample in 10-fold increments allows us to reduce the number of cells per volume to a cell density that is easier to count. Once we have reached a desired dilution of our sample, we can add the dilution to a solid medium that will support the growth of the bacteria. Once the bacteria grow to colonies (1 bacterium giving rise to 1 colony of clones), we can determine how many bacteria were plated and calculate the cell density in the original sample measured in CFUs. For example, if we serially dilute 1 g of soil sample by a factor of 10^3, spread and incubate the dilution on a solid medium, and then observe 130 colonies, we would calculate that there were 130×10^3 or 1.3×10^5 CFUs/g of soil. This number represents the number of viable cells, i.e., cells in an environmental sample that can survive lab conditions and grow in culture. While the proportion of all soil bacteria we can successfully grow in the lab remains low, plating various dilutions on different types of media and under different conditions (e.g., lighting and temperature) can increase our recovery of diverse bacteria.

How to calculate CFU/g soil:

colonies ÷ volume plated (µL) × dilution factor x 1000 µL/mL × volume of suspended soil

For example:

220 colonies on 10^{-3} plate (dilution factor = 1000)

220 colonies counted ÷ 100 µL plated × 1000 × 1000 µL/mL × 10 mL/g

= 22,000,000 = 2.2×10^7 CFU/g

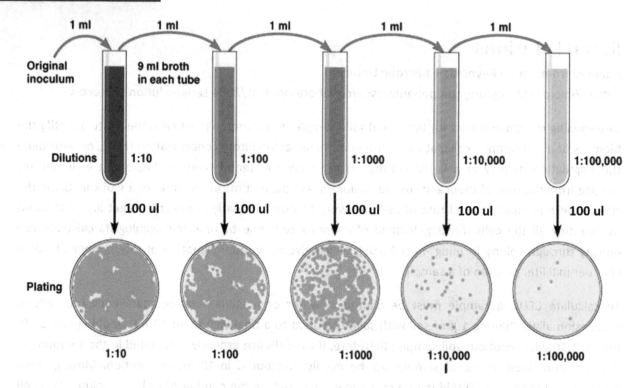

Figure 9. Serial dilution and plating schematic. A series of 10-fold dilutions is made from the original inoculum, which contains cells in suspension from the environmental sample. Each subsequent dilution plate will have 10-fold fewer bacteria than the previous one, making it possible to count individual colonies. To calculate CFU in the original inoculum, be sure to account for the effect of plating only 100 µL of a 10-mL sample. http://faculty.irsc.edu/FACULTY/TFischer/micro/serial%20dilution.jpg

MATERIALS

- Choice of media plates*
- Conical tubes or test tubes
- Soil sample
- Sterile water
- Sonicator or vortex mixer

*Refer to Media Menu at the end of this protocol.

PROTOCOL

1. Obtain and label appropriate number of plates and 1.5 mL microcentrifuge tubes (one for each subsequent dilution). Dilutions should be made in increments of 10 (10^{-1}, 10^{-2}, 10^{-3}, etc.).
2. Weigh 1 g of soil sample.
3. Transfer to test tube or 15-mL conical tube.
4. Add 9 mL of water to 1 g of soil.
5. Place tube in sonicator bath and sonicate for 30–60 sec, or vortex.

6. Determine the dilution series and calculate appropriate volumes for each. Again, dilutions should be made in increments of 10, thus add 900 μL of diluent (water) into each dilution tube. 900 μL diluent + 100 μL specimen transferred = 1000 μL

7. Remove 100 μL of soil+water with micropipette from 15-mL conical tube and add to 900 μL of water in Eppendorf tube. This is 10^{-1} dilution.

8. Mix with vortexer.

9. Remove 100 μL of 10^{-1} dilution and add to 900 μL of water in another microcentrifuge tube. Mix by vortexing.

10. Continue to transfer 100 μL of previous dilution to 900 μL of diluent until reach desired dilution.

11. When finished with dilution series, plate 100 μL of each dilution to appropriate plates.*

12. Note volume and dilutions plated.

*Check with your instructor about spread plating technique.

SAFETY

Tubes and agar plates should be discarded properly in a biohazard container for proper sterilization. The pipettes will also be sterilized (washed first if using reusable glass pipettes). Do not pipette by mouth. Use aseptic technique in the transfer of microorganisms from tube to tube, as well as in the production of the pour plates. The ASM advocates that students must successfully demonstrate the ability to explain and practice safe laboratory techniques. For more information, read the laboratory safety section of the ASM Curriculum Recommendations: Introductory Course in Microbiology and the Guidelines for Biosafety in Teaching Laboratories.

COMMENTS AND TIPS

Greater than 300 colonies on the agar plate and less than 30 leads to a high degree of error. Air contaminants can contribute significantly to a really low count. A high count can be confounded by error in counting too many small colonies or difficulty in counting overlapping colonies. Use sterile pipettes for the dilutions and use different pipettes for each dilution. To do otherwise will increase the chances of inaccurate estimates because of the carryover of cells. Accuracy in quantitation is determined by accurate pipette use and adequate mixing of the diluted samples.

Adapted from:

Reynolds, J. (2005). "Serial Dilution Protocols". Laboratory Protocols. **Microbe Library**. *American Society for Microbiology*. Accessed 17 Oct 2013. http://microbelibrary.org/component/resource/laboratory-test/2884-serial-dilution-protocols>

Tiny Earth
studenthourcing antibiotic discovery

Serial Dilution Observations and Results Sheet

Pick 1–2 dilution plates from your initial serial dilution on LB and 1–2 dilution plates of your media of choice. Specify the medium in the plate and period of incubation when colonies were counted; e.g., LB at 24 hours. Express your dilution factor (usually a factor of 10) and CFU/g of soil in scientific notation (e.g., 9.7×10^7). Fill and expand the table a below as necessary.

Medium / Incubation period	Dilution factor	Volume of dilution plated	Final dilution on plate	Number of colonies	Count Cells per g of soil (CFU/g)

CFU Practice Exercises and Serial Dilution Questions

1. You are given a test tube containing 10 mL of a solution with 8.4×10^7 cells/mL. You are to produce a solution that contains less than 100 cells/mL. What dilutions must you perform in order to arrive at the desired result?

2. You have a microtube containing 1 mL of a solution with 4.3×10^4 cells/mL and you are to produce a solution that contains 43 cells/mL. What dilutions must you perform?

3. You are given a container with 5 mL of a solution containing 5.1×10^3 cells/mL. You are to produce a solution that contains approximately 100 cells/mL.

4. You are given the task to quantify the bacteria in your soil sample. You do a 10-fold serial dilution of your soil sample in sterile water and plate 1/10 of each subsequent (serial) dilution in LB agar plates with cycloheximide – an antifungal and eukaryotic cell inhibitor. If your 10^{-6} (ten to the minus sixth) dilution plate contains 97 bacterial colonies after two days of incubation, how many bacteria do you estimate were present in your initial soil sample (1 g of soil)? Show your calculation and briefly describe each step.

5. Notice this is a three- part question. For each answer, specify the number in the answer box. No need to restate the scenario.

Tiny Earth
studentsourcing antibiotic discovery

Scenario: If you are determining the CFU of a sample of ocean water, how would the following scenarios (1–3) affect your CFU/mL estimate and the diversity of bacteria you observe:

1) The cells in the sample stick together in clumps

2) Most bacteria require high salt and minimal nutrients but you plate them on LB

3) You make your calculations entirely on 10-fold dilutions, but in your first dilution you put 10 µL of seawater in 1 mL of water (pay close attention to the units)

6.   Is CFU/g of soil a diversity estimate or an abundance estimate? How is a diversity estimate different from an abundance estimate?

CFU Practice Exercises and Serial Dilution Answers:

1) ANSWER: You should perform a series of three 1:100 dilutions to yield 84 cells/mL.

1 mL of original solution to 99 mL of water = 8.4×10^5 cells/mL.

1 mL of second solution to 99 mL of water = 8.4×10^3 cells/mL.

1 mL of third solution to 99 mL of water = 8.4×10^1 or 84 cells/mL.

2) ANSWER: You could perform the following dilutions:

10 µL of original solution to 990 µL of water = 4.3×10^2 cells/mL.

100 µL of second solution to 900 µL of water = 4.3×10^1 or 43 cells/mL.

3) ANSWER: You would perform the following dilutions:

0.5 mL of original solution to 4.5 mL of water = 5.1×10^2 cells/mL

1 mL of second solution to 4 mL of water = 1.02×10^2 cells/mL or 10^2 cells/mL

4) ANSWER:

colonies / dilution factor = CFU/g of soil

97 colonies / 10^{-6} = 9.7×10^7 CFU/g of soil

5) ANSWER:

1) You will likely underestimate CFU/mL estimate; colonies may contain various genetically distinct cell types; colonies will merge; cells may compete for resources and grow disproportionately; you would not get a reliable determination of diversity.

2) You will get a low CFU/mL estimate (assuming that these cells prefer to grow on high salt, minimal media versus rich media like LB). In addition, fast-growing cells may obscure growth or visualization of those cells preferring minimal nutrients (which are likely to grow more slowly).

Tiny Earth
studenthourcing antibiotic discovery

3) You have been consistent with the 1:10 ratio; you will underestimate your CFU estimate by a factor of 10; you may not get a good determination of diversity in your sample.

6) ANSWER:

Diversity – phylogenetically/genetically distinct bacteria, which may exhibit different morphologies, growth rates, metabolites, activity; different species/genera/other classifications; for our purposes – a more qualitative way to look at a sample.

Abundance = number of bacteria, usually determined by dilution plating and calculating CFU/g of sample

Silica Column Chromatography

In another section, Thin Layer Chromatography (TLC), a diagnostic tool that provides information about the polarity of an extract's active components is described. In this section, you will use the information gathered from the TLC process to guide silica column chromatography, a technique that separates organic compounds into various fractions based on polarity.

Like TLC, silica column chromatography requires a solvent system. However, the choice of solvents for the column is somewhat more complicated; rather than using just a single mixture of solvents as in the TLC protocol, you will now use a progression of increasingly polar solvent gradients. Luckily, the optimal solvent found for TLC can be used to determine the starting point of this progression. In general, it is best to begin the process with a mixture of solvents that is slightly less polar that the optimal TLC mixture. For instance, if a 4:1 hexane:ethyl acetate system proved effective in separating compounds on a TLC plate, you might begin silica column chromatography with a 6:1 hexane:ethyl acetate mixture. From this starting point, you will progress to more polar gradients. For example, a progression of gradients might begin with 6:1 hexane:ethyl acetate and continue with 4:1, 2:1, 1:1, 1:2, 1:4, 1:6, and finally 100% ethyl acetate.

MATERIALS
- 1 glass Pasteur pipette (5 ¾")
- Three-arm stand
- Wooden stick
- Cotton
- Small filter paper
- Silica gel (230–400 mesh)
- Sand
- Pipette bulb
- Solvents making up the optimal solvent system found using the "Thin Layer Chromatography (TLC)" protocol.
- Organic extract, suspended in the less polar of the chosen solvents
- 8–12 small glass test tubes (numbered)

PROTOCOL
1. Determine the progression of solvent gradients that will be used. This process is discussed above. Your system should have 5–10 different gradients.
2. Secure the Pasteur pipette on the three-arm stand with the tip pointing down.
3. Break off a small piece of cotton and insert it into the top of the pipette. Use the wooden stick to push the cotton down into the top of the narrow tip of the pipette and tamp it down gently. The cotton should be secure enough to stop the escape of silica from the column, but should not be large enough or tight enough to prevent the flow of solvents through the pipette.
4. Fold the filter paper into a small funnel. Use the funnel to pour silica gel into the top of the pipette. The level of the silica should be halfway in between the cotton plug and the indent near the top of the pipette. Tap the pipette gently until the surface of the silica settles flat.

Tiny Earth
studentsourcing antibiotic discovery

5. Use the paper filter to add sand. The sand layer should be about 1 cm in height.

6. Put the bulb on the top of the pipette and squeeze slowly and gently. This will help push pockets of air from the column. (Caution: Do not release pressure on the bulb while it is still attached to the column. This sudden decrease in pressure will cause the silica and sand to be sucked up the pipette. Always remove the bulb from the pipette before releasing pressure.)

7. Wash the column with the more polar of the two solvents. For instance, if you plan to start with a 6:1 hexane:ethyl acetate gradient, wash with pure ethyl acetate. To do this, use another glass pipette to add this solvent to the top of the column. Add until the solvent reaches the indent near the top of the pipette. Push this solvent through with the bulb so that the solvent level is just above the sand. (Note: Never let the level of liquid in the column fall below the sand. Whenever pushing through solvent or extract, stop just before the liquid reaches the top of the sand.) Repeat once more, for a total of two washes.

8. Wash the column with the less polar of the two solvents. For instance, if you plan to start with a 6:1 hexane:ethyl acetate gradient, wash with pure hexane. Repeat once more, for a total of two washes.

9. Add the extract, suspended in the less polar of your two solvents. Add enough so that the level of the extract is halfway in between the top of the sand and the indent near the top of the pipette. Place your first test tube (#1) under the bottom of the pipette and use the bulb to push the extract down to just above the top of the sand.

10. Remove test tube #1 and replace with test tube #2. Add the first solvent gradient, filling up to the indent near the top of the pipette. Use the bulb to push the solvent down to just above the top of the sand.

11. Switch test tubes and add the next solvent gradient. Repeat this process until all gradients have been added and all fractions have been collected.

Analyzing fractions:

1. Perform a TLC of each fraction and of the raw extract (See "Thin Layer Chromatography" protocol). The stain patterns of the various fractions should "add up" to the stain pattern of the raw extract. That is, each of the components stained in the raw extract should also be visible in the same location on one or more of the fraction plates. (Note: It may not be possible to visualize some of the raw extract's components on the fraction plates due to a low concentration of the compound [for example, if the compound were spread across a large number of the fractions].)

2. Perform an overlay bioassay of all fractions using the procedure described in the "Analyze Extraction for Antibiotic Activity" section of the "Analyzing Organic Extracts for Antibiotic Production" protocol.

Soil Sampling

Soil harbors an abundance of microbial biodiversity, coming in different forms and different packages. Studies of soil samples across the planet show that even the most remote and extreme environments are rich in microbial life. Local and familiar soils are rich and dynamic, and remain largely uncharted in the laboratory. The goal in this protocol is to demonstrate just how "exotic" local soil environments can be, and how much we can learn and discover from them. Your task is to choose an ecosystem, and bring a soil sample to study in the laboratory. Pick a sample that encapsulates a good representation of your ecosystem of choice and that is rich in biodiversity.

MATERIALS
- Container: conical tube or sandwich bag
- Soil collection worksheet (paper or electronic)

PROTOCOL
- Define what biodiversity means to you and write down what indicates that an ecosystem or soil environment is rich in biodiversity
- Write down a set of criteria for picking a soil sample and choose location(s) you wish to study. Note: Be sure to check legal requirements in your state or country before transporting soil across borders. Many areas have laws regulating import or export of soil to protect natural resources, respect ownership of biodiversity, and movement of pathogens.
- Obtain 1 or 2 containers to collect a soil sample and a soil collection worksheet
- Go out into the environment and collect a small soil sample – pick 5–10 g of soil or roughly a handful of soil.
    - For conical tube, take the cap off and use the open tube to scoop soil directly
    - For sandwich bag, turn the bag inside out, grab a handful of soil, and wrap bag around soil
- Close your container and keep until next lab session. Try to keep cool and way from the sun.
- Fill in your soil collection worksheet with information about your soil sample: location, date and time, weather conditions, habitat, surrounding plant and animal life, and other descriptive information. For location and weather, feel free to use maps or weather app to get an estimate.
- Develop hypotheses about your soil sample. What do you speculate you will learn or discover from your soil sample? How does that match your original set of criteria?

TinyEarth
studentsourcing antibiotic discovery

Soil Sample Data Collection Sheet (Authored by: Kristen Butela – Seton Hill University)

Collected By:	
Date of Collection:	
Deth:	
Type of Soil:	
Temperature of Air:	
Temperature of Soil:	
Weather Conditions on Date of Collection:	
General Location:	
GPS Coordinates via Google Earth:	
Sample Site Descriptors:	
Additional Data to be Determined in Lab:	
pH of Soil	
Water Content	
Organic Content	

Additional Documentation:

- Photo of sample site
- Identify any plant species present near site
- Photo of soil in collection tube

Soil Sampling Kit Contents:

- Data sheets
- 50-mL conical tubes
- Lab marker
- "Scientific Soil Sample Collection Device" (plastic knife or spoon)
- Alcohol pads (used to disinfect collection device, thermometer, ruler in between samplings)
- Thermometer
- Site-marking flag (if return to site necessary)
- Plastic ruler

Printout of "Guide of Texture by Feel": <http://soils.usda.gov/education/resources/lessons/texture/>

Spread Plate

Adapted from: Kathryn Wise – Microbe Library

<http://microbelibrary.org/component/resource/laboratory-test/3085-preparing-spread-plates-protocols>

PURPOSE

One method of distributing bacteria evenly over the surface of an agar plate medium is commonly referred to as the spread plate method. Classically, a small volume of a bacterial suspension is spread evenly over the agar surface by using a sterile bent glass rod or glass beads as the spreading device. The goal in evenly distributing the bacterial suspension is typically to permit the growth of colonies that can be enumerated subsequently (see Serial Dilution Protocols) or sampled following incubation. Each plate is spread with a single inoculum of the bacterial suspension. An alternative approach to spreading a single-inoculum volume with a smooth device is to apply a smaller volume and tip the plate, allowing gravity to distribute the inoculum in a band or track (track method) or to allow the inoculum to dry in place (drop method). With this alternative approach, several sample dilutions can be distributed on a single-agar plate.

HISTORY

Since the development of the agar plate in Robert Koch's laboratory, several methods have been used to achieve an even distribution of bacterial growth on or in the agar. The most common methods used to achieve this type of distribution are: spread, pour, thin layer, layered, and membrane filter(Koch,.1994).

PRINCIPLES

Using the spread method a small volume of a bacterial suspension is distributed evenly over the surface of an agar plate using a smooth sterilized spreader (Koch, 1994). In the case of track plates, gravity is used to spread the inoculum down the agar in a column forming a track (Jett et al., 1997).

PROTOCOL
Agar plates:

Select and prepare an agar medium based upon the type of bacteria to be enumerated or selected. Freshly prepared plates do not work as well as dry plates as it takes longer for the inoculum to absorb into the agar. Plates may be dried by keeping them at room temperature for roughly 24 hours. Plates will dry faster in lower humidity, so placing them in a laminar flow hood will speed the drying process. Once dried, plates may be used or refrigerated in closed bags or containers until required. Refrigerated plates should be warmed to room temperature prior to use.

Inoculations:

When enumerating colony-forming units (CFUs), plates with 20–200 CFUs can be used to calculate the number of CFUs/mL of the original sample. Typically, a dilution series is prepared, often a ten-fold dilution series, using a suitable diluent such as phosphate-buffered saline.

Serial Dilution Protocols:

A convenient inoculum volume, in terms of spreading, absorption, and calculations, is 0.1 mL (100 µL). Since some bacteria rapidly attach to the agar surface, the inoculum should be spread soon after it is applied. Working from the most dilute suspension to the most concentrated is advised. Proceeding from most dilute to most concentrated makes it unnecessary to change pipette tips between the dilutions.

Spreading:

A reusable glass or metal spreader should be flame sterilized by dipping in alcohol (such as 70% isopropyl or ethanol), shaking off the excess alcohol, and igniting the residue. The spreader is then allowed to cool. The spreader is placed in contact with the inoculum on the surface of the plate and positioned to allow the inoculum to run evenly along the length of the spreader. Apply even, gentle pressure as the plate or spreader is spun or rotated. If glass beads are used, ensure they have been properly autoclaved and stored under sterile conditions. Pour 5–10 beads onto a plate either prior to the addition of inoculum and shake to evenly distribute until the liquid is absorbed into the plate. Used beads can be washed with soap and water or just rinsed with water prior to autoclaving.

The goal is to evenly distribute the inoculum and to allow it to be absorbed into the agar. The plate, or spreader, should be rotated long enough to avoid pooling along the spreader once the rotation is stopped.

Incubation:

After the spread plates have been permitted to absorb the inoculum for 10–20 minutes they may be inverted and incubated as desired.

Observe the plates before the colonies have had time to fully develop. Closely positioned colonies may be difficult to resolve as separate colonies later, so it may necessary to shorten the incubation period to avoid overgrowth. Incubation in closed humidified containers will help avoid plates drying out when working with slow-growing colonies.

Counting and Selection:

After incubation, plates are inspected. When plating a dilution series, the growth on the plates should reflect the predictable drop in CFUs/plate as illustrated in a 10-fold dilution series prepared from an overnight broth culture of *Escherichia coli*.

COMMENTS AND TIPS

- Make sure plates are sufficiently dry prior to use.
- Plates should be prepared in duplicate or triplicate.
- Do not delay in spreading the inoculum once it has been applied to the plate since some cells will rapidly attach to the agar, especially if the plate agar is dry.
- Avoid spreading the inoculum to the edge of the agar because it is more difficult to inspect and count colonies along the agar's edge.
- Once the dilution series has been made, inoculate plates within 30 minutes to minimize changes in the number of cells in each dilution due to cell division or death.
- Make sure even pressure is applied to the spreader so that fluid is evenly distributed along its length as the plate or spreader is rotated.
- Once the dilutions are made, work backward spreading the most dilute samples first.
- When making your own spreaders do not make the spreading edge too long, it should conveniently fit into the alcohol container as well as the plate. Fire-polish the end of the spreader the student will hold. Bending the glass to form a triangle rather than an "L" will help ensure that only smooth even surfaces touch the agar and minimize pooling.
- Distributing the organisms by rotating the spreader rather than the plate tends to cause more pooling of the inoculum.

REFERENCES

Jett, B. D., Hatter, K. L., Huycke, M. M., & Gilmore, M. S. (1997) Simplified agar plate method for quantifying viable bacteria. BioTechniques 23:648–650.

Koch, A. C. (1994) Growth measurement, p. 254–257. In Gerhardt, P., Murray, R. G. E., Wood, W. A., and Krieg, N. R. (ed.), *Methods for General and Molecular Bacteriology*. Washington, DC: ASM Press.

Adapted from:
Wise, K. (2006) "Preparing Spread Plates Protocols". *Laboratory Protocols*. **Microbe Library**. *American Society for Microbiology*. Accessed 10 Oct 2013.

<http://microbelibrary.org/component/resource/laboratory-test/3085-preparing-spread-plates-protocols>

Streak Plate

Adapted from: D. Sue Katz – Microbe Library

<http://microbelibrary.org/component/resource/laboratory-test/3160-the-streak-plate-protocol>

HISTORY

The modern streak plate procedure has evolved from attempts by Robert Koch and other early microbiologists to obtain pure bacterial cultures in order to study them, as described in an 1881 paper authored by Koch.

The earliest appearance of the three-sector streak pattern (called the T streak) commonly used today may be the 1961 photos published in Finegold and Sweeney (1960). An illustration of how to perform this streak is in the 1968 edition of the Manual of BBL Products and Laboratory Procedures. In addition to the T streak, the BBL Manual illustrates the three- and four-way streak methods, which are most commonly used today.

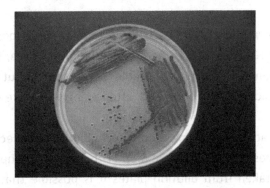

Figure 10. Four-way streak plate showing the growth of *Serratia marcescens* thinning as the streaking moves clockwise.

PURPOSE

The purpose of the streak plate is to obtain isolated colonies from an inoculum by creating areas sequentially diluting the inoculum on a single plate. Isolated colonies represent a clone of cells derived from a single precursor cell. When culture media are inoculated using a single isolated colony, the resulting culture grows from that single clone. Historically, most microbiology research and microbial characterization has been done with pure cultures.

THEORY

One bacterial cell will create a colony as it multiplies. The streak process is intended to create a region where the bacteria are so dilute that when each bacterium touches the surface of the agar, it is far enough away from other cells so that an isolated colony can develop. In this manner, spreading an inoculum containing many bacteria will result in the isolation of individual clones.

MATERIALS

- Specimen to be streaked (most likely from Master Plate)
- Wooden stick, plastic, disposable transfer loop, or reusable metal transfer loop (usually nichrome, a nickel-chromium alloy, or platinum; the single-use disposable plastic loop can be discarded between sectors rather than resterilized)
- Bunsen burner
- Sterile Petri dish with appropriate bacterial medium
- Labeling pen
- Sterile cotton swabs (if necessary to remove condensation from the agar surface and from around the inner rim of the Petri dish)

PROTOCOL

1. Label Petri dish: Petri dishes are labeled on the bottom rather than on the lid. In order to preserve an area to observe the plate after incubation, write close to the edge of the bottom of the plate. Labels usually include the organism name, type of agar, date, and the plater's name or initials.

2. Obtain sterile loop or wooden stick or sterilize a metal transfer loop by flaming in Bunsen burner so that the entire wire is red-hot: When manipulating bacteria, transfer loops, sticks, etc. are usually held like a pencil. If plastic disposable loops are being utilized, they are removed from the packaging to avoid contamination and, after a single use, are discarded into an appropriate container.

3. Open your Master Plate briefly, using aseptic technique, and collect a small number of cells from isolate patch of interest using the sterile loop or the sterile toothpick/wooden stick. Because of how patches were taken from dilution plates it is possible that each patch contains several different bacterial species or strains.

4. Streak the plate: Inoculating the agar means that the lid will have to be opened. Minimize the amount of agar and the length of time the agar is exposed to the environment during the streaking process.

   - Streak the first sector: Remove the Petri dish lid; touch the loop/toothpick on the agar in the region of the first sector and spread with bacteria by moving your loop across the dish in a zig-zag manner. Make the movements close together and cover the entire first region. The loop/toothpick should glide over the surface of the agar; take care not to dig into the agar. Discard the loop/toothpick or flame reusable loop when this is completed.
   - Between sectors: Remove the loop from the Petri dish and obtain another sterile loop/toothpick before continuing to the second sector. Either incinerate the material on the loop or obtain a sterile loop/toothpick if using disposable. Metal reusable loops must be cool before streaking can continue. Metal loops can be touched to an uninoculated area of agar to test whether they are adequately cooled. If the loop is cool, there will be no sizzling or hissing and the agar will not be melted to form a brand. If a brand is formed, avoid that area when continuing with the streaking process.

- Streak the second sector: Open the Petri dish and insert the loop. Touch the loop to the first sector once, drawing a few of the bacteria (invisible to your eye) from the first sector into the second sector. The second sector is streaked less heavily than the first sector, again using a zig-zag motion.
- Obtain a sterile loop for the third sector (see step 2, above).
- Streak the third sector: Open the Petri dish and insert the loop again. Touch the loop once into the second sector and draw bacteria from the second sector into the third sector. Streak the third sector with a zig-zag motion. This last sector has the widest gap between the rows of streaking, placing the bacteria a little further apart than in the previous two sectors. Watch closely to avoid touching the first sector as the streak is completed.
- Dispose the loop/toothpick or flame loop to sterilize for proper storage.

SAFETY

Always dispose of used loops, sticks, or any inoculating tools appropriately. Flame the metal loop one last time to sterilize for proper storage.

COMMENTS AND TIPS

- Alternative streak patterns and different culture media: A variety of alternative streak patterns are possible. Some are used for specific sources of inocula, such as urine specimens. The patterns also differ in the number of sectors as well as in the number of times the loop is sterilized. The four-quadrant streak pattern would be recommended for use when large amounts of bacteria are expected in the inoculum. The extra sector will provide additional dilution and increase the probability of isolated colonies on the plate. The four-quadrant streak plate is described in a variety of references, e.g., in Cappuccino and Sherman's *Microbiology, A Laboratory Manual*, 8th ed. (2008).
- Sometimes cultures will be streaked on enrichment media or various selective and differential media. For instance, a culture which is expected to have a Gram-negative pathogen will be streaked on a MacConkey agar plate, which inhibits the growth of Gram-positive organisms.
- Incinerating material on transfer loops—flaming: Reusable microbiological loops and needles are sterilized by flaming. A Bunsen burner is traditionally used for this process. Most microbiology manuals show the microbiologist positioned with his/her hand above the burner, with the loop placed into the flame. To avoid possible contact with the flame, the microbiologist might consider placing his/her hand below the flame with the loop/needle above the hand in the flame. The flame of the Bunsen burner should be adjusted to blue, with the darker blue cone of cooler air visible in the center of the flame. The loop or needle should be placed into the hotter part of the flame and kept there until it glows red. When flaming, the wire loop is held in the light blue area of a Bunsen burner just above the tip of inner flame of the flame until it is red hot. There is a possible aerosol hazard if the loop or needle contains liquid or a bacterial clump. Loops and needles should be placed into the heat slowly so that the moisture evaporates rather than sputters. Once sterile, the loop is allowed to cool by holding it still. Do not wave it around to cool it or blow on it.

- If an incinerator such as a Bacti-Cinerator is used to sterilize the loop, the loop is to remain inside the incinerator for 5–7 seconds. When warmed up (which will take 5 minutes), the temperature inside the incinerator is 815°C. The incinerator will take 5–10 minutes to warm up to working temperature.
- Several techniques decontaminate transfer loops between sectors of a streak plate: flame, dig into agar, flame once, and rotate loop
- There are various methods to remove organisms from the loop between sectors. Beginning students are generally taught to sterilize the loop between each sector by incinerating and then cooling the loop. Clinical microbiologists practice a variety of methods. Some flame once after the initial sector and then rotate the loop so that the next sectors can be streaked with an unused side of the loop. Other laboratorians (as clinical microbiologists call themselves) stab the loop several times into the agar to reduce the bacterial load on the loop between sectors.
- Isolated colony appearances: Isolated colonies can be described using the traditional colony descriptions. The Colony Morphology Atlas-Protocol project provides information about bacterial colony appearance and characteristic photographs. The appearance of an organism can vary. For instance, a colony of an organism growing in a crowded sector of the plate will not grow as large as the same organism growing in isolation. The media composition, pH, and moisture, as well as the incubation time and temperature can all affect the organism's appearance. Colonies selected for subculturing should be colonies that are isolated, i.e., there is no other colony visibly touching the colony.
- Agar with a surface layer of water is not suitable for obtaining isolated colonies. Obvious water drops should be removed from the surface of the plate and from the rim of the plate by using sterile cotton swabs. Plates should be incubated agar side up, to avoid condensation that would drop onto the growing colonies on the agar surface.
- Flaming tube mouths: Many protocols suggest flaming the tube mouth before and after removing organisms from a tube. Flaming is often thought to sterilize the mouth of the tube, and this was important when test tubes were capped with cotton plugs. A more important reason to flame the opening of the tube is warm the air in it, causing it expand, thereby creating a flow of air out of the tube. This reduces the chance that air will flow into the tube, possibly carrying contaminants with it. Only flame glass tubes and use extreme caution.
- Rehearsing the streak procedure: Some instructors have students practice the streaking procedure on a piece of paper. The process helps the student visualize the completed product and practice the fine muscle movements that are required in successful streaking for isolation.
- Students may also find that they can visualize the pattern better if they mark the back of the Petri dish (for instance, a T streak divide the plate into three sectors).
- Before learning to streak, students should have had the opportunity to work with 1.5% agar media. Ideally they will have had the opportunity to practice using a loop on a plate to determine the best angle of approach and the amount of force required to glide the loop over the surface of the agar without gouging the surface.
- Holding the plate while streaking: If possible, adequate lighting should be available to help the microbiologist follow the tracings of the loop on the agar. For most labs, this means that the Petri dish should be held in one's hand while being streaked in order to reflect the light properly.

Additionally, the length of time the Petri dish lid is removed should be minimized in order to limit contamination. There are several ways to hold the Petri dish. Beginning students may find that they obtain the best results leaving the plate on the lab bench and lifting the lid to work. Other students may find that they can place the plate upside down on the workbench and lift the agar-containing bottom, hold it to streak and then quickly replace it into the lid. Yet other students may have the manual dexterity to manipulate the entire dish in their hand, raising the lid with thumb and two fingers while balancing the plate in the rest of their hand.

REFERENCES

BBL. (1973) *BBL manual of products and laboratory procedures.* Cockeysville, MD: Becton Dickson Microbiology Systems.

Buchanan, E. D., & Buchanan, R. E. (1938) *Bacteriology for Students in General and Household Science* (4th ed.). New York, NY: Macmillan Company.

Cappuccino, J. G., & Sherman, N. (2008) *Microbiology a Laboratory Manual* (8th ed.). San Francisco, CA: Pearson/Benjamin Cummings.

Finegold, S. M., & Sweeney, E. E. (1960) New selective and differential medium for coagulase-positive staphylococci allowing rapid growth and strain differentiation. J Bacteriol 81(4):636–641.

Lammert, J. M. (2007) *Techniques in Microbiology. A Student Handbook.* Upper Saddle River, NJ: Pearson/Prentice Hall.

Levine, M. (1939) *An Introduction to Laboratory Technique in Bacteriology* (revised ed.). New York, NY: The Macmillan Company.

Pelczar, M. J., Jr., & Reid, R. D. (1958) *Laboratory Exercises in Microbiology*, p. 45–47. New York, NY: McGraw-Hill Book Company, Inc.

Salle, A. J. (1954) *Laboratory Manual on Fundamental Principles of Bacteriology* (4th ed.), p. 39. New York, NY: McGraw-Hill Book Company, Inc.

Sherwood, N. P., Billings, F. H., & Clawson, B. J. (1992) *Laboratory Exercises in Bacteriology and Diagnostic Methods* (7th ed.). Lawrence, KS: The World Co.

Williams, H. U. (1908) *A Manual of Bacteriology* p. 100. Revised by B. M. Bolton. Philadelphia, PA: P. Blakiston's Son & Co.

Williams, C. L., & Letton, H. P. (1916) A note on the preparation of agar agar culture media. J Bacteriol 1:547–548.
http://jb.asm.org/cgi/reprint/1/5/547?maxtoshow=&HITS=10&hits=10&RESULTFORMAT=&author1=williams&author2=letton&titleabstract=agaragar&searchid=1&FIRSTINDEX=0&tdate=3/31/1931&resourcetype=HWCIT.

Tiny Earth
studentsourcing antibiotic discovery

Adapted from:
Katz, D. S. (2008) "The Streak Plate Protocols". *Laboratory Protocols*. **Microbe Library**. *American Society for Microbiology*. Accessed 18 October 2013.
<http://microbelibrary.org/component/resource/laboratory-test/3160-the-streak-plate-protocol>

Sulfide, Indole, and Motility

Adapted from: Clifford Grimsley – Gaston College

SIM media is a semisolid differential medium, which enables detection of hydrogen sulfide, indole, and bacterial motility. Because this medium allows for the movement of bacteria, and not just growth, it will be necessary to use an inoculating needle instead of an inoculating loop to introduce the culture into the tube. Inoculating needles are essentially the same as inoculating loops; however, the wire is straight and is used to stab into the agar medium instead of spreading the bacteria on top of the agar.

Some bacteria produce hydrogen sulfide (H_2S) through the metabolism of certain amino acids containing sulfur or through the reduction of inorganic sulfur compounds in the environment, such as sulfate or sulfide. The hydrogen that is released can be detected by adding a heavy metal salt, such as lead, bismuth, or iron, into the medium. Hydrogen sulfide reacts with these compounds to produce black-colored metal sulfides.

Indole is produced when the amino acid tryptophan (yes, the one found in turkey) is metabolized. Indole production can be detected by adding a reagent known as Kovac's Reagent. If indole is produced, the Kovac's reagent will create a cherry red liquid layer on the top of the bacterial culture medium.

Bacteria have evolved several types of motility, but the most common type is driven by a motor that rotates a thick tail, called a flagellum. Motile cells can move throughout SIM medium as it is a semisolid, and they will show diffuse growth along the line of inoculation. The production of H_2S is intensified by cultures that are also motile. Therefore, if the culture is both motile and able to produce H_2S, the entire tube may turn black. Motility can also be assessed by creating a hanging drop slide of the culture and observing for motility within.

It is important to test for motility and H_2S production before testing for the presence of indole, as the test for indole production may sometimes obscure the observation of the other results.

MATERIALS
- 3 tubes of SIM media per group
- Kovac's reagent
- Cultures of test isolates and positive and negative controls
- Inoculating needle

PROTOCOL
1. Inoculate each of the cultures, respectively, into a separate tube of SIM media. Stab the wire straight down through the agar to the bottom of the tube and quickly withdraw it along the same path. Do not move the wire around in the agar.
2. Incubate the tubes at optimal growth temperature (for isolates typically 25-30°C) for 24 hours.
3. Examine the tubes for evidence of hydrogen sulfide production (browning or blackening of the media). Record the results.
4. Examine the tubes for evidence of motility of the organism. A motile species grows away from the stab line into the surrounding agar, producing lines of growth or even a general turbidity

Tiny Earth
studentsourcing antibiotic discovery

throughout the tube. The growth of a non-motile organism is restricted to the path of the stab. Record your observations.

5. Perform the Kovac test for the presence of indole, as follows:

    a) Pipette 2 mL of Kovac's reagent and add it to the SIM tube, being careful not to mix the reagent with the medium.

    b) Observe the color of the Kovac layer and record your results.

Sulfide and Indole Production and Motility Data Sheet

Isolate name	Sulfide	Indole	Motility

Thin Layer Chromatography (TLC)

Using organic solvents, we can extract the active compound from antibiotic-producing isolates (see the "Analyzing Organic Extracts for Antibiotic Production" protocol). However, this extraction process is quite crude, meaning that the result of this process is not a pure active compound, but rather a mixture of many compounds. In order to further isolate the active compound, we can use a series of techniques that separate compounds based on their chemical properties. This process can be guided by the use Thin Layer Chromatography (TLC) plates.

A TLC plate is a flat glass sheet that is covered on one side with a solid absorbent (often silica). When the bottom of the plate is placed in a mixture of organic solvents, the solvents will flow through the silica and travel up the plate. If extracts are spotted onto a TLC plate, this upward solvent flow will carry with it various components of the extract. However, different compounds will flow at different rates, with nonpolar components generally traveling more quickly and polar components typically traveling more slowly. In this manner, the various compounds that make up the extract can be separated along the length of the plate, with more nonpolar molecules near the top of the plate and more polar molecules near the bottom.

The mixture of organic solvents used in this process (called the "solvent system") can also be varied to achieve different separations of the extract. For instance, the use of a more polar solvent (like methanol, for example) often carries polar compounds further up the plate, meaning that the polar compounds in the extract will be separated to a greater degree. If a more nonpolar solvent system is used, on the other hand, the result will likely be greater separation of nonpolar compounds. In general, a 1:1 mixture of hexane:ethyl acetate is a good starting point for a TLC solvent system. Other common systems include 4:1 chloroform:methanol and 1:1 dichloromethane:ethyl acetate.

Although the compounds contained in organic extracts are often white or colorless, making it difficult to identify the locations of different compounds, there are several techniques that can be used to visualize extract components and to determine which are bioactive. First, various stains can be applied to the TLC plate, resulting in the coloration of particular classes of organic compounds. In the procedure below, we recommend the use of anisaldehyde, a broad-range stain that will result in a wide range of colorations. Other stains, like ninhydrin and potassium permanganate, tend to be more specific. (For instance, ninhydrin stains amino acids and small peptides, while potassium permanganate stains oxidizable compounds.) Second, bioassay overlays can be used to determine the movement of active compounds on the plate. In this technique, a thin layer of soft agar inoculated with a bacterial tester strain is laid on top of TLC plate. After growth under the appropriate conditions, zones of inhibition can be observed, revealing the position of the active compound(s).

MATERIALS
- 2 small silica TLC plates (about 6 cm in height and 2–4 cm in length)
- Organic extract
- 50 mL beaker
- Solvents
- Micropipettes or glass capillary tube

- Black Sharpie marker (as a "control")
- Forceps
- UV lamp
- Anisaldehyde stain (prepared by teaching assistant)
- Heat dryer or hot plate
- LB top agar (0.75%)
- Liquid culture of tester strain

PROTOCOL

1. Obtain dried organic extract.
2. Re-suspend extract in 100ul of the solvent used in extraction.
3. Draw a thin pencil line on the silica side of each TLC plate about 0.75 cm from the bottom. Be gentle so as not to scratch the silica from the glass surface. In addition, label one plate to indicate which will be used for staining and which will be used for the bioassay.
4. Use micropipette or a thin glass capillary tube to spot 2ul of extract on a point along the pencil line.
5. Wait for the extract spot to dry nearly completely. Then, once again spot 2ul of extract at the same point on the pencil line. Continue this process until 10 spots have been placed on the stain plate and 20 spots have been placed on the bioassay plate.
6. Choose another point on the pencil line and gently tap tip of black Sharpie marker on plate until a small black dot is formed. Be sure to get a sufficient amount of ink on the plate, but be careful not to pull the silica off the glass surface. The marker will act a control and allow you to visualize movement up the plate with the solvents.
7. Select solvent system and mix solvents in 50ml glass beaker. The total volume of the system should be 1 mL. For instance, if the 1:1 hexane:ethyl acetate system is chosen, 500 µL of hexane and 500 µL of ethyl acetate should be added to the beaker.
8. Use forceps to gently pick up each plate from the top. Place the plate in the beaker such that the plate sits level (not crooked). The solvent system should cover the bottom of the plate, but be well below the pencil line. Cover the beaker with aluminum foil to prevent evaporation of solvents. You should be able to see solvent line moving upward across the silica.
9. Allow the solvent to run until the solvent front is about 0.5 cm from the top of the plate. At this point, use forceps to remove the plate and gently blot edges with paper towel. Allow excess solvent to evaporate completely in the fume hood.
10. Shine UV lamp on the TLC plate prepared for staining and make note of areas of the plate that fluoresce. Try not to shine UV light on plate for more than a few seconds.

For staining TLC plate:

1. Obtain the anisaldehyde stain prepared by your teaching assistant. **Note:** This stain contains sulfuric acid; handle this stain carefully. Using forceps, pick up the plate prepared for staining by its top edge. Dip entire plate into anisaldehyde and quickly remove. Plate can be placed on a Petri dish lid or other surface to prevent staining the chemical fume-hood surface.

Tiny Earth
studentsourcing antibiotic discovery

2. Blot edges of stained plate on paper towel. Dry and heat plate using heat dryer or hot plate until background of plate is light pink and spots of various colors appear. Take pictures shortly after heating, as colors may begin to fade.

For the bio-assay plate:
1. Dampen a KimWipe with ethanol and gently wipe back and edges of the plate prepared for bioassay. Place this cleaned plate face up in an empty Petri dish.
2. Obtain a liquid culture of a bacterial tester strain of your choice. This strain should be one that was inhibited by your organic extract. Inoculate 12 mL of warm LB top-agar or soft agar for overlay (0.75%) with 240 µL of liquid culture.
3. Pour spiked soft agar into the Petri dish. Swirl gently, ensuring that agar is distributed evenly across Petri dish and that the entirety of the TLC plate is covered.
4. Incubate under appropriate conditions for the tester strain. Keep the Petri dish face up to avoid disturbing the agar.

Further Steps
Observe the results of the anisaldehyde staining and the bioassay overlay to determine how well your chosen solvent system separated the components of your extract. An ideal separation would have compounds spread over the entire length of the TLC plate rather than grouped closely together in one small section of the plate. Adjust the solvent system to try to optimize separation. In general, if the components are closely grouped at the bottom of the plate, make the solvent system more polar. For example, if a 4:1 chloroform:methanol system results in a tight group of compounds at the bottom of the plate, you might make the system more polar by adjusting the ratio to 2:1 chloroform:methanol. If, on the other hand, the components are closely grouped at the top of the plate, make the solvent system more nonpolar. If, for example, a 1:1 hexane:ethyl acetate results in tight group of compounds near the top of the plate, you might make the system less polar by adjusting the ratio to 3:1 hexane:ethyl acetate. Repeat this process of trials and readjustment until the optimal solvent system is achieved.

Typical Media Menu

This list includes common microbiological media (and their recipes). Most media come premixed in a dehydrated powder form that we mix with deionized water. Check which media types are available (ask your instructor) and select a media type to grow your soil sample – you will be using this medium for serial dilutions and to grow the your isolate from your dilution plates. Also, pay close attention to their ingredients and how they relate to bacterial nutrition. For more media types and recipes, refer to the Difco "Manual of Microbiological Culture Media" (part of BD Bioscience). <http://www.bd.com/ds/technicalCenter/misc/difcobblmanual_2nded_lowres.pdf>

Luria Broth or Lysogeny Broth (LB)

Rich media for propagation and maintenance of *E. coli* used in molecular biology.

- Tryptone – 10 g
- Yeast Extract – 5 g
- Sodium Chloride – 10 g
- Agar - 15 g

pH ~7.0

Tryptic Soy Agar (TSA) – in 1/10 or 1/2 strength

General medium used for cultivation of a wide variety of microorganisms.

- Pancreatic Digest of Casein – 17 g
- Papaic Digest of Soybean – 3 g
- Dextrose (Glucose) – 2.5 g
- Sodium Chloride – 5 g
- Dipotassium Phosphate – 2.5 g
- Agar – 15 g

pH ~7.3V V

Potato Dextrose Agar (PDA)

Cultivation of yeasts and molds

- Potato Starch – 4 g
- Dextrose (Glucose) – 20 g
- Agar – 15 g

pH ~5.1

All Culture (AC)

For cultivating a wide variety of microorganisms

- Proteose Peptone No. 3 – 20 g
- Beef Extract – 3 g
- Yeast Extract – 3 g

- Malt Extract – 3 g
- Dextrose (Glucose) – 5 g
- Ascorbic Acid – 0.2 g
- Agar - 15 g

pH ~7.2

R2A

Low nutrient (minimal) medium for enumeration and cultivation of bacteria from potable water.

- Yeast Extract – 0.5 g
- Acid Digest of Casein – 0.5 g
- Pancreatic Digest of Casein – 0.25 g
- Peptic Digest of Animal Tissue – 0.25 g
- Dextrose (Glucose) – 0.5 g
- Soluble Starch – 0.5 g
- Sodium Pyruvate – 0.5 g
- Potassium Phosphate, Dibasic – 0.3
- Magnesium Sulfate – 0.024 g
- Agar – 15 g

pH ~7.2

Brain Heart Infusion (BHI)

Cultivation of fastidious (fussy) microorganisms, including streptococci, pneumococci, and meningococci

- Brain Heart, Infusion from (Solids) – 6 g
- Peptic Digest of Animal Tissue – 6 g
- Sodium Chloride – 5 g
- Dextrose (Glucose) – 3 6
- Pancreatic Digest of Gelatin – 14.5 g
- Disodium Phosphate – 2.5 g
- Agar - 15 g

pH ~7.4

Todd Hewitt (TH)

Cultivation of group A streptococci or as a blood culture medium

- Heart, Infusion from 500 g – 3.1 g
- Neopeptone – 20.0 g
- Dextrose (Glucose) – 2 g
- Sodium Chloride – 2 g
- Disodium phosphate – 0.4 g
- Sodium carbonate – 2.5 g
- Agar – 15 g

pH ~7.8

Lab Notes

Lab Notes

Lab Notes

Lab Notes

Lab Notes

Lab Notes

Lab Notes

Lab Notes

EXPERIMENTS
IN
GENERAL CHEMISTRY

CH 103L — 104L — 105L

CH 111L — 112L — 113L

Fourth Edition

W. D. PERRY

ROBYN REYNOLDS-VAUGHN

AUBURN UNIVERSITY

DEPARTMENT OF CHEMISTRY

CPC *CONTEMPORARY PUBLISHING COMPANY*

508 ST. MARY'S STREET, RALEIGH, N.C. 27605—(919) 821-4566

Art Work
by
Woody Jones

ISBN: 0-89892-110-4

TABLE OF CONTENTS

PREFACE

The Experiments in this manual are intended to supplement the material presented to you in lecture and to introduce you to new material. Whenever possible, the laboratory experiments are synchronized with the lecture course.

You are encouraged to read the appropriate sections in your text book before doing your experiment. This is particularly important for material that you have not covered in lecture. The time that you spend doing this will actually save you considerable time when you write up your lab report.

W. D. Perry
Robyn Reynolds - Vaughn
Spring 1993

LABORATORY POLICIES

ATTENDANCE

Due to the large number of students enrolled in the general chemistry labs, only absences due to personal illness, participation in a university approved function or an extreme family emergency will be excused. Requests for make-ups for university approved functions must be filled out **prior to the absence**. If you know in advance that you will be missing a lab (e.g., a scheduled dental or doctor's appointment) you must fill out a make-up form in advance. **Absences due to personal illness must be substantiated by a doctor's written excuse with the doctor's signature**. An excuse from Drake Student Health Center must also have an in/out time. Make-up lab request forms are located in SN 214. **You must request a make-up lab within one week of the missed lab** — after this time you will not be allowed to make up the lab.

If you miss a lab, **it is your responsibility to get the lab report turned in the day and time it is due.** Do not save it for when you see about a make-up lab. Leave the report in the stockroom (SN 214). The stockroom attendant will sign and date the report. Lab reports turned in after the quiz will be penalized 10 points, and 10 points will be deducted for each additional day the report is late. Lab reports more than 5 days late can receive no more than 10 points.

SAFETY RULES FOR THE LABORATORY

STUDENTS WHO REFUSE TO FOLLOW LABORATORY SAFETY REGULATIONS WILL BE ASKED TO LEAVE THE LABORATORY.

1. Know the location of fire extinguishers, eye wash stations, safety showers and exits.
2. Eye protection (safety glasses) must be worn at all times in the laboratory.
3. Eating, drinking, and smoking are not allowed in the laboratory.
4. Appropriate clothing must be worn, including a protective apron. Confine long hair and loose clothing. Closed shoes must be worn at all times — open-toed shoes, sling-backs, clogs, and sandals are not permitted.
5. Horseplay, pranks, or other acts of mischief are especially dangerous and are prohibited.
6. Mouth suction must never be used to fill pipets.
7. Report any accident, however minor, to the instructor at once.
8. Students who are pregnant or who become pregnant must inform their instructors so that appropriate precautions may be taken.

GENERAL LABORATORY RULES

1. Students will never work in a lab room by themselves and will not perform unauthorized experiments.
2. Students must clean their benches and their work spaces (balance rooms, etc.) before they leave the laboratory.
3. All chemicals should be returned to their proper places immediately after they are used. Unused chemicals should never be poured back into their original containers.
4. Proper liquid and solid waste containers should be used at all times. The instructor will tell the students where to dispose of waste materials.

LABORATORY EQUIPMENT

Each student is responsible for the equipment issued to him/her. The equipment in your drawer is to be returned at the end of each quarter complete and in good condition. You will be charged for any missing or broken equipment at the end of the quarter. You are also responsible for the equipment that you will occasionally borrow from the storeroom. Please be certain that all equipment is present when you check in on the first day of lab. If you forget your key on the day of your lab, a fee must be paid (to Chem Supply, room 128 Saunders) before your drawer can be unlocked. If you lose your key, a replacement key can be purchased from Chem Supply in 128 SN. When you check out of lab you must return the key to the drawer assigned to you. Failure to return the key will result in a $25.00 charge which must be paid (to the Bursar's Office) before a grade will be given for the lab.

I have read the above laboratory policies and agree to abide by them.

Desk Number		Lab Course	Time	Day

	Signature		Date

LABORATORY POLICIES

ATTENDANCE

Due to the large number of students enrolled in the general chemistry labs, only absences due to personal illness, participation in a university approved function or an extreme family emergency will be excused. Requests for make-ups for university approved functions must be filled out **prior to the absence**. If you know in advance that you will be missing a lab (e.g., a scheduled dental or doctor's appointment) you must fill out a make-up form in advance. **Absences due to personal illness must be substantiated by a doctor's written excuse with the doctor's signature**. An excuse from Drake Student Health Center must also have an in/out time. Make-up lab request forms are located in SN 214. **You must request a make-up lab within one week of the missed lab** — after this time you will not be allowed to make up the lab.

If you miss a lab, **it is your responsibility to get the lab report turned in the day and time it is due.** Do not save it for when you see about a make-up lab. Leave the report in the stockroom (SN 214). The stockroom attendant will sign and date the report. Lab reports turned in after the quiz will be penalized 10 points, and 10 points will be deducted for each additional day the report is late. Lab reports more than 5 days late can receive no more than 10 points.

SAFETY RULES FOR THE LABORATORY

STUDENTS WHO REFUSE TO FOLLOW LABORATORY SAFETY REGULATIONS WILL BE ASKED TO LEAVE THE LABORATORY.

1. Know the location of fire extinguishers, eye wash stations, safety showers and exits.
2. Eye protection (safety glasses) must be worn at all times in the laboratory.
3. Eating, drinking, and smoking are not allowed in the laboratory.
4. Appropriate clothing must be worn, including a protective apron. Confine long hair and loose clothing. Closed shoes must be worn at all times — open-toed shoes, sling-backs, clogs, and sandals are not permitted.
5. Horseplay, pranks, or other acts of mischief are especially dangerous and are prohibited.
6. Mouth suction must never be used to fill pipets.
7. Report any accident, however minor, to the instructor at once.
8. Students who are pregnant or who become pregnant must inform their instructors so that appropriate precautions may be taken.

GENERAL LABORATORY RULES

1. Students will never work in a lab room by themselves and will not perform unauthorized experiments.
2. Students must clean their benches and their work spaces (balance rooms, etc.) before they leave the laboratory.
3. All chemicals should be returned to their proper places immediately after they are used. Unused chemicals should never be poured back into their original containers.
4. Proper liquid and solid waste containers should be used at all times. The instructor will tell the students where to dispose of waste materials.

LABORATORY EQUIPMENT

Each student is responsible for the equipment issued to him/her. The equipment in your drawer is to be returned at the end of each quarter complete and in good condition. You will be charged for any missing or broken equipment at the end of the quarter. You are also responsible for the equipment that you will occasionally borrow from the storeroom. Please be certain that all equipment is present when you check in on the first day of lab. If you forget your key on the day of your lab, a fee must be paid (to Chem Supply, room 128 Saunders) before your drawer can be unlocked. If you lose your key, a replacement key can be purchased from Chem Supply in 128 SN. When you check out of lab you must return the key to the drawer assigned to you. Failure to return the key will result in a $25.00 charge which must be paid (to the Bursar's Office) before a grade will be given for the lab.

I have read the above laboratory policies and agree to abide by them.

_____

Desk Number   **Lab Course**   **Time**   **Day**

_____

                                  Signature   **Date**

LABORATORY POLICIES

ATTENDANCE

Due to the large number of students enrolled in the general chemistry labs, only absences due to personal illness, participation in a university approved function or an extreme family emergency will be excused. Requests for make-ups for university approved functions must be filled out **prior to the absence**. If you know in advance that you will be missing a lab (e.g., a scheduled dental or doctor's appointment) you must fill out a make-up form in advance. **Absences due to personal illness must be substantiated by a doctor's written excuse with the doctor's signature**. An excuse from Drake Student Health Center must also have an in/out time. Make-up lab request forms are located in SN 214. **You must request a make-up lab within one week of the missed lab** — after this time you will not be allowed to make up the lab.

If you miss a lab, **it is your responsibility to get the lab report turned int he day and time it is due.** Do not save it for when you see about a make-up lab. Leave the report in the stockroom (SN 214). The stockroom attendant will sign and date the report. Lab reports turned in after the quiz will be penalized 10 points, and 10 points will be deducted for each additional day the report is late. Lab reports more than 5 days late can receive no more than 10 points.

SAFETY RULES FOR THE LABORATORY

STUDENTS WHO REFUSE TO FOLLOW LABORATORY SAFETY REGULATIONS WILL BE ASKED TO LEAVE THE LABORATORY.

1. Know the location of fire extinguishers, eye wash stations, safety showers and exits.
2. Eye protection (safety glasses) must be worn at all times in the laboratory.
3. Eating, drinking, and smoking are not allowed in the laboratory.
4. Appropriate clothing must be worn, including a protective apron. Confine long hair and loose clothing. Closed shoes must be worn at all times — open-toed shoes, sling-backs, clogs, and sandals are not permitted.
5. Horseplay, pranks, or other acts of mischief are especially dangerous and are prohibited.
6. Mouth suction must never be used to fill pipets.
7. Report any accident, however minor, to the instructor at once.
8. Students who are pregnant or who become pregnant must inform their instructors so that appropriate precautions may be taken.

GENERAL LABORATORY RULES

1. Students will never work in a lab room by themselves and will not perform unauthorized experiments.
2. Students must clean their benches and their work spaces (balance rooms, etc.) before they leave the laboratory.
3. All chemicals should be returned to their proper places immediately after they are used. Unused chemicals should never be poured back into their original containers.
4. Proper liquid and solid waste containers should be used at all times. The instructor will tell the students where to dispose of waste materials.

LABORATORY EQUIPMENT

Each student is responsible for the equipment issued to him/her. The equipment in your drawer is to be returned at the end of each quarter complete and in good condition. You will be charged for any missing or broken equipment at the end of the quarter. You are also responsible for the equipment that you will occasionally borrow from the storeroom. Please be certain that all equipment is present when you check in on the first day of lab. If you forget your key on the day of your lab, a fee must be paid (to Chem Supply, room 128 Saunders) before your drawer can be unlocked. If you lose your key, a replacement key can be purchased from Chem Supply in 128 SN. When you check out of lab you must return the key to the drawer assigned to you. Failure to return the key will result in a $25.00 charge which must be paid (to the Bursar's Office) before a grade will be given for the lab.

I have read the above laboratory policies and agree to abide by them.

Desk Number   **Lab Course**   **Time**   **Day**

Signature   **Date**

GUIDELINES FOR LAB REPORTS

GENERAL RULES

Write as **neatly** as possible. Take your time. Points will be taken off for messy reports. **Do not** scribble out mistakes. Draw a single horizontal line through the mistake and then rewrite it correctly.

Do not use pencil, erasable ink or "whiteout" on a lab report.

Do not write on the backs of pages.

Do not scribble notes or make any stray marks in the margins.

Your handwritten lab procedure is signed by one of your lab instructors when your lab report for the previous week is turned in and **before** the quiz.

Your data sheet(s) are to be signed and a copy left with your lab instructor **before** you leave lab.

Each page of the lab report should have your name and desk number at the top right-hand corner.

ORDER OF THE LAB REPORT (all reports should be stapled in the upper left corner)

1. **Title Page**
   Name of the experiment, your name, your desk number, your lab instructors' names

2. **Handwritten Procedure**
   Outline or step form and initialed by lab instructor

3. **Data Sheet**
   Data is to be written in **INK**. One line through errors, do not write over previously taken data, no "whiteout", must be signed by lab instructor

4. **Conclusions and Calculations Sheet**
   Units and significant figures are to be used in all lab reports.
   a. There should be a formula for each calculation used, no matter how simple.
   b. There should be a formula with the numbers and correct units plugged into the formula.
   c. The answer with the correct units and the proper number of significant figures.
   d. If there is more than one calculation for a formula, only the answer needs to be written for the subsequent calculations.
   e. If a reference book is used, the book title and page number need to be recorded in the report.
   f. All answers to questions should be in complete sentences with reasoning included in the answer.

5. **Graphs (if required):**

   a. Graph paper which is graduated to 10 divisions to the centimeter should be used for all graphs.

   b. Graphs should fill the entire page if possible.

   c. Graphs should have a title and both axes should be properly labeled.

   d. The graduated intervals used for plotting data should be clearly labeled and easy to interpret.

   e. All data points should be circled.

   f. All curves or straight lines should be completely drawn on the graph.

   g. All important points should be labeled (stoichiometric points, equivalence points, etc.)

   h. There should be a separate graph for each set of data points.

CHECK IN / CHECK OUT

The following items of permanent equipment should be in your desk. Check items against the list below, both for presence and condition. List any missing items on the bottom of this sheet and obtain the missing items by presenting this sheet to the laboratory stockroom.

ITEMS AND SIZE	QUANTITY	CATALOG NO.
Beaker, 50 ml	2	2-540
Beaker, 150 ml	2	2-540
Beaker, 250 ml	3	2-540
Beaker, 400 ml	1	2-540
Beaker, 1000 ml	1	2-540
Beaker Cover (Watch Glass) 75 mm	1	2-610
Beaker Cover (Watch Glass) 90 mm	1	2-610
Bottle, Narrow Mouth 4 oz	1	2-883
Bottle, Narrow Mouth 16 oz	1	2-883
Bottle, Vial, 17 x 60 mm, 2 dm	1	3-338
Bottle, Vial, 23 x 85 mm, 6 dm	1	3-338
Bottle, Washing, 8 oz.	1	3-409
Brush, Test Tube.	1	3-606
Burner, Bunsen	1	3-962
Clamp, Test Tube	1	3-841
Clamp, Pinchcock, Day.	1	5-867
Cylinder, Graduate, 10 ml.	1	8-550
Cylinder, Graduated, 100 ml	1	8-550
Dish, Evaporating Size No. 00A	1	8-690
File, Triangular	1	9-735
Flask, Boiling, Flat Bottom, 250 ml.	1	10-035
Flask, Boiling, Flat Bottom, 500 ml.	1	10-035
Flask, Erlenmeyer, 50 ml	1	10-040
Flask, Erlenmeyer, 125 ml	2	10-040
Flask, Erlenmeyer, 250 ml	4	10-040
Forceps, Straight, 125 mm	1	10-280
Funnel, Long Stem, 75 mm. Dia. 150 mm Stem	1	10-362
Glass Stirring Rods, 5 x 200 mm	4	11-380
Pipet, Dropping (medicine Dropper)	2	13-700
Pipette, Serological, 10 ml	1	13-674
Spatula, Scoop	1	14-357
Support, Test Tube (wooden rack)	1	14-770
Test Tubes, 13 mm x 100 mm	6	14-957
Test Tubes, 20 mm x 150 mm	10	14-957
Test Tubes, 25 mm x 200 mm	1	14-957
Thermometer, 0° to 150°C	1	14-985
Tongs, Crucible	1	15-195
Triangle, 1½ or 2 inches	2	15-260
Wire Gauze, 5 x 5	1	15-590

You will be expected to have every item of permanent equipment present in perfect condition in your desk, breakages must be replaced immediately by purchases from the **CHEMISTRY SUPPLY STORE, (Room 128)**.

Certain expendable equipment is also required for this course. In CH-103 or CH-111, this equipment is provided to you through your lab fee. If you need additional equipment for another course you will have to purchase it.

After you have determined that all equipment is present and in good condition, please sign and present to your laboratory instructor.

NAME

DESK NO.   **DATE:**

COMMON LABORATORY EQUIPMENT

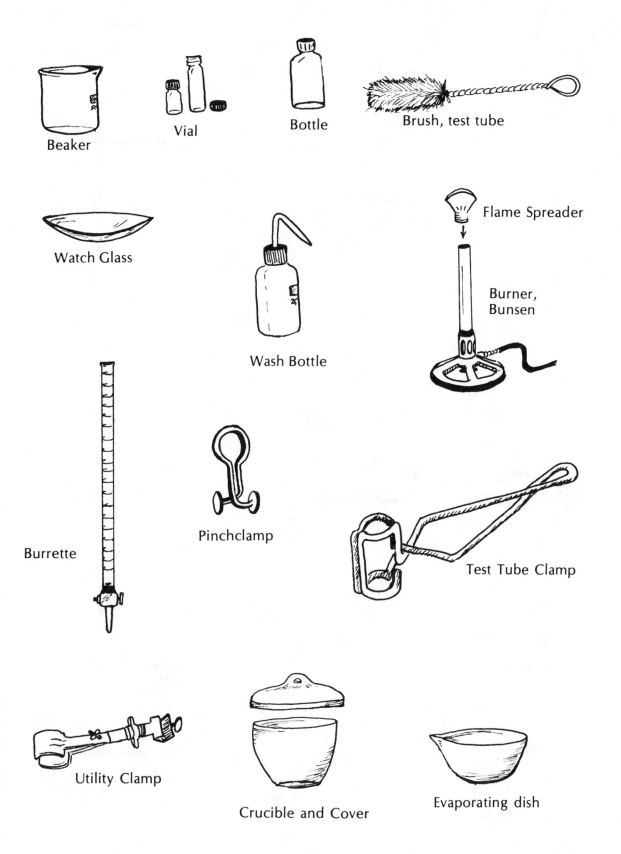

Beaker

Vial

Bottle

Brush, test tube

Watch Glass

Wash Bottle

Flame Spreader

Burner, Bunsen

Burrette

Pinchclamp

Test Tube Clamp

Utility Clamp

Crucible and Cover

Evaporating dish

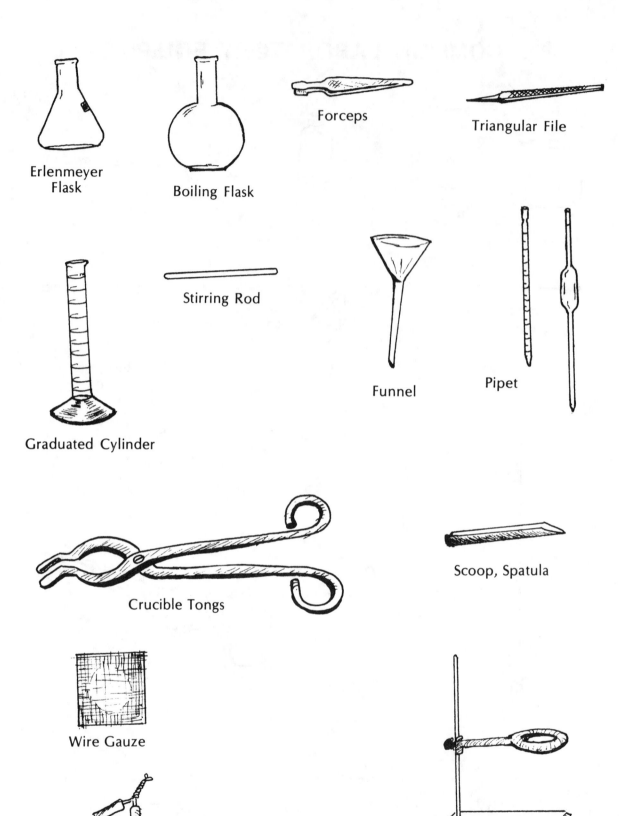

Erlenmeyer Flask

Boiling Flask

Forceps

Triangular File

Graduated Cylinder

Stirring Rod

Funnel

Pipet

Crucible Tongs

Scoop, Spatula

Wire Gauze

Clay Triangle

Ring Stand

DETERMINATION OF DENSITY

PURPOSE AND GOALS

To learn the use of analytical balances, how to measure volumes and how to use significant figures.

PRINCIPLES

TYPES OF PROPERTIES AND CHANGES

Chemistry is often defined as the study of **Matter**. A more detailed description states that it is the study of the chemical and physical properties of different kinds of matter, the changes that can be made to occur in the form and composition of matter and the corresponding changes in energy. The changes in composition of substances which occur in a chemical reaction are one of the primary interests of the chemist, but from examination of any simple chemical experiment it is apparent that without a knowledge of some of the physical properties of substances, little can be determined about the changes in composition that accompany a chemical reaction.

At this point it will be helpful to review some of the specialized terms of chemistry discussed in the opening chapters of your text. The following discussion assumes that the student is familiar with terms such as; sample, homogeneous, heterogeneous, mixture, substance, compound, element, atom and molecule. It is important to note that in chemistry the term pure substance refers exclusively to a compound or an element. Samples of wood, sea water and air are not pure substances but mixtures of two or more substances (see **Figure 1**).

A **physical change** can be defined as any change that does not involve the production of new chemical species. Examples of physical changes are: the freezing or evaporation of water (liquid water, ice and water vapor are all composed of H_2O particles), the shattering of glass, the dissolution of salt or sugar in water and the sublimation of moth balls. (Sublimation is the process whereby a substance undergoes the physical change from a solid directly to gas without going through the liquid state).

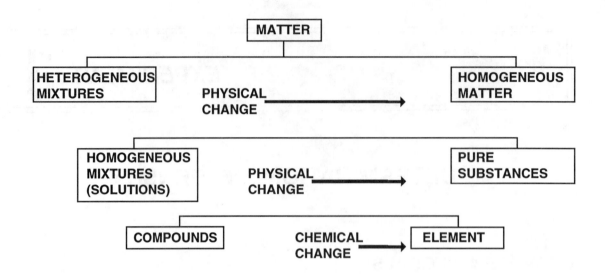

FIGURE 1. Classification of Matter

A **chemical change** is usually defined as a change in which substances are converted into new substances. An example of this is the electrolysis of the compound water (H_2O) to yield samples of hydrogen gas (H_2) and oxygen gas (O_2) (electrolysis is the application of electrical energy to force a chemical reaction to occur).

$$2H_2O \; (\textit{liquid}) \xrightarrow{\text{electrolysis}} 2H_2 \, (\textit{gas}) \; + \; O_2 \, (\textit{gas})$$

The smallest discrete particles present in the initial sample of water are all composed of two hydrogen atoms chemically bound to one oxygen atom. The smallest discrete particles in the final sample are composed of either two hydrogen atoms chemically bonded together or two oxygen atoms chemically bonded together.

From casual observation it is easy to determine that hydrogen gas or oxygen gas have different **physical properties** than those of water. For example, they are gaseous at room temperature and atmosphere pressure, while water exist mainly as a liquid under these conditions. It is equally straight forward to determine that water has different **chemical properties** from a mixture of molecular hydrogen gas and oxygen gas. We can observe experimentally that water vapor is not affected by exposure to a lighted splint but a mixture of hydrogen and oxygen explodes violently as it reacts to produce water vapor. Careful measurement of the amounts of

$$2H_2 \, (\textit{gas}) + O_2 \, (\textit{gas}) \xrightarrow{\text{lighted} \atop \text{splint}} 2H_2O \; (\textit{liquid}) + \text{energy}$$

water, hydrogen and oxygen involved would reveal that the quantity of water produced is characteristic of the amounts of hydrogen and oxygen ignited.

A **chemical property** of a substance is one that describes the chemical changes (kinds of reactions) that the substance undergoes. The property of hydrogen gas described above (it will react explosively with oxygen gas in the presence of a spark to produce water) is an example of a chemical property. Other common examples of chemical properties include the rusting of iron on exposure to moist air ($H_2O + O_2$) and the reaction of certain hydrocarbons (for example, gasoline) with oxygen gas to produce carbon dioxide $(CO_2)^+$ water vapor and enough energy to power the internal combustion engine of an automobile.

Similarly a **physical property** is a property of matter which can be observed without changing the composition of the matter present in the sample. At one atmosphere pressure water freezes at a particular temperature (generally taken to be $0.0°C$) which is referred to as its freezing point or melting point. This property of water is a physical property since the chemical composition of the sample does not change during melting or freezing. The weight of a specified number of particles of H_2O or the weight of a particular volume of water at a given temperature are also examples of physical properties.

Many physical properties of pure substances are easily measured and prove useful in the identification of substances, the determination for their purity and the prediction of their behavior under a variety of conditions. Properties can be divided into **extensive** and **intensive properties.** **Extensive properties** depend upon the size of the sample. **Intensive properties** characterize a substance but are independent of the amount of material. Two common examples of intensive properties are boiling point and freezing point. Both of these properties are highly sensitive to trace impurities and have been used as indicators of sample purity for many years. Both the boiling point and freezing point are directly measurable but are meaningless unless the conditions of the experiment are specified, since the values of these quantities are dependent on the pressure.

In some cases intensive properties are not directly measurable but can be computed from combinations of extensive properties. An example is density: a property we will determine in this experiment. It is necessary to specify the conditions at which the density is measured because density varies with temperature (and in some cases with pressure also). This laboratory exercise is intended to give you a brief introduction to the indirect measurement of selected intensive properties which are often useful in distinguishing between substances.

The mathematical relationships between a large number of intensive physical properties have been determined. The values for many physical properties of many substances have also been determined under a variety of conditions. *The Chemical Rubber Company: Handbook of Chemistry and Physics* tabulates much of this information. One can also find the definitions of common physical properties along with their mathematical relationships to other selected physical properties in your text book. Vapor pressure and viscosities of liquids are common examples of physical properties whose values are generally determined indirectly.

Density is defined as the amount of mass per unit volume of the substance. For liquids and solids density is usually expressed in grams per cubic centimeter (g/cm^3 or g cm^{-3}) or in grams per milliliter.

$$\text{density} = \text{d} = \frac{\text{mass (grams)}}{\text{volume (ml)}} \tag{1}$$

Densities of gases are much smaller than the densities of liquids and solids and are usually expressed in grams per liter (g/l). Another term that you may encounter in reading about density is specific gravity. **Specific gravity** is the ratio of the density of a substance to the density of water at some specified temperature and is a dimensionless quantity.

$$\text{Specific gravity} = \frac{\text{density of substance}}{\text{density of water}}$$

An important intensive property of a substance is the **gram molecular weight** (or gram atomic weight for elements). This is defined as the mass of a specific number (one mole) of the smallest discrete particles of a substance. The term mole is analogous to the terms dozen and gross. One dozen contains 12 particles, one gross contains 144 particles while one mole contains 6.022×10^{23} particles. This number of particles is often referred to as Avogadro's Number or simply a mole and will be determined experimentally in the next experiment. Several different methods of molecular weight determination will be encountered by the student during the freshman chemistry courses since molecular weight is one of the most important intensive physical properties for use in the characterization of a substance. The volume of a mole of particles, another intensive property, may be calculated from the density and the molecular weight (see Table 1):

Since   **density = mass/volume = grams/ml**   **(2)**

and   **molecular weight   = mass/mole of substance**

                                         = grams/mole

Then   **volume of one mole   = molecular weight/density**

                                           = ml/mole of substance   **(3)**

TABLE 1. Some Physical Properties of Common Substances at Selected Temperatures*					
Substance	Temp. (°C)	State (form)	Density in g/ml	Gram Molecular or gram atomic weight in g/mole	Molar volume (ml/mole)+
Gold (Au)	1063	Solid	19.31	197.0	10.20
Sodium Chloride (NaCl)	25	Solid	2.165	58.4	26.99
Mercury (Hg)	20	Liquid	13.60	200.6	14.75
Water (H_2O)	0	Solid	0.9168	18.02	19.66
	4	Liquid	1.000	18.02	18.02
Carbon Dioxide (CO_2)	0	Gas	0.001977	44.01	22,261
	-79	Solid	1.560	44.01	28.21
Oxygen (O_2)	0	Gas	0.001429	32.0	22,392
	-183	Liquid	1.149	32.00	27.85

    *   Data from CRC Handbook of Chemistry and Physics (at one atmosphere pressure)

    +   Calculated from Density and gram molecular weight

EXAMPLE 1.

Calculation of Molar Volume of Hg at 20°C
from Mass, Volume, and Gram Atomic Weight.

A 75.042 g sample of mercury occupies 5.52 ml at 20°C and one atmosphere of pressure. From equation (**1**) its density is:

$$\text{Density} = \frac{\text{mass Hg sample}}{\text{volume Hg sample}} = \frac{75.042g}{5.52\ ml} = 13.6\ g/ml$$

The gram atomic weight of mercury is 200.6 g/mole of Hg. From equation (**3**) its molar volume is:

$$\text{Molar volume of Hg} = \frac{\text{gram atomic weight}}{\text{density Hg}} = \frac{200.6\ g/mole}{13.6\ g/ml\ of\ Hg}$$

$$= 14.8\ ml/mole\ of\ Hg$$

PROCEDURE

Obtain two samples (one having a volume between 1 and 10 ml the other having a volume of 10 ml or more) of the assigned solid unknown and record its number on the Data Sheet.

Determine the mass of a clean 50-ml beaker on both the analytical balance and the semi-analytical balance, and record on the Data Sheet.

Determine the mass of each sample of the unknown on both the analytical balance and the semianalytical balance by weighing them in the beaker. Be sure to note the number of significant figures in each case.

Determine the volume of each sample of the unknown by completely immersing it in a graduated cylinder containing a recorded amount of water, see **Figure 2**. Be careful to immerse the samples slowly and to tilt the cylinder to avoid breaking it with the more dense samples. The volume of the solid is given by the difference in the final volume reading and the initial volume of water contained in the graduated cylinder.

Repeat the mass and volume determinations two more times with two new (different) samples each time. The average value from multiple determinations is more reliable than the value of any single determination.

Note: For one set of determinations, use a triple-beam balance instead of a semi-analytical balance. Be sure to note the number of significant figures.

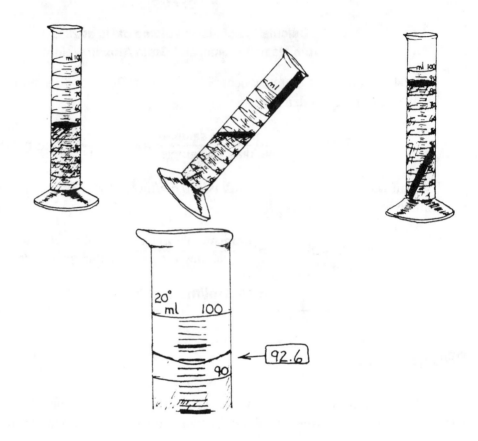

- Read from the bottom of the meniscus
- Estimate the last digit.

Figure 2: Measuring volume of sample in graduated cylinder.

CONCLUSIONS AND CALCULATIONS

Use the correct number of significant figures in all cases.

1. Calculate the mass of each sample in each run for both balances from the mass of the container plus the sample and the mass of the container. Note the difference in the number of significant figures for the different samples and balances.

2. Calculate the volume of each sample in each run from the final and initial volume readings of the graduated cylinder. Note the difference in the number of significant figures caused by sample size.

3. Calculate the density of the unknown for each sample in each run from both balances. Note the difference in the number of significant figures caused by sample size. Did it matter which balance you used in this experiment?

4. Calculate the average density of the sample from the data which gives you the maximum number of significant figures possible.

5. Given that the unknown metal is aluminum, copper, iron, lead, magnesium, tin or zinc, indicate your conclusion about the identity of your unknown metal.

6. Consult the *CRC Handbook of Chemistry and Physics* and obtain the true density and gram molecular weight of your metal from the section on physical constants of inorganic compounds. Calculate the molar volume of the assigned substance from the information obtained.

7. Calculate the % error in the determination of the density of your unknown.

$$\% \text{ error} = \frac{\text{Observed Value} - \text{Accepted Value}}{\text{Accepted Value}} \times (100\%)$$

8. The density of solid carbon dioxide (dry ice) is 1.560 g/ml. What volume would 6.9 grams of dry ice occupy?

9. The specific gravity of mercury is 13.60. What would be the mass of a sample of mercury that occupies a volume of 4.55 ml?

DETERMINATION OF AVOGADRO'S NUMBER

PURPOSE AND GOALS

An estimation of Avogadro's Number will be made by measuring the area of a monolayer of known weight of oleic acid.

PRINCIPLES

The number of molecules in a mole of an element or a compound is called Avogadro's Number. It is possible to "count" the number of molecules of known volume in a monomolecular film of a known weight of oleic acid (see **Figure 1**). If one knows the number of molecules in a given weight of oleic acid, then the number of molecules per mole can be calculated.

The value for Avogadro's Number has been calculated by a variety of different experimental methods. In this experiment, a known weight of the acid is placed on a water surface and the area of the surface film is measured. From the area of the surface film, it is possible to calculate the thickness of the film. One assumes some reasonable shape and orientation for the molecule in the film and assumes that the film is one molecule thick. From the film thickness, the molecular weight and density of the acid in the film, we will show how it is possible to calculate Avogadro's Number, "N".

This experiment uses an unusual property of certain large organic molecules. When a drop of an organic fatty acid is placed upon a water surface, the acid spreads to give a layer on the water surface that is one molecule thick. The quantity of acid in the acid film must be very small or the area covered would be too large to measure conveniently.

This spreading of the acid is due to the interactions of these large water-insoluble molecules with water. These acids have a long, water-insoluble hydrocarbon chain with a water-soluble acid group at one end, as shown in **Figure 1**. In water, the soluble end of the acid goes into the water and the hydrocarbon chains align themselves in a near vertical position.

The acid film has a natural tendency to exist in the smallest possible area, which is circular. The

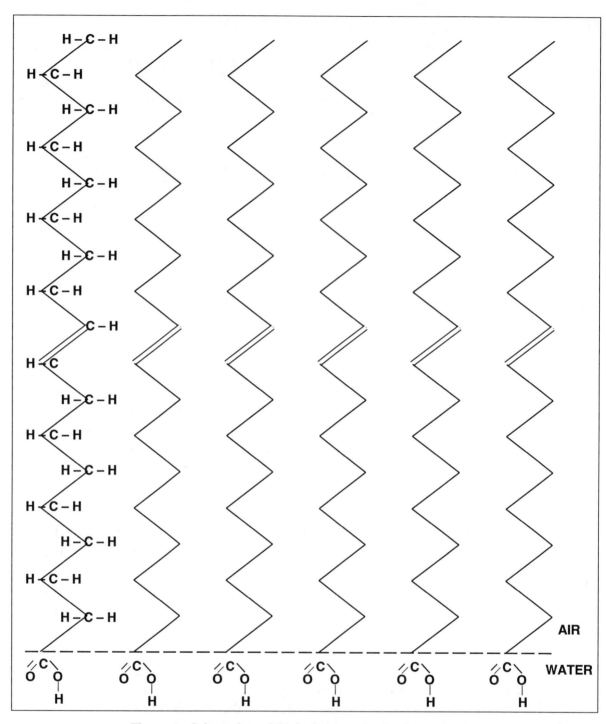

Figure 1. Orientation of Oleic Acid on the Surface of Water

oleic acid film is made visible by addition of lycopodium powder to the surface of the water. The oleic acid film will push back the lycopodium powder, forming a circular area (under ideal conditions) on the surface of the water. The area of this resulting film can be determined by tracing the area on graph paper and counting the squares or by cutting out the area and weighing.

The oleic acid has a gram molecular weight of 282.5 g/mole and its density is 0.892 g/ml.

Once the weight of oleic acid in the monomolecular layer and the area of the monomolecular layer are known, an estimation of Avogadro's Number can be made. If the total volume of the acid is known,

$$\text{density} = \frac{\text{mass acid}}{\text{volume acid}}$$

$$\text{volume acid} = \frac{\text{mass acid}}{\text{density}}$$

then the volume of one molecule can be calculated,

$$\text{Volume} = \text{area} \times \text{thickness of layer}$$

$$\text{Thickness of layer} = \text{volume} \div \text{area}$$

if the molecule is assumed to be cubic, then

$$\text{Volume of 1 molecule} = (\text{thickness of layer})^3$$

Since Avogadro's Number is the number of molecules in one mole, the volume of one mole and the volume of one molecule can be used to obtain a value for Avogadro's Number.

$$\text{Avogadro's Number} = \frac{\text{volume one mole}}{\text{volume one molecule}}$$

PROCEDURE

Obtain approximately 900 ml of tap water in a 1 liter beaker. Add three drops of 6 M HCl and mix. Fill the aluminum pan to overflowing with this very dilute acid solution. Using a plastic ruler, clean the surface of the water in the tray by pulling the edge of the ruler across the surface of the water.

Cover the surface of the water in the tray with piston oil by touching the water surface with a 0.5 mm glass rod previously dipped in the piston oil preparations. Allow the pan of water with the prepared surface to stand undisturbed until it is involved in another step.

Weigh a clean, dry 6-inch (150 mm) test tube to the nearest 0.001 gram. Add 4 drops (about 100 mg) of oleic acid and reweigh the tube plus acid to the nearest 0.001 gram. Any amount of oleic acid between 80 and 120 mg (0.080 and 0.120 gram) is satisfactory as long as the actual

Figure 2. Pipetting Oleic Acid

quantity of acid is accurately known. Using a pipet, add 10.0 ml of petroleum ether to the oleic acid in the test tube (see **Figure 2**). Stopper the tube to reduce evaporation. Mix well by holding the tube loosely at the top between two fingers and flicking the bottom of the tube with a fingernail. This imparts a swirling motion to the liquid and mixes it without getting the liquid in contact with the stopper.

CAUTION: PETROLEUM ETHER IS FLAMMABLE!

Transfer 1.0 ml (use a 1 ml transfer pipet) of this petroleum ether solution to a second test tube; dilute with 9.0 ml of petroleum ether, stopper, and mix well. Transfer 1.0 ml (use a 1 ml transfer pipet rinsed once with pure petroleum ether) of the petroleum ether solution from the second test tube to a third tube; again, dilute with 9.0 ml of petroleum ether, stopper, and mix thoroughly.

Dust the oil surface in the aluminum pan very lightly with lycopodium powder. The purpose of the lycopodium powder is to make it easier to see the film of oleic acid on the surface of the water.

Using a graduated 1 ml pipet (rinsed once with pure petroleum ether) place exactly 0.10 ml of the third (last) solution of oleic acid in petroleum ether on the center of the water surface. Wait 5 minutes for the petroleum ether to evaporate.

Support the glass plate just above the water surface on wooden blocks. Do not let the glass touch the film surface. See **Figure 3**.

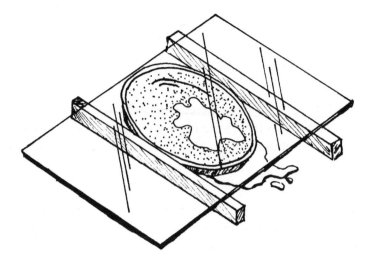

Figure 3: Set up for pan and Glass plate

Transfer the outline of the film to the glass plate using a wax marking pencil, and then transfer the outline of the film from the glass plate to a piece of graph paper (10×10 to 1 cm).

Carefully cut out a 5 cm $\times$ 5 cm piece of graph paper and weigh it. Then carefully cut out and weigh the trace of the oleic acid film.

CONCLUSIONS AND CALCULATIONS

1. From the outline of the acid film on the graph paper find the area of the film surface. (Graph paper used should be attached to the report for this experiment and turned in).

2. Calculate the mass (weight) of oleic acid in 0.10 ml of the final petroleum ether solution, which is the mass (weight) of acid left as a film on the surface of the water.

3. Calculate the volume of acid in the film. (Assume that the density of the acid is the same in bulk and in the film).

4. Calculate the thickness of the acid film from the volume of acid and the area of the film surface.

5. Calculate the volume of one molecule of the acid based on the assumption that the acid film is one molecule thick and on the assumption that the acid molecule is a cube.

6. From the density and molecular weight of the acid in bulk, calculate the volume of 1.0 mole of acid.

7. Calculate Avogadro's Number, "N".

8. Compare your value for "N" with the accepted value which you can find in your text book. List and explain all sources of error in the experiment, consider all assumptions used in the calculations, and try to account for the difference between your value and the accepted value for "N".

9. Now assume that the acid molecule is shaped like a brick, twice as tall as it is broad. Calculate the volume of one molecule of the acid and from this, Avogadro's Number "N". (In this case x corresponds to the thickness of the layer).

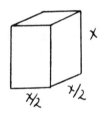

6.022×10^{23}

DETERMINATION OF THE FORMULA
OF A HYDRATE

PURPOSE AND GOALS

Stoichiometric relationships will be used to determine the number of moles of water of hydration in an unknown hydrate.

PRINCIPLES

Certain inorganic salts can exist in either anhydrous conditions or with a number of water molecules bound to each salt molecule. However, if the water is simply mechanically trapped in the crystal lattice, the number of water molecules per metal atom could be a non-integer number. The amount of water in this case is said to be non-stoichiometric. For every metal ion in this type of salt, there might be 0.003 or 1.05 molecules of water. By chance exactly 1.00 or 2.00 molecules of water per metal ion could be present, but this would be a mere coincidence.

In cases where the water is chemically bound (not mechanically trapped), then there usually is a stoichiometric amount of water present, 1.00 or 2.00, etc., for each metal ion. The water present may be either bound to one or more specific metal ions or it may bind to an anion. The hydrates used in this experiment contain chemically bound water.

The formula for the hydrated salt (hydrate) is represented by the formula for the anhydrous salt followed by a dot and the appropriate number of water molecules. Thus, the formula for magnesium chloride hexahydrate is $MgCl_2 \cdot 6H_2O$, indicating that 6 waters of hydration are present for each magnesium chloride unit.

Water of hydration can frequently be removed by heating the salt. In this experiment you will determine the number of waters of hydration present in a pure hydrate from the weights of a sample of pure hydrate before and after heating, and the formula of the anhydrous salt.

For example:

$$CuSO_4 \cdot XH_2O \; (s) \longrightarrow CuSO_4 \, (s) + XH_2O \; (g)$$

The weight loss that you will observe corresponds to the water that is driven off as a gas when the sample is heated.

PROCEDURE

Obtain a sample with an unknown number of waters of hydration and record sample number on data sheet. Also obtain a metal crucible and crucible cover from the stockroom.

Do not wash the crucible. Most of the solid material may be removed by use of your scoop spatula. It is not necessary that the crucible be absolutely clean; only that it be brought to constant weight before the sample is placed in it. Mount the crucible and cover on a ring stand. See **Figure 1**.

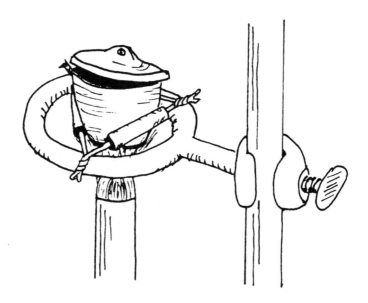

Figure 1. Heating a Crucible

The ring should be adjusted above the Bunsen burner so that the deep blue cone in the flame just touches the bottom of the crucible (this is the hottest part of the flame). Heat your crucible and cover gently for about 3 minutes and then strongly for 5 minutes. Remove your crucible and cover from the ring stand with your crucible tongs and allow to cool to room temperature. Weigh the crucible and cover and record their mass to the nearest 1 mg (0.001 g). **DO NOT** touch either the crucible or cover with your fingers after you start the initial heating. Repeat the process of heating, cooling, and weighing until two consecutive determinations agree to within 3 mg (.003 g). **Note:** Hold the crucible with your crucible tongs, and hold a wire gauze underneath the crucible when you carry the crucible and cover to be weighed on the balance.

After you have established the mass of your crucible and cover, pour about 1 g of your hydrate into the crucible. Replace the cover and determine the mass of the hydrate and crucible to the nearest 1 mg. Record this mass on the data sheet. Put the crucible and cover containing the hydrate (leave a small opening between crucible and cover) on the ring stand and begin to drive out the water by gently heating the crucible. It is necessary to heat gently at first because some of the hydrated mixture might splatter if heated too vigorously and escape through the small opening between the crucible and cover. After a 5 minute period of gently heating, slowly increase the size of the flame. Heat the hydrate for a minimum of 10 minutes at maximum heat. Remove the crucible, cover and mixture, and allow to cool to room temperature. Weigh and record the mass to the nearest 1 mg. Repeat this procedure until two consecutive determinations agree to within 3 mg. This procedure will be carried out in duplicate.

CONCLUSIONS AND CALCULATIONS

In this experiment there are basically two types of calculations you must do. One is the calculation of the **number of moles of a substance**.

$$\text{Number of moles} = \frac{\text{Mass of substance (g)}}{\text{Molecular weight of substance (g/mole)}}$$

The other calculation is that of finding the percent of water in the sample. In general, when you want to express a given quantity as a percentage of another quantity, you divide the given number by the number with which it is being compared an multiply by 100;

$$\text{Percent } H_2O = \frac{\text{Mass of } H_2O}{\text{Mass of original sample}} \times 100\%$$

DETERMINATION OF THE COMPOSITION
OF A COMPOUND

PURPOSE AND GOALS

A reaction between magnesium and oxygen will be carried out and the percentage composition of the product will be determined.

PRINCIPLES

In this experiment, the composition of magnesium oxide is to be determined by synthesis. A weighed amount of a metal is allowed to react with an excess of a nonmetal to form the compound. The mass of the compound is then carefully determined;

$$\textbf{Metal} \; + \; \textbf{Nonmetal} \; \longrightarrow \; \textbf{Compound}$$
$$\textbf{(Mg)} \qquad \textbf{(O}_2\textbf{)} \qquad\qquad \textbf{(Magnesium oxide)}$$

The mass of the nonmetal which reacted is then determined by subtracting the mass of the metal from the mass of the compound:

Mass of compound – mass of metal = mass of nonmetal that reacted

From the masses of the elements that compose a given mass of the compound, the percentage composition by mass is calculated.

$$\textbf{\% metal} \; = \; (\frac{\textbf{mass metal}}{\textbf{mass compound}}) \times \textbf{100\%}$$

$$\textbf{\% nonmetal} \; = \; (\frac{\textbf{mass nonmetal}}{\textbf{mass compound}}) \times \textbf{100\%}$$

If the combustion is carried out in pure oxygen, the product of the combustion would be solely magnesium oxide (MgO). However, magnesium is an active metal, and when burned in air, it unites with oxygen and nitrogen, so that the product at this stage is a mixture of magnesium oxide and magnesium nitride (MgO and Mg_3N_2).

In order to get all of the magnesium in the form of MgO, we take advantage of the fact that Mg_3N_2 reacts with H_2O

$$Mg_3N_2 \text{ (s)} + 6H_2O \text{ (l)} \longrightarrow 3 Mg(OH)_2 \text{ (s)} + 2NH_3 \text{ (g)}$$

and that the resulting $Mg(OH)_2$ can be converted to MgO by heating

$$Mg(OH)_2 \text{ (s)} \xrightarrow{\Delta} MgO \text{ (s)} + H_2O \text{ (g)}$$

PROCEDURE

Obtain a ceramic crucible and cover from the stockroom. Do not wash the crucible. Heat the crucible and cover **gently** for about 3 minutes and then strongly for 5 minutes. Remove the crucible and cover from the ring stand with the crucible tongs and allow to cool to room temperature. Weigh the clean crucible and cover and record this mass on the Data Sheet. Repeat this procedure until two successive weighings on the same crucible and cover agree within 0.002 g (this is called bringing the crucible and cover to constant mass weight). **DO NOT** touch either the crucible or cover with your fingers. **Note:** Hold the crucible with your crucible tongs and hold a wire gauze underneath the crucible when you carry the crucible and cover to be weighed on the balance.

Secure about 0.4 to 0.6 g of magnesium ribbon. The ribbon is to be rolled and folded into a spherical wad whose diameter is about ¾ of an inch. To do this, start with a small circle of magnesium and build up the sphere by rolling and folding the ribbon loosely in all directions so as to make a ball with an open structure.

The objective here is to fit the ribbon in a crucible and to have the maximum amount of the surface of the magnesium in contact with air.

Place the magnesium in the crucible and weigh with the crucible lid. All weighings are to be made to the nearest 0.001 g. Record this mass on the Data Sheet. Transfer the crucible and contents to a clay triangle mounted on a ring stand, see **Figure 1**. Remove the lid of the crucible with forceps. Heat the bottom of the crucible with a flame. Hold the lid with forceps near the crucible while heating. At the instant the magnesium ignites put the cover on the crucible.

Although the magnesium oxide which is formed by the burning is a solid, it is very finely divided and some will be lost as a white smoke unless the crucible is covered as soon as possible. After a brief period, raise the cover about an inch to admit enough air to start the magnesium burning again. At the instant it begins to burn, replace the cover. Continue admitting air in this way at short intervals. The objective is to keep the magnesium burning at a slow rate and in such a manner that no MgO will be lost as white smoke. After most of the magnesium ribbon has burned, shorten the intervals at which you raise the crucible cover. When the contents no longer burn with the lid raised, cover about seven-eights of the opening of the crucible with the lid and then heat the bottom of the crucible with a hot flame for 5 to 10 minutes, then let the crucible cool.

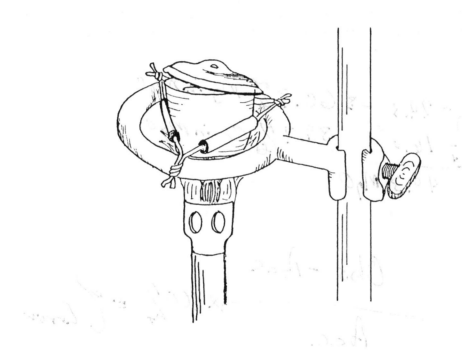

Figure 1. Experimental Set-up for Heating Magnesium

In order to convert any magnesium nitride that formed into magnesium oxide, proceed as follows.

After the crucible has cooled, moisten the products with about 10 drops of distilled water. This will change magnesium nitride to magnesium hydroxide:

$$Mg_3N_2\,(s) + 6H_2O\,(aq) \longrightarrow 3Mg(OH)_2\,(s) + 2NH_3\,(g)$$

Reheat the crucible with lid in place (leave small opening) gently at first to avoid spattering, then strongly for 5 to 10 minutes. The second heating brings about the decomposition of magnesium hydroxide into magnesium oxide:

$$Mg(OH)_2\,(s) \longrightarrow MgO\,(s) + H_2O\,(g)$$

Remove the flame and let the crucible stand until cool and weigh. Reheat and weigh the crucible until you get a constant weight. Record the mass on the Data Sheet.

CONCLUSIONS AND CALCULATIONS

1. From your data, calculate the percentage by weight of magnesium and oxygen in magnesium oxide.

2. Using the known formula of magnesium oxide (MgO) and a table of atomic weights, calculate the true percentage composition and your percentage error. Write equations for the combustion of magnesium in air.

$$M_g = 24.3 \longrightarrow 60.3\% \ M_g \ in \ M_gO$$
$$O = 16.0 \qquad 39.7\% \ O \ in \ M_gO$$
$$+$$
$$\overline{\ 40.3 \ M_gO}$$

$$\frac{Obs - Acc}{Acc} \longrightarrow \times 100\% = \% \ Error$$

67.7

.NON

THE PERCENTAGE BARIUM IN A MIXTURE OF
$BaCl_2 \cdot 2H_2O$ and $BaCl_2$

PURPOSE AND GOALS

To determine the percentage barium in a mixture of $BaCl_2 \cdot 2H_2O$ and $BaCl_2$ by precipitation of $BaSO_4$ and by weight loss.

PRINCIPLES

Certain inorganic salts can exist in either anhydrous conditions or with a number of water molecules bound to each salt molecule. However, if the water is simply mechanically trapped in the crystal lattice, the number of water molecules per metal atom could be a non-integer number. The amount of water in this case is said to be non-stoichiometric. For every metal ion in this type of salt, there might be 0.003 or 1.05 molecules of water. By chance exactly 1.00 or 2.00 molecules of water per metal ion could be present, but this would be a mere coincidence.

In cases where the water is chemically bound (not mechanically trapped), then there usually is a stoichiometric amount of water present 1.00 or 2.00, etc., for each metal ion. The water present may be either bound to one or more specific metal ions or it may bind to an anion. The hydrates used in this experiment contain chemically bound water.

The formula for the hydrated salt (hydrate) is represented by the formula for the anhydrous salt followed by a dot and the appropriate number of water molecules. Thus, the formula for copper sulfate pentahydrate is $CuSO_4 \cdot 5H_2O$, indicating that 5 waters of hydration are present for each copper sulfate molecule.

This experiment will be done in two parts. **Part I** of the procedure will be done the first week and **Part II** the second week. Parts I and II will be written up and turned in separately.

PERCENT Ba FROM THE MASS OF BARIUM SULFATE PRECIPITATE

The difference in the solubilities of two or more substances in some particular solvent can be used to separate the substances. If one component of a mixture is essentially insoluble while the other components are soluble, the soluble components can be dissolved and the insoluble removed by filtration.

Reactions in which insoluble substances are formed from a mixture of soluble substances are referred to as precipitation reactions (precipitates). Some examples of compounds which precipitate from aqueous solutions are $AgCl$, $PbCl_2$, CuS, CdS, and $BaSO_4$.

Both $BaCl_2$ and $BaCl_2 \cdot 2H_2O$ are soluble in water and react with H_2SO_4 (sulfuric acid) to produce $BaSO_4$ which is essentially insoluble in water. The other products of this reaction are water and HCl (hydrochloric acid), which are very water soluble as is H_2SO_4. We need only to add a sufficient amount of H_2SO_4 and heat to make sure all the $BaCl_2$ and $BaCl_2 \cdot 2H_2O$ are converted to water insoluble $BaSO_4$ and remove $BaSO_4$ from the rest of the reaction mixture by filtration

$$BaCl_2\,(aq) + H_2SO_4\,(aq) \longrightarrow BaSO_4\,(s) + 2HCl\,(aq)$$

or

$$BaCl2 \cdot 2H_2O\,(aq) + H_2SO_4\,(aq) \longrightarrow BaSO_4\,(s) + 2HCl\,(aq) + 2H_2O\,(l)\,.$$

You have two pieces of data for this calculation, the original mass of the mixture used, m_o, and the mass of the precipitate of barium sulfate, m_p. All of the barium that was the original mixture is now present as barium sulfate. Since the molecular weight of barium sulfate is 233 g/mole and the atomic mass of barium is 137 g/mole, then the mass of barium originally present is:

$$\text{mass of Ba} \;=\; (m_p,\ \text{grams } \cancel{BaSO_4}) \cdot \left(\frac{137\text{ g Ba}}{233\text{ g } \cancel{BaSO_4}} \right)$$

$$\text{Mass of Ba} \;=\; \left(\frac{137}{233} \right) \cdot m_p \text{ g Ba}$$

The percent barium would be determined by dividing the mass of Ba by the mass of the mixture times 100:

$$\% \text{ Ba} \;=\; \frac{\left(\dfrac{137}{233} \right) \cdot m_p}{m_o} \times 100\%$$

PROCEDURE

Obtain a sample containing an unknown mixture of $BaCl_2$ and $BaCl_2 \cdot 2H_2O$ from the stockroom. **Write your sample number on the data sheet.** This same sample will be used in Parts I and II, so **be certain to save part of your sample for next week.** You will also need to obtain a 9 cm circle of Whatman # 40 quantitative filter paper for Part I. Place the mixture in a large weighing bottle. About 8 g of mixture is sufficient.

Weigh the screw cap vial containing the mixture to the nearest 1 mg. Empty about 2 grams of the mixture into a 250 ml beaker that has been thoroughly cleaned. Again weigh the vial and record its mass to the nearest 1 mg. Add 50 ml distilled water to the 250 ml beaker and dissolve the mixture. Add 2 ml of 6 M hydrochloric acid to this solution and bring it to nearly boiling. Add 10 ml of 3 M sulfuric acid to the solution with stirring. When you remove your stirring rod you should rinse any precipitate adhering to it back into the beaker by gently squirting distilled water from a wash bottle down the stirring rod.

At this point you should observe a white precipitate of barium sulfate form. Cover the beaker with a watch glass. Continue heating this mixture to nearly boiling for about twenty minutes. Remove the heat and allow the beaker and precipitate to cool. If the 250 ml beaker is allowed to sit for a few minutes the barium sulfate precipitate will settle to the bottom. At this point you should test for the completeness of the precipitation by the following procedure. When all of the barium sulfate has settled to the bottom, add one or two drops of 3 M sulfuric acid to the solution.

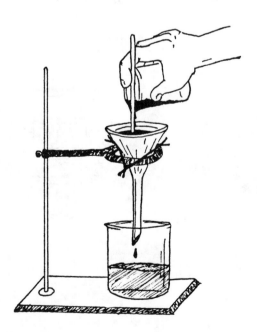

Figure 1. Gravity Filtration of Barium Sulfate

Carefully observe the solution where the sulfuric acid was added. If it remains clear, your precipitation was complete. If the solution turns cloudy, add another 5 ml of 3 M sulfuric acid before continuing. Carefully fold the piece of Whatman filter paper in the manner described by your lab instructor. Place this piece of filter paper on a watch glass and determine the mass of both to the nearest 1 mg. Place the piece of filter paper in a long stemmed funnel and moisten it with distilled water so that it is sealed to the glass surface.

After the solution containing the barium sulfate precipitate has cooled it is to be filtered. Mount the funnel in a ring stand and use a clean 400 ml beaker to catch the filtrate. The funnel should be mounted so that the tip of the funnel is just touching the side of the beaker and the funnel should extend not more than $\frac{1}{3}$ of the way into the beaker, see **Figure 1**.

Place a stirring rod across the top of the beaker, which contains the barium sulfate, so that the rod is sitting in the mouth of the beaker. By placing your forefinger on the rod and holding the beaker in your thumb and remaining fingers you can carefully pour most of the liquid from the beaker through the funnel without disturbing the precipitate, see **Figure 1**. Pour this mixture slowly into the funnel making sure the level of the fluid in the funnel never comes closer than $\frac{1}{2}$ inch from the top of the filter paper. Examine the filtrate to make sure it is clear. If it is clear it can be discarded. If the liquid is cloudy, some of the $BaSO_4$ passed through and it should be filtered again. If some of the precipitate sticks to the walls of the beaker, it can be removed with a rubber policeman. Use distilled water in your wash bottle to help rinse out any remaining precipitate.

Figure 2. Drying Filter Paper and Barium Sulfate

Make sure all of the precipitate is lodged in the filter paper cone. It is important that none of the precipitate is lost. Use about three 10 ml portions of distilled water to rinse the precipitate then rinse with two 10 ml portions of acetone to help the precipitate dry quicker. Carefully remove the moist filter paper and place it on the watch glass. Make sure that the filter paper does not extend beyond the edge of the watch glass. (This is done by selecting a watch glass which is larger than the filter paper). Place the watch glass, filter paper, and precipitate on top of a beaker about half-full of water and heat the water to boiling, see **Figure 2**.

CAUTION: ACETONE IS FLAMMABLE

The steam heats the watch glass and evaporates the water and acetone from your sample. When the sample is dry; determine the mass of the watch glass, filter paper, and precipitate to the nearest 1 mg. Reheat the sample and determine the mass of the nearest 1 mg. If the second weight was smaller, there may be some water or acetone still left in the precipitate. If so, reheat, reweigh, etc.

CONCLUSIONS AND CALCULATIONS

1.   Determine the mass of the unknown mixture.

2.   Determine the mass of the barium sulfate precipitate.

3.   Calculate the mass of Ba in the barium sulfate precipitate.

4.   Calculate the % Ba in the unknown sample.

Name _____ Lab Instructor: _____ Date: _____

DATA SHEET: PART I – DETERMINATION OF % Ba FROM THE MASS OF BARIUM SULFATE PRECIPITATE

Unknown Number_____	**RUN I**	**RUN II**
Mass of vial and mixture	_____	_____
Mass of vial and remains	_____	_____
Mass of mixture transferred (m_o)	_____	_____
Mass of watch glass and paper	_____	_____
Mass of watch glass, paper, and precipitate after heating	_____	_____
After reheating	_____	_____
% Ba in your sample	_____	_____

DETERMINATION OF % OF Ba BY WATER LOSS

Since water of hydration can frequently be removed by heating the salt; the number of waters of hydration present in a pure hydrate may be found from the weights of a sample of pure hydrate before and after heating, and the formula of the anhydrous salt. **The weight loss upon heating corresponds to the weight of water that was present in the hydrate.**

$$ZnSO_4 \bullet XH_2O \ (s) \xrightarrow{\Delta} ZnSO_4 \ (s) + XH_2O \ (g)$$

This heating method also allows the calculation of the % of anhydrous salt and the % of hydrated salt in a mixture (Xg $BaCl_2 \bullet 2H_2O$ + Yg $BaCl_2$) of the two from the initial and final weights of a sample of the mixture and the formula of the **hydrated** salt. (**NOTE: If the number of waters of hydration is not known; it cannot be calculated from data recorded for the mixture**).

One of the purposes of this exercise is to demonstrate the usefulness of mathematical concepts in the solution of chemical problems. You will do a graphical solution of simultaneous equations. You have two pieces of data for Part II: the mass of the original mixture, m_i; and the mass of the mixture after heating m_f (m_i and m_f stand for the initial and final mass, respectively). Since the mixture originally contained only $BaCl_2$ and $BaCl_2 \bullet 2H_2O$, the mass of the original mixture is simply the sum of the mass of each component. If X grams of $BaCl_2 \bullet 2H_2O$ and Y grams of $BaCl_2$ were originally present, then:

$$m_i = \text{Xg } BaCl_2 \bullet 2H_2O + \text{Yg } BaCl_2 \qquad (1)$$

After heating, the water that was present in the $BaCl_2 \bullet 2H_2O$ has been driven off.

$$BaCl_2 \bullet 2H_2O \ (s) \xrightarrow{\Delta} BaCl_2 \ (s) + 2H_2O \ (g)$$

If 1 mole of $BaCl_2 \bullet 2H_2O \ (s)$, 244 g, is heated, we obtain 1 mole of $BaCl_2 \ (s)$, 208 g, and 2 moles of $H_2O \ (g)$, 36 g, are driven off.

The second piece of data is the mass of the mixture minus the mass of the water that was lost.

If we have X grams of $BaCl_2 \bullet 2H_2O \ (s)$ before heating, then after heating we will have produced

$$(\text{Xg } \cancel{BaCl_2 \bullet 2H_2O} \ ) \ (\frac{208 \text{ g } BaCl_2}{244 \text{ g } \cancel{BaCl_2 \bullet 2H_2O}}) = (\frac{208}{244}) (\text{Xg } BaCl_2)$$

according to the balanced equation above.   Therefore we can write for the final mass:

$$m_f = \left[\left(\frac{208}{244}\right)(Xg\ BaCl_2)\right] + Yg\ BaCl_2 \qquad (2)$$

Remember that the equation for a straight line is generally written as:

$$y = ax + b$$

where x and y are independent variables and a is the slope of the line and b is the y-intercept. If we recast our two equations, (1) and (2), into this form we get:

from equation (1)
$$Yg\ BaCl_2 = -Xg\ BaCl_2 \bullet 2H_2O + m_i \qquad (3)$$

from equation (2)
$$Yg\ BaCl_2 = -\left[\left(\frac{208}{244}\right)(Xg\ BaCl_2)\right] + m_f \qquad (4)$$

We do not know the value of either X or Y but we have two equations and two unknowns. If we plot these two equations we will find that they have a point of intersection. This one point corresponds to the solution of the simultaneous equations. **An example will illustrate.** A student determined the mass of his original mixture to be exactly 2.000 g. After heating, the mass had been reduced to 1.786 g. Using equations (3) and (4), we obtain

from equation (3)
$$Yg = -Xg + 2.000\ g \qquad (5)$$

from equation (4)
$$Yg = -\left[\left(\frac{208}{244}\right)(Xg)\right] + 1.786\ g \qquad (6)$$

The mass of $BaCl_2$, .55 g, and $BaCl_2 \bullet 2H_2O$, 1.45 g, can be read directly off the graph, see **Figure 3**. Calculation of the percentage barium in the sample is now straightforward. We now have a value for X and Y obtained from the intersection of equation (5) and (6). The amount of barium from the $BaCl_2$ is given by:

$$\left(\frac{137\ g\ Ba}{208\ g\ BaCl_2}\right)(Yg\ BaCl_2) = \left(\frac{137}{208}\right)(Yg\ Ba)$$

and the amount of barium from the $BaCl_2 \bullet 2H_2O$ is given by:

$$\left(\frac{137\ g\ Ba}{244\ g\ BaCl_2 \bullet 2H_2O}\right)(Xg\ BaCl_2 \bullet 2H_2O) = \left(\frac{137}{244}\right)(Xg\ Ba)$$

The percentage barium is the mass of barium divided by the original mass of the mixture, m_i, times 100. Therefore:

$$\%\ Ba = \frac{\left(\frac{137}{244}\right)Xg\ Ba + \left(\frac{137}{208}\right)Yg\ Ba}{m_i} \times 100\%$$

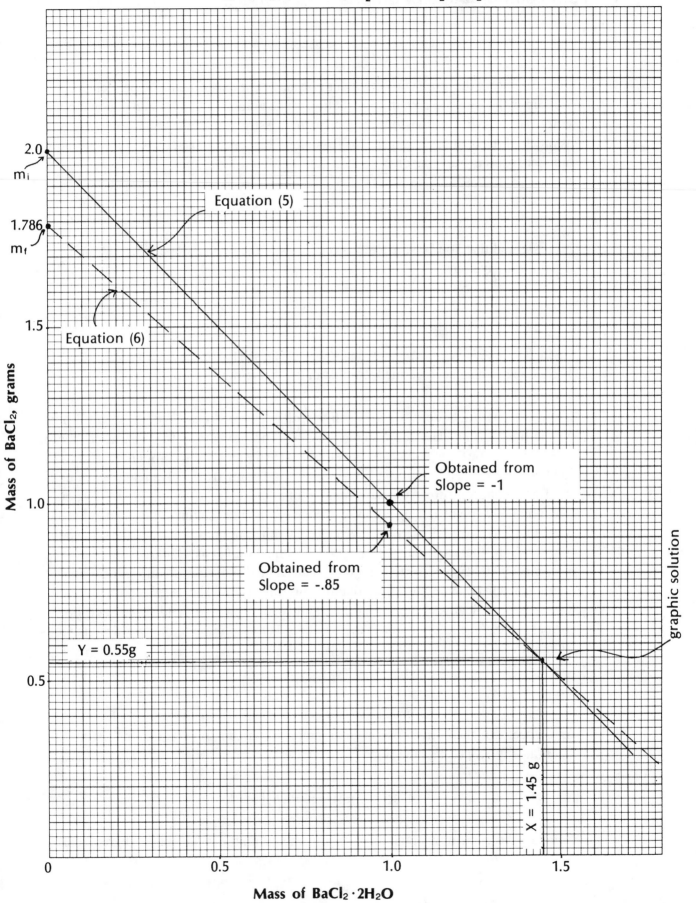

Figure 3. Determination of the Composition of a Mixture of BaCl$_2$ and BaCl$_2 \cdot$ 2H$_2$O

Notes on construction of graphs:

1.   The accuracy of the result you get for this portion of this experiment is dependent, in great part, upon the care you take in construction of the graph. It is suggested that you obtain graph paper having 10 divisions per cm. In the construction of the graph you want to use as much of the area of the paper as is feasible. This reduces the errors made in reading numbers off the graph paper.

2.   It is essential that you be able to construct lines of the proper slope. For a straight line the slope is given by:

$$\text{slope} = \frac{Y_2 - Y_1}{X_2 - X_1}$$

where X_2, Y_2. and X_1, Y_1 are the X and Y coordinates of two respective points on the line. The slope has also been defined simplistically as rise/run.

In our case, as will be seen: we are dealing with negative slopes. We know only 1 point on the line, in this case, the Y-intercepts, b. The problem is to construct a line of appropriate slope through point b. For equation (3) the slope is -1 through point m_i. This can be accomplished by starting from point m_i and going over a given number of units, say 1 gram, and then down the same number of units, and placing a point at that spot. A line joining this point and m_i will have a slope of -1 since the run or horizontal distance was 1 unit and the rise or vertical distance was 1 unit. The construction of the second line is similar. In this case the slope is given by equation (4) as $-(208/244)$. This is approximately -0.85. Similar to the process determined above, locate m_f on the y-axis. If once again you counted 1 unit horizontally, this time it would be necessary to go only .85 units down vertically. Connecting this point with m_f would yield the second line of correct slope. The intersection of the two lines is the solution to the two simultaneous equations.

3.   As a check for the correctness of your graphs, you can solve equations (3) and (4) algebraically. Since Y is the same in both cases:

$$-X + m_i = -[(\frac{208}{204})(X)] + m_f$$

Compare the value of X obtained by this method with the value obtained graphically.

PROCEDURE

Do not wash the crucible. Remove any solid material in the crucible with your spatula scoop. It is not necessary that the crucible be absolutely clean; only that it be brought to constant weight before the sample is placed in it. When the crucible is clean, mount the crucible and cover on a ring stand, see **Figure 4**.

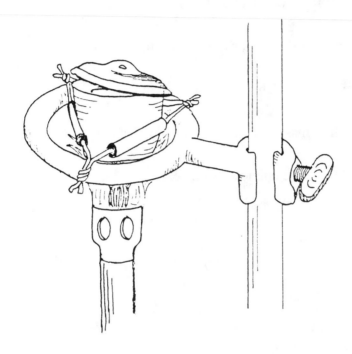

Figure 4. Heating the Crucible

The ring should be adjusted so that when the Bunsen burner is operating the light blue cone in the flame just touches the bottom of the crucible. Heat the crucible and cover gently for about 3 minutes and then strongly for 5 minutes. Remove the crucible and cover from the ring stand using your crucible tongs and allow to cool to room temperature. Weigh the crucible and cover and record their mass to the nearest 1 mg (0.001 g). **DO NOT** touch either the crucible or cover with your fingers after you start the initial heating. Hold the crucible with your crucible tongs and hold a wire gauze underneath the crucible when you carry the crucible and cover to be weighed on the balance. Repeat the process of heating, cooling, and weighing until two consecutive determinations agree to within 3 mg.

After you have established the mass of your crucible and cover, pour about 2 g of your hydrate mixture into the crucible. Replace the cover and determine the mass of the mixture to the nearest 1 mg. Record this mass. Put the crucible and cover containing the mixture on the ring stand and begin to drive out the water by gently heating the crucible. It is necessary to heat gently at first because some of the hydrated mixture might splatter if heated too vigorously and escape through the crack between the crucible and cover. After a 5-minute period of gently heating begin to slowly increase the size of the flame. Heat the mixture for a minimum of 10 minutes at maximum heat. Remove the crucible, cover and mixture, and cool to room temperature. Weigh and record the mass to the nearest 1 mg. Repeat this procedure until two consecutive determinations agree to within 3 mg. This procedure will be carried out in duplicate.

CONCLUSIONS AND REFLECTIONS

1.   Determine the mass of the unknown mixture (m_i).

2.   Calculate the mass of the dehydrated sample (m_f).

3.   Construct a graph of mass of $BaCl_2$ vs. mass of $BaCl_2 \cdot 2H_2O$.

4.   Calculate the % Ba in the unknown sample.

Name _____ Lab Instructor: _____ Date: _____

DATA SHEET: PART II – DETERMINATION OF % Ba BY WATER LOSS

Unknown Number_____	**RUN I**	**RUN II**

Mass of crucible and cover
after heating   Ist heating   _____   _____

                      2nd heating   _____   _____

                      3rd heating   _____   _____

Mass of crucible, cover,
and mixture   _____   _____

Mass of mixture (m_i)   _____   _____

Mass of crucible, cover,
and mixture   Ist heating   _____   _____

                      2nd heating   _____   _____

                      3rd heating   _____   _____

Mass of dehydrated sample (m_f)   _____   _____

% Ba in your sample   _____   _____

STOICHIOMETRIC RATIO

PURPOSE AND GOALS

To experimentally determine the stoichiometric ratio between two reactants.

PRINCIPLES

Stoichiometry is the branch of chemistry that deals with the mole ratio between reactants and products in a chemical reaction.

The net result of a chemical reaction can be described by a balanced chemical equation. The balanced equation for the reaction gives the formulas for chemical species present initially (reactants) and after the reaction has occurred (products). The balanced equation also gives the mole ratio of reactants to products (this is the stoichiometric ratio). For example:

$$Mg\ (s)\ +\ 2HCl\ (aq)\ \longrightarrow\ MgCl_2\ (aq)\ +\ H_2\ (g)$$

This balanced equation states that 1 particle of magnesium metal reacts with 2 particles of hydrochloric acid to produce 1 particle of magnesium chloride and 1 particle of hydrogen gas. Since a mole of any substance contains the same number of particles (Avogadro's Number), the coefficients in the equations also give the relative number of moles of reactants and products involved in the reaction.

Thus the above equation states that the reaction occurs in the ratio of one mole Mg (s) plus two moles HCl (aq) to yield one mole $MgCl_2$ (aq) plus one mole H_2 (g).

Before a balanced chemical equation can be written to describe a particular reaction, the identity of all the reactants and products involved must be known. The chemist uses a variety of techniques to isolate and determine the identity of the chemical species involved. Many of these techniques are based on the intensive properties of the substances, with which you are already familiar. One must also determine the relative number of moles of reactants and products involved in the reaction. The purpose of this exercise is to determine experimentally the stoichiometric ratio in the reaction of sodium hypochlorite (NaOCl) with sodium sulfite (Na_2SO_3) or sodium thiosulfate ($Na_2S_2O_3$):

$$\text{a } Na_2SO_3\,(aq) + \text{b } NaOCl\,(aq) \longrightarrow \text{products} + \text{heat}$$

Since reactions are characterized by a particular stoichiometric ratio, the quantity of a particular product is dependent on the quantities of the various reactants used. The reactants will combine in a characteristic ratio until one or both of them is used up. The reactant which is exhausted first is called the limiting reagent because it limits the amount of product produced. Consider the reaction:

$$Pb(NO_3)_2\,(aq) + 2NaCl\,(aq) \longrightarrow PbCl_2\,(s) + 2NaNO_3\,(aq)$$

This balanced equation tells us that lead nitrate and sodium chloride react in a 1:2 mole ratio and that lead chloride and sodium nitrate are produced in a 1:2 mole ratio.

In experiments #1 and #2, in Table 1, below, the lead nitrate and sodium chloride are present in the 1:2 mole ratio given by the balanced equation and using this stoichiometric ratio we determine the number of moles of product produced.

In experiment #3, Table 1, the reactants are not present in the 1:2 mole ratio given by the balanced equation, therefore, one of the reactants will be used up (limiting reagent) and one will be in excess (there will be some left over at the end of the reaction). In this case the reaction stoichiometry tells us that 0.5 mole of $Pb(NO_3)_2$ is the limiting reagent.

TABLE 1					
	Reactants			**Products**	
Experiment	$Pb(NO_3)_2$ (aq)	+ 2NaCl (aq)	$\longrightarrow$	$PbCl_2$ (s)	+ 2NaNO$_3$ (aq)
#1	1 mole*	2 moles*		1 mole	2 mole
#2	0.5 mole*	1 mole*		0.5 mole	1 mole
#3	0.5 mole*	2 moles		0.5 mole	1 mole
#4	2 moles	0.5 mole*		0.25 mole	0.5 mole

* Indicates the limiting reagent

The limiting reagent is used to determine the theoretical number of moles of product obtained in a given experiment. From experiment #4 in Table 1:

$$? \text{ Moles } PbCl_2 = 0.5 \text{ moles } NaCl \frac{1 \text{ mole } PbCl_2}{2 \text{ moles } NaCl} = 0.25 \text{ mole } PbCl_2$$

This comes from the stoichiometry of the reaction

If we imagine an investigation in which $Pb(NO_3)_2$ is always the limiting reagent, one would expect that as the number of moles of $Pb(NO_3)_2$ used is increased, the amount of precipitate formed increases. **Figure 1** illustrates this.

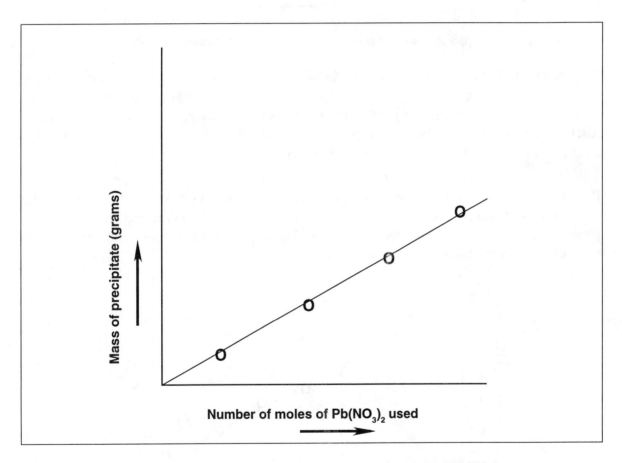

Figure 1. Mass of precipitate vs. number of moles of $Pb(NO_3)_2$

Now consider a similar investigation in which NaCl is always the limiting reagent. This time the amount of precipitate formed depends on the amount of NaCl used. This case is represented by the graph in **Figure 2**.

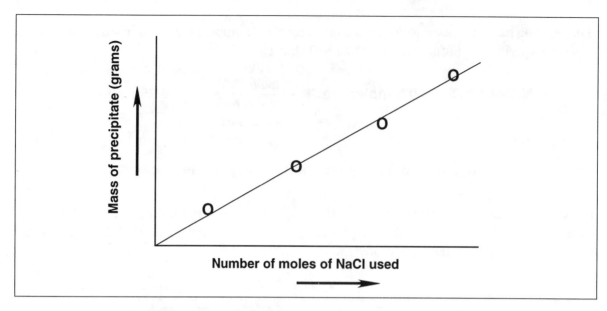

Figure 2. Mass of precipitate vs. number of moles of NaCl

If we react a different number of moles of $Pb(NO_3)_2$ and NaCl while holding the total number of moles of reactants constant and plot the mass of precipitate recovered from the reaction mixture as a function of the number of moles of the reactants used, the ratio of moles involved in the reaction between $Pb(NO_3)_2$ and NaCl can be determined. The mass of precipitate formed will be a maximum at the stoichiometric ratio for the reaction.

If we increase the number of moles of $Pb(NO_3)_2$ used from left to right and the number of moles of NaCl used from right to left; our graph will be of the form shown in **Figure 3**. Note that at any point on the x–axis, the total number of moles of $Pb(NO_3)_2$ and NaCl remains the same (in this particular experiment it is 0.12 moles).

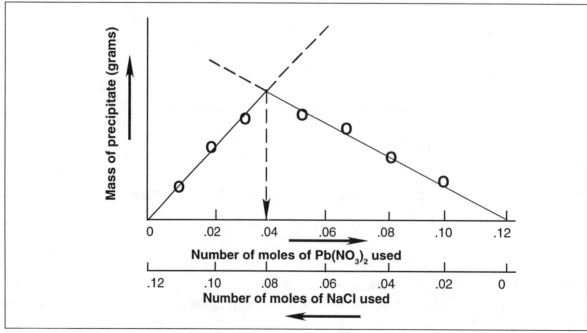

Figure 3. Mass of precipitate vs. moles of $Pb(NO_3)_2$ and moles of NaCl

It is apparent that the $Pb(NO_3)_2$ is the limiting reagent on the left hand side of the graph (where very little $Pb(NO_3)_2$ is used) and NaCl is the limiting reagent on the right hand side of the graph. The plotted points fall into two distinct groups and the best straight line is drawn through each group. The point of intersection corresponds to maximum product formation on the y–axis and corresponds to the stoichiometric ratio of $Pb(NO_3)_2$ and NaCl on the x–axis. The ratio from **Figure 3** is 0.04 moles $Pb(NO_3)_2$ to 0.08 moles NaCl or a 1:2 ratio.

We can determine the stoichiometry of chemical systems in which no precipitate is produced by a similar method if some product (for example, a gas) is produced which is easily measured because the amount of product formed is a function of the stoichiometry and the quantities of reactants used.

It is also true that the amount of heat absorbed or evolved in a reaction is a stoichiometric quantity. We will take advantage of this fact in order to determine the stoichiometric ratio in the reaction of NaOCl (sodium hypochlorite or bleach) with Na_2SO_3 (sodium sulfite) or with $Na_2S_2O_3$ (sodium thiosulfate).

$$\textbf{a NaOCl (aq) + b Na}_2\textbf{S}_2\textbf{O}_3 \textbf{ (aq)} \longrightarrow \textbf{products + Q}$$

where **Q** represents the amount of heat that is evolved. This evolution of heat results in an increase in temperature of the solution.

$$\Delta T = (T_{final} - T_{initial})$$

The rise in temperature, ΔT, is directly related to the amount of heat, **Q**, given off in the reaction. Therefore, the change in temperature can be used to monitor the amount of heat that is released in the reaction.

If we carry out a series of reactions between NaOCl and Na_2SO_3 (or $Na_2S_2O_3$), where the total number of moles of reactants is held constant, then the maximum amount of heat, **Q**, will be given off when the reactants are present in the correct stoichiometric ratio. This is the same principle as the $Pb(NO_3)_2$ and NaCl example discussed above.

In carrying out this experiment, you will use a solution of 0.50 M NaOCl and a basic solution of 0.50 M $Na_2S_2O_3$ (or 0.50 M Na_2SO_3 as your instructor directs). The expression 0.50 M means that the solution contains 0.50 mole of the solute in 1.0 liter of solution. Using solutions of known concentrations allows you to obtain a certain number of moles of a reactant simply by measuring a specific volume of solution. For instance, if you measure 1.0 liter of a 0.50 M solution of NaOCl, you know that this solution contains a 0.50 mole of NaOCl; 500 ml of this solution contains 0.25 mole of NaOCl; and so on.

$$\textbf{MV} = (\frac{\textbf{moles solute}}{\textbf{liter solution}}) \times \textbf{(liters solution)} = \textbf{moles solute}$$

PROCEDURE

Measure the appropriate amounts (see **Data Sheet**) of NaOCl and Na_2SO_3 (or $Na_2S_2O_3$) in different graduated cylinders. Determine the temperature of the reactants in both cylinders being careful to rinse the thermometer thoroughly before immersing it in either solution to avoid contamination. The temperatures of these solutions should be identical.

CAUTION: NaOCl is bleach. Do not get it on your clothes. Wash hands after handling.

Pour the NaOCl into a clean, dry styrofoam cup. Add the other reagent to the NaOCl, swirl the contents to insure good mixing of the reagents and determine the maximum temperature to which the reaction mixture rises.

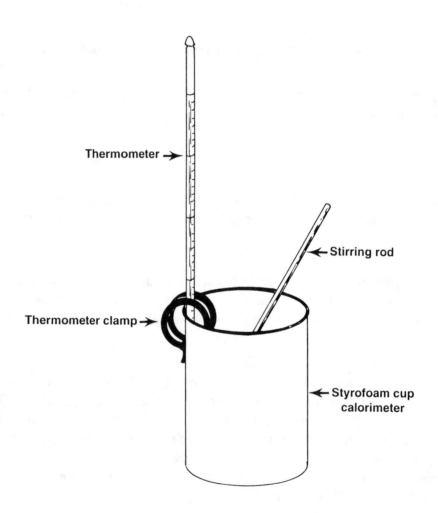

Figure 4. Experimental Set-up

CONCLUSIONS AND CALCULATIONS

1. Calculate the number of moles of each reactant used in each assignment.

2. Calculate the change in temperature for each assignment for the mixing of the solutions from the initial and final temperatures.

3. Plot the change in temperature as a function of the number of moles of NaOCl and the number of moles of Na_2SO_3 (or $Na_2S_2O_3$) used. The points will fall into two groups. Draw the best straight line through each group and determine the intersection point.

4. Determine the ratio of the number of moles of NaOCl to the other reactant from your plot, and determine which reactant is the limiting reagent in each experiment.

DATA SHEET: STOICHIOMETRIC RATIO – NaOCl + Na$_2$S$_2$O$_3$

Run Number	Volume NaOCl	Volume Na$_2$S$_2$O$_3$	Initial Temp.	Maximum Temp.	Δ T	Moles NaOCl	Moles Na$_2$S$_2$O$_3$	Limiting Reagent
I	25.0 ml	75.0 ml						
II	40.0 ml	60.0 ml						
III	60.0 ml	40.0 ml						
IV	80.0 ml	20.0 ml						
V	85.0 ml	15.0 ml						
VI	95.0 ml	5.0 ml						

STOICHIOMETRIC RATIO : _____

THE GAS CONSTANT

PURPOSE AND GOALS

To determine the value of the gas constant, R, by collecting the $H_2(g)$ produced when a known amount of magnesium reacts with acid.

PRINCIPLES

When a sample of gas is compressed at **constant temperature**, one finds that the volume change that occurs does not depend on the kind of gas used, but is determined by the initial volume and the ratio of the initial and final pressures. Similarly heating a gas sample at constant volume results in an increase in pressure which is not dependent on the nature of the gas in the sample. Gases, unlike liquids and solids, show volume – temperature – pressure behavior that can be described in terms of relationships that are as valid for methane as for helium, for air as for fluorine. The most important of these relationships is called the **ideal gas law**.

The ideal gas law is an equation which describes the relationship between the four fundamental properties of a gas, i.e., pressure, temperature, volume and amount of gas present, and may be stated as follows

$$PV = nRT$$

where P = pressure, V = volume, n = number of moles of gas, and T is the absolute temperature of the gas. T is related to the Celsius (centigrade) temperature, t, in the following way:

$$T = t + 273°$$

The quantity R is called the gas constant; it has the same value for all gases.

As you can see, the ideal gas law is an expression containing four variables and one constant. If we know the value of any three variables and we know the value of R, we can calculate what the value for the other variable must be. It is a rather remarkable equation in that it is one of the few natural laws involving as many as four variables - usually scientists perform experiments in which, hopefully, there are only two variables, since, under these conditions, it is easiest to see how one depends on the other. The ideal gas law is based on several experiments in which two variables were studied. The ideal gas law took the general form that we use today when the possibility of summarizing the results from several different experiments was realized. The ideal gas law combines three other laws:

$$\text{Boyle's Law: } V = \frac{k_a}{P} \text{ at constant n and T}$$

$$\text{Charles' Law: } V = k_b T \text{ at constant n and P}$$

$$\text{Avogadro's Law: } V = k_c n \text{ at constant P and T}$$

Boyle's Law states that at constant number of moles of gas and constant temperature, the volume is inversely proportional to the pressure.

Charles' Law states that at constant number of moles of gas and constant pressure, the volume is directly proportional to the temperature.

Avogadro's Law states that at constant temperature and constant pressure, the volume is directly proportional to the number of moles of the gas present.

If we combine all three relationships we obtain

$$V \propto \left(\frac{1}{P}\right) (T) (n)$$

and

$$V = R \left(\frac{1}{P}\right) (T) (n)$$

where R = constant of proportionality, gas law constant, therefore;

$$PV = nRT \tag{1}$$

Now consider a case where we are dealing with a constant amount of gas, i.e., n remains constant. By rearranging the ideal gas law we obtain

$$nR = \frac{PV}{T}$$

If we initially take a given sample of gas under a certain set of conditions, we have:

$$nR = \frac{P_1 V_1}{T_1} \qquad (2)$$

However, if we now change the set of conditions on this same sample of gas, we have

$$nR = \frac{P_2 V_2}{T_2} \qquad (3)$$

It is immediately recognized that since nR is a constant in this case, these last two equations can be set equal to each other:

$$\frac{P_1 V_1}{T_1} = \frac{P_2 V_2}{T_2} \qquad (4)$$

We can use equation (4) to calculate one unknown variable if the other five are known.

Example

One mole of an ideal gas occupies 22.4 liters of S.T.P. (Standard Temperature and Pressure; 0°C or 273°K and 1 atmosphere) what will be its new volume at 500°K and 700 atmospheres?

Now
$$P_1 = 1 \text{ atm}$$
$$V_1 = 22.4 \text{ liters}$$
$$T_1 = 273° \text{ K}$$
$$V_2 = ?$$
$$P_2 = 700 \text{ atm}$$
$$T_2 = 500° \text{ K}$$

from equation (4):
$$V_2 = \frac{P_1 V_1}{T_1} \cdot \frac{T_2}{P_2}$$

$$V_2 = \frac{1 \text{ atm} \times 22.4 \text{ liter} \times 500°\text{K}}{273°\text{K} \times 700 \text{ atm}}$$

$$V_2 = 0.059 \text{ liters}$$

We can also rearrange the gas law equation and solve for R:

$$R = \frac{PV}{nT} \qquad (5)$$

Notice that the units of R depend on the units that the volume and the pressure are measured in, e.g., if P is in atmospheres and V is in liters, then R will have units of $atm \cdot l \cdot mole^{-1} \cdot K^{-1}$.

The value of R may be evaluated by determining the volume occupied by a given number of moles of a gas at a known temperature and pressure.

In this experiment the reaction of magnesium metal with hydrochloric acid is utilized in determining the value of R as the number of moles of hydrogen gas generated is equal to the number of moles of magnesium used as a reactant if excess hydrochloric acid is present

$$Mg\ (s)\ +\ 2HCl\ (aq)\ \longrightarrow\ MgCl_2\ (aq)\ +\ H_2\ (g)$$

The volume of hydrogen gas produced may be measured by collecting gas in an inverted graduated cylinder over water if the atmospheric pressure and the room temperature are known, all these values, on substitution into equation (5) will give a value for R.

Since the hydrogen is collected over water in this experiment, the pressure of the gas collected (barometric pressure) is the sum of the hydrogen gas pressure and water vapor pressure.

$$P_{Bar}\ =\ P_{H_2} +\ P_{H_2O}$$

In order to obtain the pressure of the hydrogen gas, the vapor pressure of the water at room temperature must be subtracted from barometric pressure (see **Table 1**).

$$P_{H_2}\ =\ P_{Bar}\ -\ P_{H_2O} \tag{6}$$

Where P_{H_2} = Pressure of H_2 gas
P_{Bar} = Barometric Pressure
P_{H_2O} = Water Vapor pressure at room temperature

TABLE 1 Vapor Pressure of Water	
Temperature (°C)	Vapor Pressure (Torr)
20.0	17.5
21.0	18.7
22.0	19.8
23.0	21.1
24.0	22.4
25.0	23.8
26.0	25.2
27.0	26.7
28.0	28.3
29.0	30.0
30.0	31.8

FRACTIONAL CRYSTALLIZATION

PURPOSE

To investigate the separation of a mixture of pure substances by fractional crystallization.

PRINCIPLES

The solubility of a solute in a given solvent is usually very dependent upon temperature. Whether the solubility of the solute increases or decreases as the temperature is raised depends upon whether or not the solution process is endothermic or exothermic.

The solubilities of solid substances in different kinds of liquid solvents vary widely. Some substances are essentially insoluble in all known solvents; the materials we classify as macromolecular are typical examples. Most materials are noticeably soluble in one or more solvents. Those substances that we call salts often have very appreciable solubility in water by relatively little solubility in any other liquids. Organic compounds, whose molecules contain carbon and hydrogen atoms as their main constituents, are often soluble in organic liquids such as benzene or carbon tetrachloride.

It is often possible to separate a mixture into its pure components by taking advantage of the differences in solubilities of the solutes and of the differences in temperature dependences of the solutes.

In this experiment you will be given a sample containing silicon carbide, potassium dichromate, and sodium chloride. Your problem will be to separate this mixture into its component parts, using water as a solvent. Silicon carbide, SiC, is a macromolecular substance and is insoluble in water. Potassium dichromate, $K_2Cr_2O_7$, and sodium chloride, $NaCl$, are water soluble ionic substances, with different solubilities at different temperatures, as indicated in **Figure 1**. Sodium chloride exhibits little change in solubility between 0°C and l00°C, whereas the solubility of potassium dichromate increases about 16-fold over this temperature range. Given a water solution containing equal weights of $NaCl$ and $K_2Cr_2O_7$ it should be clear that $K_2Cr_2O_7$ would most easily crystallize in pure form from the solution at low temperatures, and that at high temperatures the crystals that would first appear in the boiling solution would be essentially pure NaCl. The method by which we recover pure substances by making use of solubility properties such as those cited for NaCl and $K_2Cr_2O_7$ is called **fractional crystallization** and this is one of the fundamental procedures used by chemists for isolating pure materials.

The solubility of solute is usually expressed in terms of **grams solute/100 g solvent**.

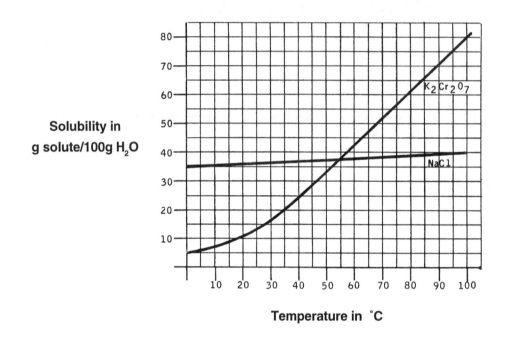

Figure 1. Solubility versus temperature for NaCl and $K_2Cr_2O_7$

PROCEDURE

Obtain a Büchner funnel, a filtering flask and a sample containing unknown percentages of SiC, NaCl and $K_2Cr_2O_7$.

CAUTION: $K_2Cr_2O_7$ (potassium dichromate) is poisonous. Wash hands after handling.

NOTE: Be sure to disconnect the rubber hose from the Büchner funnel before shutting off the water, otherwise water will back up into the flask.

Weigh the sample (about 12 g) into a clean 150 ml beaker and add about 100 ml of tap water. Make all mass measurements to 0.1 gram.

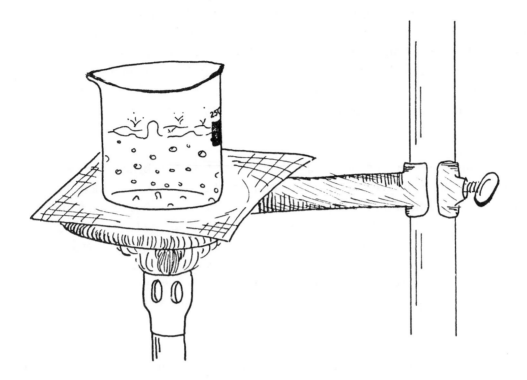

Figure 2. Heating Solution of Unknown

Figure 3. Suction Filtration Set-Up

Warm the solution to about 40°C, see **Figure 2**. Stir the solution constantly for at least 5 minutes to insure dissolution of all soluble solvents. Through a preweighed piece of filter paper in a Büchner funnel, filter the hot solution to remove the insoluble SiC, see **Figure 3**. Be sure to transfer as much of the SiC to the filter paper as possible with your rubber policeman. Rinse the beaker with 5-10 ml distilled water which has been heated to 40°C and pour onto the filter paper to wash the solid SiC. Continue to apply suction for a few minutes in order to dry the solid. Gently remove the solid and filter paper using your spatula and set it aside to air dry. When it is dry, reweigh.

Transfer the orange filtrate (approximately 55-60 ml) to a 150 ml beaker and heat the orange filtrate in the beaker gently to the boiling point and boil gently to reduce the volume to approximately 35 ml (stir continuously). The solution will become turbid and white crystals of NaCl will be visible in the liquid. The solution will have a tendency to bump, so do not heat it too strongly. Hot dichromate solution can give you a bad burn. When NaCl crystals are clearly apparent, the solution will usually appear cloudy (you may have to reduce the volume to 30 ml if you do not see solid). Wash the crystallized solids from the walls of the beaker with your medicine dropper, using the solution in the beaker. Stir the solution with a glass rod to dissolve the solids; if necessary, you may heat the solution, but do not boil it.

Cool the solution to room temperature by running tap water over the outside of the beaker, and then to about 0°C in an ice bath. Leave the beaker containing the solution in the ice bath for 10 minutes. Bright orange crystals of $K_2Cr_2O_7$ will precipitate. Stir the cold slurry of crystals for several minutes to make sure any NaCl dissolves. Add 3 ml of ice cold distilled water to dissolve any NaCl. Before filtering the $K_2Cr_2O_7$, the Büchner funnel needs to be chilled in order to prevent the solution from warming up and as a result some $K_2Cr_2O_7$ dissolving.

Assemble the Büchner funnel using a preweighed piece of filter paper; chill it by adding 100 ml ice-cold distilled water and, after a minute, draw the water through with suction. Discard the water in the suction flask. Filter the $K_2Cr_2O_7$ slurry through the cold Büchner funnel into the empty flask. Your rubber policeman may be helpful when transferring the last of the crystals. Press the crystals dry with a clean piece of filter paper, and continue to apply suction for a minute or so. Turn off the suction and pour the filtrate, which contains most of the NaCl in the sample, into a clean 150 ml beaker.

Place the Büchner funnel (containing the $K_2Cr_2O_7$) back on the filtering flask and without applying suction, add 3 ml of ice cold distilled water from your wash bottle to the funnel. Let the cold liquid remain in contact with the crystals for about ten seconds, and then apply suction; the liquid removed will contain most of the NaCl impurity. Add 10 ml of acetone to the funnel and pull it through with suction. This will remove most of the water and speed up the drying process. Continue to apply suction for about a minute to dry the purified $K_2Cr_2O_7$ crystals. Lift the filter paper and the crystals from the funnel and put the paper on the lab bench to let the crystals dry further in the air. Reweigh the filter paper and $K_2Cr_2O_7$ when dry.

CAUTION: ACETONE IS FLAMMABLE

Heat the filtrate containing the NaCl to boiling and boil gently. Continue to boil the solution until the volume of NaCl crystals (which form as the volume is reduced) is about half the volume of the liquid above the crystals. Again, wash the crystallized solids from the walls of the beaker into the solution with your medicine dropper filled with solution from the beaker. Stir to dissolve any solid $K_2Cr_2O_7$ that may be present. Reheat the solution to the boiling point.

Assemble the Büchner funnel using a third piece of preweighed filter paper (make sure the funnel is warmed), turn on the suction, and, using your tongs to hold the beaker, filter the hot solution through the funnel. Transfer as much of the solid NaCl crystals as possible, first by swirling the slurry as you pour it, and then by using your rubber policeman. Press the crystals flat with a piece of dry filter paper. At this point the NaCl will appear yellow because of the presence of residual dichromate solution.

Turn off the suction by disconnecting the hose from the suction flask. Add about 15 drops 6 M HCl (dilute HCl) to the crystals to get rid of the $K_2Cr_2O_7$ contaminate. Wait for a minute, and then re-apply suction for a minute or so to remove the liquid, which will contain most of the yellow contaminant. Wash the crystals, with suction on, using about 10 ml of acetone, which will remove the residual HCl and will readily evaporate. If this operation has been done properly your purified NaCl crystals will be nearly colorless. Remove the filter paper with the crystals from the funnel and put it aside to let the NaCl air dry further. Reweigh the filter paper and NaCl when dry.

Show your samples of SiC, $K_2Cr_2O_7$ and NaCl to your laboratory instructor for evaluation.

Waste containers will be provided for the disposal of the $K_2Cr_2O_7$ residue and filter papers.

CONCLUSIONS AND CALCULATIONS

1.   Calculate the percent SiC, $K_2Cr_2O_7$ and NaCl in your unknown. Assume 80% recovery for $K_2Cr_2O_7$ and NaCl.

2.   Calculate the total percent recovery in your fractional crystallization.

3.   Which solute did you recover the least of? Explain.

FRACTIONAL CRYSTALLIZATION

SAMPLE MIXTURE

1. Add 50 ml of distilled water, warm to 40°C and stir constantly for at least 5 minutes.
2. Filter (using preweighed filter paper) through a Büchner funnel.
3. Put 5 - 10 ml of distilled water in the same beaker, warm to 40°C, pour onto filter paper to wash the SiC.

RESIDUE (SiC)

Remove filter paper containing solid SiC, air dry, and weigh.

FILTRATE

1. Heat **gently** to boiling and continue to heat to reduce the volume to 35 ml (stir continuously), the solution becomes turbid and crystals of NaCl will appear. You should see solid, if not, heat to 30 ml. **CAUTION: Hot dichromate solution gives painful burns!**
2. Wash solid from the walls of the beaker with a medicine dropper (using the hot solution in the beaker).
3. Cool outside of beaker with tap water and then cool in ice bath.
4. Leave in the ice bath for 10 min. (should see orange crystals -- if you don't, remove and heat to reduce the volume further and proceed from #2). Stir to make sure any NaCl dissolves. Add 3 ml of ice cold distilled water to dissolve any NaCl.
5. Filter (with preweighed filter paper) through the Büchner funnel which has been chilled.

RESIDUE (Solid $K_2Cr_2O_7$)

1. Without suction, add 3 ml ice cold water. Let stand 10 seconds then add suction. With suction still on, add 10 ml of acetone to aid drying (suction 1 minute). Remove the solid $K_2Cr_2O_7$, air dry and weigh. **CAUTION: Acetone is flammable. $K_2Cr_2O_7$ is poisonous.**

FILTRATE

1. TRANSFER FILTRATE FROM FLASK TO BEAKER BEFORE PROCEEDING.
2. Heat to boiling, reduce heat and stir frequently.
3. Reduce the volume until it contains half solid and half liquid -- wash solid from the walls of the beaker with medicine dropper using hot solution in beaker.
4. Filter the hot solution (make sure the Büchner funnel has been warmed). Preweigh the filter paper.

RESIDUE (Solid NaCl, looks yellow)

1. Without suction, add 15 drops 6 M HCl to get rid of the $K_2Cr_2O_7$ contaminate (let stand for 1 minute and then suction 1 minute).
2. With suction still on, add about 10 ml of acetone to remove residual HCl and aid drying. Air dry and weigh.

FILTRATE (Discard)

Name _____ Lab Instructor: _____ Date: _____

DATA SHEET: FRACTIONAL CRYSTALLIZATION

Unknown Number _____

Determination of mass of unknown

Mass of container   _____

Mass of container
plus unknown   _____

Mass of unknown   _____

Determination of mass of SiC in unknown

Mass of Filter paper plus SiC   _____

Mass of filter paper   _____

Mass of SiC   _____

Determination of mass of $K_2Cr_2O_7$ in unknown:

Mass of filter paper
plus $K_2Cr_2O_7$ _____

Mass of filter paper   _____

Mass of $K_2Cr_2O_7$ _____

Determination of mass of NaCl in unknown

Mass filter paper plus NaCl   _____

Mass of filter paper   _____

Mass of NaCl   _____

Composition of Unknown

Percent SiC in sample   _____

Percent $K_2Cr_2O_7$ in sample
(assuming 80% recovery)   _____

Percent NaCl in sample
(assuming 80% recovery)   _____

DETERMINATION OF REACTION STOICHIOMETRY

PURPOSE

To determine the stoichiometric relationship between $Pb(NO_3)_2$ and KBr in water solution by the method of continuous variations.

PRINCIPLES

In order to investigate the experimental stoichiometric ratio between $Pb(NO_3)_2$ and KBr, we will carry out a series of reactions between different quantities of $Pb(NO_3)_2$ and KBr. The important thing is that the sum of the number of moles of $Pb(NO_3)_2$ and the number of moles of KBr will be constant for each determination. This procedure is known as **Job's Method** or the method of continuous variations.

Since we are investigating the stoichiometry of the system, some quantitative property of the system must be measured for each determination. This could be such things as a temperature change, volume change, mass of product produced or amount of gas produced. In this experiment we will measure the mass of products produced since an insoluble precipitate is formed in the reaction.

If we plot the magnitude of the quantitative feature we are measuring (in this case, mass of precipitate) versus the number of moles of reactant used, a maximum or minimum represents the stoichiometric ratio between the reactants.

As an example, consider the investigation of the reaction stoichiometry between $AgNO_3$ and Li_2CO_3 in water. The amounts of $AgNO_3$ and Li_2CO_3 reacted are listed in **Table 1**. Notice that the total number of moles of reactants remained constant for each determination. Also listed in **Table 1** is the mass of precipitate collected for each determination.

In order to find the stoichiometric ratio between the reactants we must plot the mass of the precipitate versus the number of moles of reactant. If we plot the mass of precipitate versus the moles of Li_2CO_3 we obtain **Figure 1**.

Table 1: AgNO$_3$ / Li$_2$CO$_3$ / H$_2$O System

Assignment number	Volume (ml) of 0.50 M AgNO$_3$	moles of AgNO$_3$	Volume (ml) of 0.50 M Li$_2$CO$_3$	moles of Li$_2$CO$_3$	Total number of moles of reactants	mass of precipitate, g
1	3.00	1.50×10^{-3}	27.00	1.35×10^{-2}	1.50×10^{-2}	.207
2	6.00	3.00×10^{-3}	24.00	1.20×10^{-2}	1.50×10^{-2}	.414
3	9.00	4.50×10^{-3}	21.00	1.05×10^{-2}	1.50×10^{-2}	.621
4	12.00	6.00×10^{-3}	18.00	9.00×10^{-3}	1.50×10^{-2}	.828
5	15.00	7.50×10^{-3}	15.00	7.50×10^{-3}	1.50×10^{-2}	1.035
6	18.00	9.00×10^{-3}	12.00	6.00×10^{-3}	1.50×10^{-2}	1.241
7	21.00	1.05×10^{-2}	9.00	4.50×10^{-3}	1.50×10^{-2}	1.241
8	24.00	1.20×10^{-2}	6.00	3.00×10^{-3}	1.50×10^{-2}	.828
9	27.00	1.35×10^{-2}	3.00	1.50×10^{-3}	1.50×10^{-2}	.414

DETERMINATION OF THE PERCENT ACETIC ACID IN A VINEGAR SAMPLE

PURPOSE

The percent acetic acid in a vinegar sample will be determined by a titrimetric procedure.

PRINCIPLES

Solutions of accurately known concentrations are called **standard solutions**. Standard solutions of some substances can be prepared by dissolving a carefully weighed sample in enough water to give an accurately known volume of solution. Solutions of some other compounds are prepared and then their concentrations are determined by titration.

Titration is the process by which one determines the volume of a standard solution required to react with a specific amount of pure substance, or to react with a specific volume of solution of unknown concentration. Alternately, one may determine the concentration of a solution by measuring carefully the volume of solution required to react with an exactly known amount of a **primary standard**. Ideal primary standards have the following properties:

1. Must not react with or absorb the components of the atmosphere, such as water vapor, oxygen, or carbon dioxide.
2. Must react according to one invariable reaction.
3. High percentage purity.
4. High molecular weight to minimize error in weighing.
5. Soluble in the solvent of interest.

Each of these characteristics minimizes the errors involved in analysis. Not very many substances meet these criteria, so the number of useful primary standards is quite limited. Two common primary standard bases are pure sodium carbonate and borax ($Na_2B_4O_7 \cdot 10H_2O$). Potassium hydrogen phthalate, oxalic acid dihydrate, sulfamic acid, and benzoic acid are primary standard acids.

Some common primary standard substances for oxidation-reduction reactions include arsenic(III) oxide, potassium oxide, potassium iodate, potassium dichromate, and sodium oxalate. Silver nitrate can be obtained in primary standard form for precipitation titrations.

If one of the titration reactants is not a primary standard, then a primary standard substance must be selected for purposes of standardizing one of the reactant solutions. Thus, a primary standard is used, either directly or indirectly, in the preparation of any standard solution. Hydrochloric acid solutions are commonly standardized using sodium carbonate while potassium hydrogen phthalate is commonly employed to standardize sodium hydroxide solutions.

A **secondary standard** is a solution to be used in the analysis of an unknown.

A crucial part of a successful titration is that a chemical reaction takes place. However, not all chemical reactions are equally suitable for this type of volumetric analysis. The most successful titrations involve reactions that meet or closely approach the following requirements:

1. The reaction should be rapid so that the titration is not too slow and tedious.
2. The reaction should be stoichiometric, i.e., capable of being described by a chemical equation so that volumetric data can be used directly in the titration calculations.
3. The reaction should not involve alternate or side reactions between constituents of the solutions.
4. There must be a method for determining when the reaction is complete.

Several general types of reactions come to mind which often meet these criteria. These are

(1) reactions between acids and bases,
(2) oxidation-reductions,
(3) reactions involving the formation of complexes, and
(4) precipitation reactions.

In this experiment we will consider titrations involving acid/base reactions.

In order to determine the percent acetic acid in a vinegar sample we must use a base (NaOH, in this case) of known concentration (standardized). The base is standardized by titration with a standardized acid (HCl, in this case). The acid is first standardized by titrating sodium carbonate (Na_2CO_3), which is a primary standard. Acetic acid is not titrated against sodium carbonate directly due to problems associated with determining the equivalence point of the titration of a weak base with a weak acid.

For every titration, some method must be available to determine when the reaction is complete, i.e., when the equivalence point has been reached. Although other methods are also available small amounts of certain organic dyes called indicators can be added to the titration mixture and will signal the equivalence point by changing color. Choice of the proper indicator for a specific titration should not be taken lightly because it depends on a knowledge of the chemistry of the indicator and the nature of the titration equivalence point.

In general, an indicator should fulfill the following requirements:

1. An indicator must have a strongly colored form in solution.
2. An indicator must undergo a large enough color change at the equivalence point to be observable by the human eye.
3. The final color of the indicator should persist in solution.
4. The indicator should generally be soluble in the titrated solution so that the color of the indicator is uniformly distributed in the titrated solution.

A common indicator used for the titration of a strong base such as sodium hydroxide is phenolphthalein. In acid solution, the colorless form of phenolphthalein is present, while in basic solution the red form is present.

During the titration, the point at which the indicator changes color is known as the end-point. If the indicator is carefully selected, the end-point will coincide with or occur close to the equivalence point. It should be remembered that these two terms represent distinct concepts.

In dealing with quantitative calculations involving solutions, we need to express the solution concentration in some convenient unit. In this experiment we will use the molarity. The molarity, M, of a solution is the number of moles of the substance which is dissolved per liter of solution. Therefore, one liter of a solution containing 40.00 grams of sodium hydroxide is described as a 1.000 M NaOH solution. The number of zeros is determined by the exactness with which the mass and final volumes are known.

The definitions described above can be expressed mathematically using the following symbols:

$$M = \text{molarity in units of moles per liter}$$

$$V = \text{volume in units of liters}$$

In general:

$$M(\text{moles liter}^{-1}) = \frac{\text{Number of Moles Solute}}{V\ (\text{liter})}$$

or,

$$\text{Number of moles solute} = (M)(V)$$

The equivalence point of the reaction of a monoprotic acid with a monohydroxy base is reached when the number of moles of base is exactly equal to the number of moles of acid. Therefore, at the equivalence point,

$$\textbf{(Number of moles of acid)} = \textbf{(number of moles of base)} \qquad \textbf{(1)}$$

and,

$$\textbf{(M}_{\textbf{acid}}\textbf{)} \textbf{(V}_{\textbf{acid}}\textbf{)} = \textbf{(M}_{\textbf{base}}\textbf{)} \textbf{(V}_{\textbf{base}}\textbf{)} \qquad \textbf{(2)}$$

These rather simple relationships are the foundation for all calculations that accompany acid-base titrations.

In this experiment, the concentration of a hydrochloric acid solution will be determined by titrating an accurately known amount of sodium carbonate. The hydrochloric acid solution is referred to as the titrant because it is the solution dispensed from the buret into the solution being titrated. The reaction involved in this titration is shown in Equation (**3**).

$$\textbf{2HCl(}\textit{aq}\textbf{)} + \textbf{Na}_2\textbf{CO}_3\textbf{(}\textit{aq}\textbf{)} \longrightarrow \textbf{2NaCl(}\textit{aq}\textbf{)} + \textbf{CO}_2\textbf{(}\textit{g}\textbf{)} + \textbf{H}_2\textbf{O(}\textit{l}\textbf{)} \qquad \textbf{(3)}$$

To find the concentration of the hydrochloric acid solution, the number of moles of hydrochloric acid that react with a known number of moles of sodium carbonate must be found. The stoichiometry of the reaction is such that two moles of hydrochloric acid are required to react with one mole of sodium carbonate. The number of moles of sodium carbonate used in each determination is found by:

$$\textbf{Number of moles of Na}_2\textbf{CO}_3 = \frac{\textbf{mass of Na}_2\textbf{CO}_3\textbf{, g}}{\textbf{106.00 g mole}^{-1}} \qquad \textbf{(4)}$$

From the mole ratio in Equation (**3**)

$$\textbf{Number of moles of HCl} = \textbf{(moles of Na}_2\textbf{CO}_3\textbf{)} \left(\frac{\textbf{2 moles HCl}}{\textbf{1 mole Na}_2\textbf{CO}_3} \right) \qquad \textbf{(5)}$$

then using Equations (**4**) and (**5**)

$$\textbf{Number of moles of HCl} = \left(\frac{\textbf{mass of Na}_2\textbf{CO}_3\textbf{, g}}{\textbf{106 g mole}^{-1}} \right) \left(\frac{\textbf{2 moles HCl}}{\textbf{1 mole Na}_2\textbf{CO}_3} \right) \qquad \textbf{(6)}$$

and, because

$$\textbf{Number of moles of HCl} = \textbf{M}_{\textbf{HCl}} \ \textbf{V}_{\textbf{HCl}} \qquad \textbf{(7)}$$

where

$$\textbf{M}_{\textbf{HCl}} = \textbf{Molarity of HCl in moles liter}^{-1}$$

$$\textbf{V}_{\textbf{HCl}} = \textbf{Volume of HCl in liters}$$

then,

$$M_{HCl} \ V_{HCl} = \left(\frac{\text{mass of Na}_2\text{CO}_3, \text{ g}}{106.00 \text{ g mole}^{-1}} \right) \left(\frac{2 \text{ moles HCl}}{1 \text{ mole Na}_2\text{CO}_3} \right) \tag{8}$$

To calculate the molarity of the hydrochloric acid, Equation (8) is rearranged, giving Equation (9)

$$M_{HCl} = \frac{2 \ (\text{mass of Na}_2\text{CO}_3, \text{ g})}{(106.00 \text{ g mole}^{-1}) \ (V_{HCl})} \tag{9}$$

Now that the molarity of the HCl solution is known, it can be used to determine the molarity of an unknown NaOH solution

$$\text{NaOH } (aq) + \text{HCl } (aq) \longrightarrow \text{H}_2\text{O } (l) + \text{NaCl } (aq) \tag{10}$$

where the number of moles of acid will equal the number of moles of base.

Consider, for example, the titration of a 0.100 M hydrochloric acid solution with a sodium hydroxide solution of unknown concentration. If 25.05 ml of the sodium hydroxide solution is required to titrate 25.00 ml of the hydrochloric acid solution, the molarity of the sodium hydroxide solution may be found from:

$$M_{HCl} \ V_{HCl} = M_{NaOH} \ V_{NaOH} \tag{11}$$

or

$$M_{NaOH} = \frac{M_{HCl} \ V_{HCl}}{V_{NaOH}} \tag{12}$$

$$M_{NaOH} = \frac{(0.100 \text{ moles liter}^{-1}) \ (0.0250 \text{ liter})}{(0.02505 \text{ liter})}$$

$$M_{NaOH} = 0.0998 \text{ moles liter}^{-1}$$

The analysis of vinegar can be carried out by titrating the acetic acid in the sample with the standardized solution of NaOH according to Equation (13).

$$\text{CH}_3\text{COOH } (aq) + \text{NaOH } (aq) \longrightarrow \text{CH}_3\text{COONa } (aq) + \text{H}_2\text{O } (l) \tag{13}$$

The number of moles of acetic acid in the sample titrated can be found from Equation (14).

$$\begin{array}{c} \text{Number of moles} \\ \text{of acetic acid} \\ \text{in 5.00 ml} \end{array} = (M_{NaOH}) \ (V_{NaOH}) \qquad (14)$$

where M_{NaOH} is the molarity of the sodium hydroxide solution in moles liter^{-1} and V_{NaOH} is the volume of sodium hydroxide solution in liters.

The number of grams of acetic acid in the 5.00 ml portion that was titrated can be found from Equation (15).

$$\begin{array}{c} \text{Number of grams} \\ \text{of acetic acid} \\ \text{in 5.00 ml} \end{array} = \left(\begin{array}{c} \text{Number of} \\ \text{moles} \\ \text{in 5.00 ml} \end{array} \right) \left(\begin{array}{c} \text{Molecular} \\ \text{weight of} \\ \text{acetic acid} \end{array} \right) \qquad (15)$$

By assuming the density of the vinegar sample to be 1.00 g ml^{-1}, the percent by mass of acetic acid in the vinegar sample can be found from Equation (16).

$$\text{Percent acetic acid} = \frac{\text{mass of acetic acid, g}}{\text{mass of vinegar sample, g}} \times 100\% \qquad (16)$$

PROCEDURE

PART I

STANDARDIZATION OF HCl WITH SODIUM CARBONATE

Add about 250 ml of distilled water to a 500 ml flat bottomed boiling flask (Florence flask). Measure in a 10 ml graduated cylinder about 8.4 ml of dilute hydrochloric acid (6 M). Add the hydrochloric acid to the 250 ml of water in the Florence flask. Dilute the solution to approximately 500 ml with distilled water. Stopper the flask and swirl the contents thoroughly to mix the solution. Let the solution stand until the solution comes to room temperature.

Obtain from the stockroom window a vial (weighing bottle) containing 2 to 3 grams of sodium carbonate which has been dried for you. This will serve as your primary standard.

The weighing bottle should never be handled with bare fingers. If crucible tongs are not available to handle the bottle, a clean cloth or strip of paper folded around the bottle, as shown in **Figure 1,** can be used.

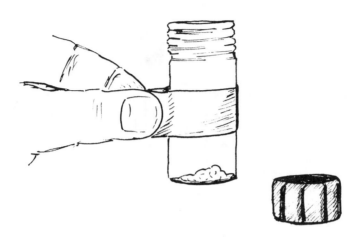

Figure 1. Proper Handling of Weighing Bottle.

Weigh the bottle and its contents to the nearest milligram on an analytical balance. Record the initial mass of the bottle and contents on the Data Sheet. Carefully pour about 0.20 to 0.25 grams of sodium carbonate into a clean 250 ml Erlenmeyer flask. Weigh the weighing bottle and the remaining contents again to the nearest milligram. Record this final mass on the data sheet. The difference between the initial mass and the final mass is the mass of the sodium carbonate transferred to the flask. Weigh to the nearest milligram two more 0.15 to 0.20 gram samples of sodium carbonate into clean 250 ml Erlenmeyer flasks, being certain that the flasks are clearly labeled so that the samples can be easily distinguished. Record the mass of each sample on the Data Sheet.

Dissolve each sample in about 30 to 50 ml of distilled water. Add three drops of bromophenol blue indicator solution to the solution in each flask.

After cleaning a buret, rinse it with three 5 ml portions of the hydrochloric acid solution to be standardized. Make certain that the rinse solution comes in contact with the entire inner surface of the buret and tip of the buret. Drain the rinse solution through the tip of the buret and discard the rinse solution. Close the buret stopcock and fill the buret with the hydrochloric acid solution to above the top calibration mark on the buret. Lower the meniscus of the solution until it reaches a calibrated portion of the buret. Make certain that the buret tip is filled with the solution. Record the initial buret reading to the nearest 0.01 ml on the Data Sheet.

Place one of the Erlenmeyer flasks containing the sodium carbonate solution under the buret and lower the buret tip until it is well into the mouth of the flask as shown in **Figure 2**.

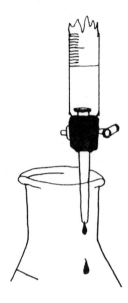

Figure 2. Relationship of buret to the flask.

Swirl the flask containing the sodium carbonate solution with one hand while controlling the stopcock with the other hand. Continue to add the titrant slowly to the sodium carbonate solution with swirling. As the titration progresses, the approach of the end point will be signaled by a temporary appearance of the green end-point color where the titrant first comes in contact with the sodium carbonate solution. As the end-point is approached more closely, these temporary flashes of color will persist longer and fractional parts of a drop of titrant should be added. Titrate the first sodium carbonate solution until the bromophenol blue indicator just begins to change color from blue to green.

Fractions of a drop may be added by allowing a droplet to begin to form on the buret tip. After touching the buret tip to the inner surface of the flask, wash down the inner surface of the flask with a stream of distilled water from a wash bottle. The titration is complete when the indicator begins to exhibit its green color for a minimum of 20 seconds. Read the final buret volume to the nearest 0.01 ml and record this volume on the Data Sheet.

Repeat the titration at least two more times with two different samples of sodium carbonate. Titrations should be done until three results are obtained which agree to within five parts per thousand.

When all of the titrations are completed, drain and thoroughly rinse the buret with distilled water. Rinse the other glassware also in order to have it ready to use for the next experiment. Save your standardized HCl solution made for this part of the experiment. You will need the HCl solution for **Part II** of this experiment.

STANDARDIZATION OF NaOH SOLUTION

Measure 8.2 ml of 6 M sodium hydroxide in a 10 ml graduated cylinder. Pour the solution into your large brown bottle. Dilute this solution to approximately 500 ml with distilled water. The volume of the sodium hydroxide solution does not have to be known accurately. This solution will be titrated in this part of the experiment to determine the concentration of the solution. Mix the solution thoroughly by inverting the bottle ten times. Insufficient mixing of solutions is a common source of error in titrations.

NOTE: Always keep the NaOH solution stoppered or capped when not in use since the NaOH slowly reacts with the CO_2 in the air (this may affect the endpoint result).

Before a titration is begun, all glassware must be thoroughly cleaned, but does not need to be dry. The glassware usually needed for a titration includes a buret, a pipet, and an Erlenmeyer flask.

Rinse a clean 25 ml volumetric pipet with a 5 ml portion of distilled water. Always use a rubber bulb to draw water or solutions into a pipet. Make certain that the rinse water contacts the entire inner surface of the pipet. Discard the rinse water. Rinse the pipet at least two times with 5 ml portions of your standard HCl solution by holding the pipet in a horizontal position and rotating it so that the solution contacts the entire inner surface of the pipet. Discard the rinse solutions.

Carefully pipet 25.00 ml of your standard hydrochloric acid solution into a 250 ml Erlenmeyer flask, holding the tip of the pipet against the inner surface of the flask to avoid splatter. When the flow of liquid from the pipet stops, continue to hold the pipet in a vertical position for 15 seconds to allow reproducible draining of the pipet. Touch off the last drop of a solution on the tip of the pipet so that the drop enters the flask. Add about 50 ml of distilled water to the acid solution in the flask to give a sufficient volume of solution in which to see a color change. The addition of about 50 ml of distilled water to the 25.00 ml of hydrochloric acid will not affect the volume of titrant, or number of moles of base to be added. Add to the acid solution three drops of phenolphthalein indicator solution and swirl the flask to thoroughly mix the solution.

After the buret has been properly cleaned, rinse the buret with a 5 ml portion of the 0.1 M NaOH solution so that the solution comes in contact with the entire inner surface of the buret and the tip of the buret. Drain the rinse solution through the tip of the buret and discard the rinse solution. Repeat this procedure twice with two new 5 ml portions of the NaOH solution. Discard the rinse solution through the tip of the buret.

Close the stopcock and fill the buret. After eliminating air bubbles in the tip of the buret, lower the meniscus of the solution until it is at a point on the calibrated portion of the buret. Record the initial buret reading to the nearest 0.01 ml on the Data Sheet. (It is not necessary that the initial buret reading be 0.00 ml, it is only important that the initial volume is known and recorded).

Place the Erlenmeyer flask containing the acid solution under the buret and lower the buret tip until it is well into the mouth of the flask as is shown in **Figure 2**.

Swirl the flask containing the acid solution with one hand as the stopcock is controlled with the other hand. If the standard HCl solution is approximately 0.1 M and the NaOH solution is approximately 0.1 M, approximately 25 ml of NaOH solution should be required for the titration. If the concentration of the NaOH is correct; 18-20 ml of titrant may be added to the acid solution without danger of adding so much titrant that the end-point of the titration is exceeded.

As the titration progresses, the approach of the end-point will be signaled by a very temporary appearance of the end-point color where the titrant first comes in contact with the acid solution. As the end-point is approached more closely, these temporary flashes of color persist longer and smaller amounts of titrant should be added. Just prior to the end-point, titrant should be added one drop at a time. Fractions of a drop may even be added by allowing a droplet to begin to form on the buret tip and, after touching the inner surface of the flask, washing with a stream of distilled water from a wash bottle.

The titrant may splatter slightly as it is added from the buret. The inner surface of the Erlenmeyer flask should be washed down thoroughly with distilled water before the end-point is reached. The titration is complete when the first barely perceptible but permanent end-point appears. The best accuracy is obtained if the intensity of the pink color is the faintest that can be seen. Place a sheet of white paper behind or under the flask to better see the faint pink color change. Divide the last drop of titrant added if possible. Read the final buret volume to the nearest 0.01 ml and record the volume on the Data Sheet.

Repeat the titration at least two more times. Titration should be done until three results are obtained which agree to within five parts per thousand. Between titrations, pour the neutralized solution from the Erlenmeyer flask and discard the solution. Rinse the flask several times with a few milliliters of distilled water. The flask need not be dried before introducing the 25.00 ml portion of acid for the next titration.

Do not discard your standardized NaOH solution until you are finished with the entire experiment.

PART III

TITRATION OF VINEGAR WITH STANDARDIZED NaOH

Obtain from labeled bottles approximately 50 ml of the assigned vinegar sample in a clean, dry 250 ml beaker. Record on the DataSheet the number of the unknown vinegar sample being analyzed. The beaker must be dry as any water present will dilute the vinegar sample and change the concentration of the vinegar sample.

Rinse a clean 5 ml volumetric pipet by drawing about 1 ml of distilled water into the pipet with a rubber bulb. Quickly disconnect the rubber bulb and place a finger over the top of the pipet. Hold the pipet in a nearly horizontal position and slowly rotate the pipet so that the water comes in contact with the entire inner surface of the pipet. Discharge the rinse water through the tip of the pipet.

Rinse the pipet with about 1 ml of the vinegar sample following the same procedure as when rinsing the pipet with water. Discard the rinse solution. Repeat this procedure with a second and a third 1 ml portion of the vinegar solution.

Carefully pipet 5.00 ml of the vinegar solution into a 250 ml Erlenmeyer flask holding the tip of the pipet against the inside surface of the flask to avoid splattering of the solution. After the solution stops flowing from the pipet, continue to hold the pipet vertically for 15 seconds to allow reproducible draining of the pipet. Remove the last drop of solution on the tip of the pipet by touching the tip of the pipet to the inside surface of the flask. Measure 40 ml of distilled water in a 100 ml graduated cylinder. Add the water to the vinegar solution in the flask to give a sufficient volume of solution in which a color change can be seen. Add to this solution 3 drops of a phenolphthalein indicator solution. Swirl the flask and contents to mix the solution thoroughly.

If a 5 ml volumetric pipet is not available, a clean 10 ml graduated pipet can be used to measure the vinegar solution. The pipet should be rinsed with distilled water and with two 2 ml portions of the vinegar solution.

If you do not already have the standardized NaOH solution in your buret refer to the procedure for cleaning and filling a buret in **Part II**.

Place the Erlenmeyer flask containing the vinegar solution under the buret. Lower the buret so that the tip of the buret is inserted an inch or more into the mouth of the flask as shown in **Figure 2**.

Swirl the flask containing the vinegar solution with one hand as the stopcock is controlled with the other hand. Begin to titrate the vinegar sample by slowly adding the standard sodium hydroxide solution. As the titration progresses, the approach of the end-point of the titration will be indicated by a momentary appearance of the pink end-point color where the titrant first comes in contact with the acid solution. As the end-point is approached more closely, these brief flashes of color will persist for a longer period of time. Reduce the flow of titrant into the vinegar solution. Immediately before the end-point of titration, when the light pink color slowly disappears, add the titrant one drop at a time. The titration is complete when the vinegar solution first turns a faint pink color which persists after swirling the flask and contents for 20 seconds. Read to the nearest 0.01 ml and record on the Data Sheet the final buret reading.

Repeat the titration until three results of the volume of sodium hydroxide added are obtained which agree to within five parts per thousand. Between determinations, discard the titration solution in the Erlenmeyer flask and thoroughly wash the flask with distilled water. The flask need not be dry when the additional samples of vinegar solution are placed in the flask because the water present will not affect the quantity of acetic acid present.

Before beginning another titration, refill the buret with standard sodium hydroxide solution. Lower the meniscus of the solution until the meniscus is at a point on the calibrated portion of the buret. Read to the nearest 0.01 ml and record on the Data Sheet the initial buret reading for the determination being done.

When all titrations are complete, drain the solution from the buret. Rinse the buret thoroughly three times thoroughly with distilled water to remove the sodium hydroxide solution. Rinse all other glassware used in the experiment with distilled water.

CONCLUSIONS AND CALCULATIONS

1.   Calculate the molarity of the HCl for each of your titrations.

2.   Calculate the average molarity of the HCl.

3.   Calculate the molarity of the NaOH for each of your titrations.

4.   Calculate the average molarity of the NaOH.

5.   Calculate the percent acetic acid in your vinegar sample.

Name _____ Lab Instructor: _____ Date: _____

DATA SHEET: DETERMINATION OF THE PERCENT ACETIC ACID IN A VINEGAR SAMPLE

PART I: STANDARDIZATION OF HCl WITH SODIUM CARBONATE

Preparation of Sample of Sodium Carbonate

	I	II	III	IV	V
Initial mass of container, g	_____	_____	_____	_____	_____
Final mass of container, g	_____	_____	_____	_____	_____
Mass of solid standard, g	_____	_____	_____	_____	_____

Titration of Sodium Carbonate Sample with approximately 0.1 M HCl

	I	II	III	IV	V
Final buret reading, ml	_____	_____	_____	_____	_____
Initial buret reading, ml	_____	_____	_____	_____	_____
Volume of titrant, ml	_____	_____	_____	_____	_____
Molarity of HCl solution, moles liter^{-1}	_____	_____	_____	_____	_____
Average molarity of HCl solution, moles liter^{-1}	_____				

ANALYSIS OF SODA ASH

PURPOSE

A standard hydrochloric acid solution will be used to titrate a sample of soda ash. The data will be used to calculate the percent of sodium carbonate in the sample.

PRINCIPLES

Commercial grade sodium carbonate is known as soda ash. Soda ash may range from 40% to 90% sodium carbonate with most of the remainder being a neutral salt such as sodium chloride.

In this experiment, an aqueous solution of soda ash will be titrated with standard hydrochloric acid. When acid is added to a solution containing carbonate ion, two reactions can take place, as shown in equations (**1**) and (**2**).

$$CO_3^{2-}\ (aq)\ +\ H^+\ (aq)\ \longrightarrow\ HCO_3^-\ (aq) \qquad \textbf{(1)}$$

$$HCO_3^-\ (aq)\ \ H^+\ (aq)\ \longrightarrow\ CO_2\ (g)\ +\ H_2O\ (l) \qquad \textbf{(2)}$$

Reaction (**1**) is essentially complete at any pH less than 8, while reaction (**2**) is not essentially complete unless the pH is less than 3. From the stoichiometry of Equations (**1**) and (**2**), the concentration of carbonate ion can be determined. By using an appropriate indicator, the equivalence point of either reaction can be detected.

The overall reaction of the carbonate ion with acid is given by equation (**3**):

$$CO_3^{2-}\ (aq)\ +\ 2H^+\ (aq)\ \longrightarrow\ CO_2\ (g)\ +\ H_2O\ (l) \qquad \textbf{(3)}$$

The normality of the HCl made in **Part B** of the procedure can be calculated using Equation (**4**).

$$N_{acid} \, V_{acid} \; = \; N_{base} \, V_{base} \tag{4}$$

where V is volume used in liters or milliliters

$$N = \text{normality in equivalents} \cdot \text{liter}^{-1}$$

Equation (3) shows that 2 moles of HCl are required to titrate each mole of Na_2CO_3 in the soda ash sample. Therefore one gram-equivalent weight of Na_2CO_3 will be one–half the mass of one mole of Na_2CO_3 or 53.00 grams per gram-equivalent. Therefore, the number of gram-equivalents of sodium carbonate used in each determination is found by:

$$\text{Number of gram-equivalents of } Na_2CO_3 \; = \; \left(\frac{\text{mass of } Na_2CO_3\text{, g}}{53.00 \text{ g gram-equiv}^{-1}} \right)$$

Since

$$\text{Number of gram-equivalents of HCl} \; = \; \text{Number of gram-equivalents of } Na_2CO_3$$

then

$$\text{Number of gram-equivalents of HCl} \; = \; \left(\frac{\text{mass of } Na_2CO_3\text{, g}}{53.00 \text{ g gram-equiv}^{-1}} \right)$$

and because

$$\text{Number of gram-equivalents of HCl} \; = \; (N_{HCl}) \, (V_{HCl})$$

then

$$(N_{HCl}) \, (V_{HCl}) \; = \; \left(\frac{\text{mass of } Na_2CO_3\text{, g}}{53.00 \text{ g gram-equiv}^{-1}} \right) \tag{5}$$

You can calculate the mass of Na_2CO_3 in your sample by using equation (5).

PROCEDURE

A.   Preparation of Approximately 0.1 N HCl

Using a clean graduated cylinder, measure 400 ml of deionized water into your clean large brown bottle (volume approximately 450 ml). Use a clean 10 ml graduated cylinder, measure out 6.8 ml of dilute hydrochloric acid (approximately 6 N) and add it to the water in the bottle.

Screw the cap tightly on the bottle and mix the solution thoroughly by inverting and re-inverting the bottle at least 12 times. Label the brown bottle "**HCl solution**".

B. Standardization of HCl Solution with Standardized NaOH

In this and subsequent parts of the experiment, it is essential that proper care be taken to insure that pipets and burets are cleaned properly, rinsed with the solution to be used, and then filled and discharged properly. If you do not know how to use a buret or pipet, ask your instructor to demonstrate it for you.

Pipet 25.00 ml of your approximately 0.1 N HCl solution (prepared in **Part A**) into a clean 250 ml Erlenmeyer flask which you have previously rinsed out with deionized water. Wash all of the HCl solution from the sides and neck of the Erlenmeyer flask using deionized water from your wash bottle. Add three drops of the phenolphthalein indicator to the HCl in the flask and titrate with the standardized NaOH solution until the trace of faint pink color of the phenolphthalein indicator remains for at least 20 seconds after you have swirled the flask. Be certain to record the normality of the standardized NaOH on your Data Sheet. Repeat the titrations two more times, record those results on the data sheet, and after the lab period calculate the exact normality of the HCl solution as outlined in the **PRINCIPLES** section. You have now standardized (you will know the exact normality of) your HCl solution.

A primary standard must be used, either directly or indirectly, in the preparation of any standard solution. The NaOH solution used in this experiment was standardized with potassium hydrogen phthalate (KHP), a primary standard acid. KHP is the monopotassium salt of a diprotic organic acid (phthalic acid). The reaction of NaOH with KHP is,

$$H_5C_8O_4^- \, (aq) \; + \; OH^- \, (aq) \; \longrightarrow \; H_4C_8O_4^{2-} \, (aq) \; + \; H_2O \, (l)$$

indicating the stoichiometry of the reaction is one mole of NaOH to one mole of KHP. Since the formula weight of KHP is 204.1 g mole^{-1}, it would require 20.00 ml of 1.000 N NaOH solution to titrate 4.082 g of KHP using phenolphthalein as an indicator.

C. Determinations of % Na$_2$CO$_3$ in Soda Ash

Obtain from the stockroom window a 3 g sample of soda ash in a screw cap bottle. This sample has already been dried for you and care should be taken to avoid unnecessary exposure to moisture. Immediately record the number of your unknown on your Data Sheet.

Weigh the vial and contents to the nearest .001 g. Record this initial mass of the vial and sample on the Data Sheet.

Transfer 0.4 to 0.6 g of the sample to a clean 250 ml Erlenmeyer flask, be especially careful not to spill any. Reweigh the vial and contents to the nearest .001 g. The difference between this weight and the initial weight of the vial and contents is equal to the weight of soda ash transferred to the Erlenmeyer flask, if you did not spill any! Repeat the above described weighing procedure twice more so that a total of three soda ash samples (probably not to exactly equal weight) will be ready for titration with the HCl standardized in **Part B**. Dissolve each in approximately 25 ml of deionized water.

Arrange the three samples in order of lowest to highest weight of soda ash.

Titrate first the soda ash sample with the lowest weight by using the standardized HCl solution. Bromophenol blue is used as the indicator, and the soda ash solution is titrated with HCl until a green color remains after swirling the solution for 15 seconds. Record the results on the Data Sheet.

The titrations of the next highest weight soda ash sample can be done by rapidly running the standardized HCl solution in the buret down to the end point volume reading of the first soda ash sample (the one with lowest weight) and then very slowly, drop by drop, adding more HCl until the end–point is reached. The titration of the third sample (highest weight) is done similarly.

CONCLUSIONS AND CALCULATIONS

1. Calculate the average normality of the HCl for the three determinations and use this average value as the exact normality of the standardized HCl.

2. Using equation (**5**), calculate the mass of Na_2CO_3 in your sample of soda ash.

3. Calculate the percent sodium carbonate in each of your three soda ash samples.

4. Calculate the mean (average) percent Na_2CO_3 in your soda ash sample.

Name _____ Lab Instructor: _____ Date: _____

DATA SHEET: ANALYSIS OF SODA ASH

PART B: STANDARDIZATION OF HCl SOLUTION WITH STANDARDIZED NaOH

Normality of NaOH Stock Solution _____

	Determinations		
	.1	2	3
Volume of approx. 0.1 N HCl	_____	_____	_____
Final buret reading, ml	_____	_____	_____
Initial buret reading, ml	_____	_____	_____
Volume NaOH used, ml	_____	_____	_____
Calculated normality of HCl	_____	_____	_____
Average normality of HCl	_____		

PART C: DETERMINATION OF % Na_2CO_3 IN SODA ASH

Unknown Number _____

Initial mass of weighing vial + sample, g	_____	_____	_____
Final mass of weighing vial + sample, g	_____	_____	_____
Mass of soda ash sample, g	_____	_____	_____
Final buret reading, ml	_____	_____	_____
Initial buret reading, ml	_____	_____	_____
Volume of HCl used, ml	_____	_____	_____
Calculated mass of Na_2CO_3 present in each soda ash sample	_____	_____	_____
% Na_2CO_3 in each sample	_____	_____	_____
Average % Na_2CO_3 in your soda ash sample	_____		

MOLECULAR WEIGHT DETERMINATION BY FREEZING POINT DEPRESSION

PURPOSE

The molecular weight of an unknown substance will be determined by measuring the freezing point depression in paradichlorobenzene.

PRINCIPLES

Colligative properties of solutions are properties which (in dilute solution) depend only on the relative number of solute and solvent particles present; not on the nature of the particles. Colligative properties include vapor pressure, osmotic pressure, boiling point, and freezing point.

The vapor pressure of any solution, (P_{total}), is the sum of the partial pressure of the components (P_A, P_B, and so on). Thus for a binary solution consisting of a solute dissolved in a solvent:

$$P_{total} \ = \ P_{solute} + P_{solvent} \tag{1}$$

For ideal solutions the partial pressure of each component can be calculated from the mole fraction of the component present in the solution (X_A) and the vapor pressure of the **pure** component (P_A°) at the temperature in question. Thus,

$$P_{solute} = X_{solute} \, P^{\circ}_{solute} \tag{2}$$

$$P_{solvent} = X_{solvent} \, P^{\circ}_{solvent} \tag{3}$$

By substitution of equations (2) **and** (3) **in equation** (1) **we obtain**

$$P_{total} \ = \ X_{solute} \, P^{\circ}_{solute} \ + \ X_{solvent} \, P^{\circ}_{solvent} \tag{4}$$

This expression is known as **Raoult's Law**. If the solute is nonvolatile, as it is in this experiment, $P°_{solute}$ is essentially zero and equation (**4**) reduces to

$$P_{total} = X_{solvent} P°_{solvent} \qquad \qquad \textbf{(5)}$$

$$P_{total} = (1-X_{solute}) P°_{solvent}$$

and we see that the total vapor pressure over the solution is proportional to the mole fraction of solute present.

As can be seen from the above relationships, **the addition of a nonvolatile solute lowers the vapor pressure of the liquid solvent.** This decrease in the vapor pressure of the solvent results in other easily observable physical changes; the boiling point of the solution is higher than that of the pure solvent and the freezing point is lower.

In **Figure 1**, the vapor pressure of a pure liquid versus temperature and the vapor pressure of the liquid as a solvent versus temperature are plotted. At all temperatures the vapor pressure of the solvent over the solution (with non-volatile solute) is lower than the vapor pressure of the pure liquid. If the barometric pressure is one atmosphere, a pure liquid or liquid solution will boil (by

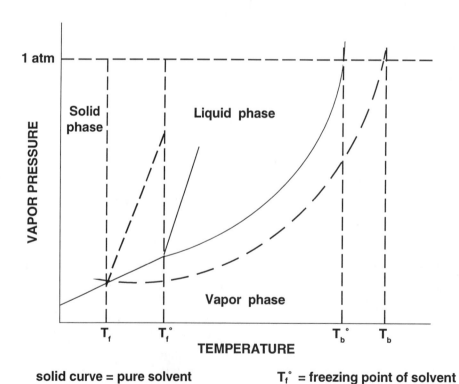

solid curve = pure solvent
dashed curve = solution of
nonvolatile solute

$T_f°$ = freezing point of solvent
T_f = freezing point of solution
$T_b°$ = boiling point of solvent
T_b = boiling point of solution

Figure 1. Vapor Pressure as a Function of Temperature

definition) when the vapor pressure over the solution reaches one atmosphere. Thus, as a result of the vapor pressure lowering due to the addition of a nonvolatile solute to the pure liquid, the boiling point of the solution will be higher than that of the pure liquid.

At the other end of the curve, the freezing point of the solvent in the solution can be seen to be less than that of the pure liquid. The depression of the freezing point of the pure liquid is proportional to the lowering of the vapor pressure and hence is proportional to the mole fraction of solute. In dilute solutions, the concentration is usually expressed in terms of molality of solute rather than in terms of the mole fraction of the solute:

$$\text{molality of A} \; = \; m \; = \; \frac{\text{number of moles A dissolved}}{\text{number of kg solvent}}$$

For non-volatile, non-dissociating solute, it is found empirically that the boiling point elevation, $T_b - T_b^\circ$ (ΔT_b), and the freezing point depression, $T_f - T_f^\circ$ (ΔT_f), in $^\circ$C at low concentrations are given by the equations:

$$\Delta T_b \; = \; k_b m \qquad \Delta T_f \; = \; k_f m \qquad\qquad (6)$$

Where k_b and k_f are characteristic of the solvent used.
For water, $k_b = 0.52^\circ$C/m and $kf = -1.86^\circ$C/m. For benzene, $k_b = 2.53^\circ$C/m and $k_f = -5.10^\circ$C/m.

For solutes which dissociate, the number of dissociated particles per molecule of solute must be taken into consideration since colligative properties depend on the **number** of particles present.

For example, one mole of sodium sulfate dissociates into **three moles** of particles:

$$Na_2SO_4 (s) \xrightarrow{\; H_2O \;} 2Na^+ (aq) \; + \; SO_4^{2-} (aq)$$

One of the main uses of the colligative properties of solutions is in connection with the determination of the molecular weight of unknown substances. If we dissolve a known amount of solute in a given amount of solvent and measure ΔT_b and ΔT_f of the solution produced, and if we know the appropriate **k** for the solvent we can find the molality and hence the molecular weight of the solute. In the case of freezing point depression, the relation would be:

$$\Delta T_f \; = \; k_f m \; = \; k_f \cdot \left(\frac{\text{number of moles solute}}{\text{number of Kg solvent}}\right)$$

$$\Delta T_f \; = \; k_f \cdot \left(\frac{\text{number g solute}}{\text{molecular weight solute}}\right) / (\text{number of Kg solvent}) \qquad (7)$$

In this experiment you will be asked to estimate the molecular weight of an unknown solute using this equation. The solvent used will be paradichlorobenzene, (PDB), which has a convenient melting point and a relatively large value of $k_f = -7.10^\circ$C/m. The freezing points will be obtained

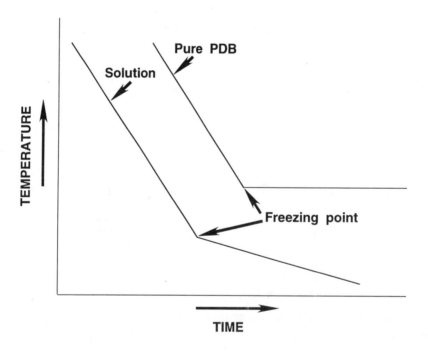

by studying the rate at which liquid paradichlorobenzene and some of its solutions containing the unknown cool in air. Temperature-time graphs, called cooling curves or heating curves, reveal the freezing points very well, since the rate at which a liquid cools is typically quite different from that of a liquid-solid equilibrium mixture (see **Figure 2**).

Figure 2. Cooling Curve

In this experiment, the freezing point of pure PDB and the freezing point of a solution of an unknown sample in PDB will be determined. The pure PDB will be melted and air-cooled. The temperature will be recorded at set time intervals. The temperature of the system will then be plotted against time. The curve obtained will show a change of slope at the temperature at which the PDB freezes. A typical temperature/time plot is given in **Figure 3**.

ENTHALPY OF HYDRATION

PURPOSE

To demonstrate the use of **Hess's Law** by determining the enthalpy of hydration of $MgSO_4$.

PRINCIPLES

The vast majority of chemical reactions occur with the liberation or absorption of heat. This heat change is called the enthalpy of the reaction; if heat is liberated, the enthalpy has a negative sign and the reaction is said to be **exothermic**; on the other hand, if heat is absorbed, the enthalpy has a positive sign and the reaction is said to be **endothermic**.

A simple example of a chemical reaction involving heat change is the dissolution of an ionic salt in water; lithium carbonate dissolves in water, taking in heat from the surroundings, i.e., the reaction is endothermic, hence the solution cools down below room temperature while the solid dissolves. Silver nitrate, however, dissolves in water in an exothermic reaction, i.e., heat is released to the surroundings and the temperature of the solution rises until all the silver nitrate dissolves.

Some ionic salts possess the interesting property of forming hydrated compounds which are stable at room temperature and pressure. The hydrates, as they are called, have a fixed number of water molecules attached to each ionic salt molecule, e.g., $CuSO_4 \bullet 5H_2O$, $BaCl_2 \bullet 2H_2O$, and $Na_2CO_3 \bullet 10H_2O$. Each of these hydrates can be formed from the corresponding anhydrous compound by the addition of the exact number of water molecules required by the ratios shown above. The addition of too few results in only partial hydration, and the addition of too many molecules of water result in hydration followed by dissolution, i.e., the hydrate formed begins to dissolve in the excess water. The addition of the required number of molecules to form the hydrate also involves a heat change. However, it can be seen that experimentally this may not be easy to measure directly, especially if the exact number of molecules that need to be added is not known. How then can we measure the value indirectly?

The simplest method is to make use of Hess's Law, which states that if a particular chemical reaction can be expressed as the sum of two or more other chemical reactions, the enthalpy change (or heat change) will also be the sum of the enthalpy changes of the other chemical reactions. Consider the following reaction:

$$CuSO_4(s) + \text{"excess"} H_2O \xrightarrow[\Delta H_1]{} Cu^{2+}(aq) + SO_4^{2-}(aq)$$

The above reaction could be considered to occur in two steps rather than in just one (**Hess's Law**).

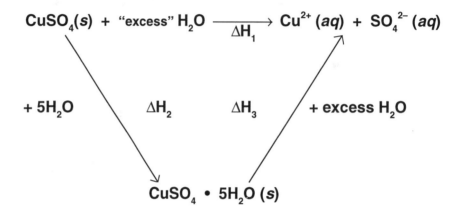

Applying Hess's Law we find that

$$\Delta H_1 = \Delta H_2 + \Delta H_3 \qquad\qquad (1)$$

ΔH_1 and ΔH_3 represent **enthalpies of dissolution**, that is, the heat change when one mole of solute dissolves in water. ΔH_2 represents the **enthalpy of hydration**, that is, the heat change when one mole of solute takes up a fixed number of moles of water.

Enthalpies of hydration are difficult to measure directly, but we can take advantage of Hess's Law and determine an enthalpy of hydration by measuring two enthalpies of dissolution. From equation (**1**) we obtain

$$\Delta H_2 = \Delta H_1 - \Delta H_3 \qquad\qquad (2)$$

The following example will demonstrate how to calculate enthalpy changes from the calorimeter data.

EXAMPLE: Calculation of the Enthalpy of Dissolution

An experiment was conducted in which 5.19 g of Na_2CO_3 was dissolved in 75.0 g of distilled water.

$$Na_2CO_3(s) + \text{``excess''} H_2O \xrightarrow{\Delta H_{diss}} 2Na^+(aq) + CO_3^{2-}(aq)$$

A temperature increase of the system of 3.8°C was observed. The heat change, Q, for such a process can be found from the expression

$$Q = -C\Delta T$$

Where C = heat capacity of the system and ΔT = observed temperature change;

$$C = (\text{Mass of Mixture, g}) \times (\text{Specific Heat of Mixture, } J g^{-1} deg^{-1})$$

$$\text{Mass of mixture} = 75.0 g + 5.19 g = 80.19 g$$

$$Q = -(80.19 g) \times (3.820 J g^{-1} °C^{-1}) \times (3.80°C)$$

$$Q = -1164.0 \text{ Joules}$$

The specific heat of the mixture is a known constant obtained from the chemical literature. Note that if the reaction is exothermic, Q is negative.

By assuming that the heat transferred to the calorimeter is negligible, the enthalpy of dissolution of one mole of Na_2CO_3 can be calculated by the expression

$$\Delta H_{diss} = \frac{Q}{\text{Number of moles of solute}}$$

therefore,

$$\Delta H_{diss} = \frac{-1164.0 J}{4.9 \times 10^{-2} \text{ moles}}$$

$$\Delta H_{diss} = -23.76 \times 10^3 J \text{ mole}^{-1} = -23.76 \text{ KJ mole}^{-1}$$

Note that if the change in temperature had been **negative**, i.e., the reaction was endothermic, the H_{diss} calculated would have been a positive number.

The calculations in this experiment require ΔT to be a measure of the instantaneous heat change in the reaction, i.e., the heat should be released or absorbed immediately. However, this is not what happens experimentally. All calorimeters have heat leaks and not all the compound will dissolve immediately, therefore, the highest (or lowest) temperature change is never observed. To determine the instantaneous heat change, draw a vertical line on your graph parallel to the y-axis at the point of the x-axis where the solute was first added (this should be after 5 minutes). Draw the best **straight line** through the plotted points after mixing; the line is extrapolated (i.e., extended) until it intersects the vertical line at the time of mixing. This intersection point represents the maximum (or minimum) temperature that would have been achieved had there been no heat loss (or gain) to the surroundings. It is this difference between the initial and final temperatures that is used in the calculation (See **Figure 1**).

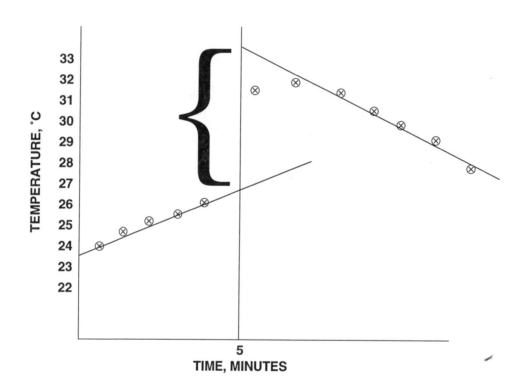

Figure 1. Time vs. Temperature Plot for an Exothermic Reaction

In this experiment you will determine the enthalpy of hydration of anhydrous magnesium sulfate

$$MgSO_4\,(s) \;+\; 7H_2O\,(l) \quad MgSO_4 \bullet 7H_2O\,(s)$$

by experimentally determining the enthalpy of dissolution of anhydrous magnesium sulfate, $MgSO_4(s)$, and of hydrated magnesium sulfate, $MgSO_4 \bullet 7H_2O\,(s)$.

CHEMICAL KINETICS

PURPOSE

To investigate how the concentration of reactants and the temperature affect the rate of a chemical reaction.

PRINCIPLES

When looking at any chemical reaction two of the basic questions that we are interested in are:

1. Does a chemical reaction occur?
2. How fast does the reaction occur?

The first question is answered by **chemical thermodynamics**, the second by **chemical kinetics**; thermodynamics only tells us whether a particular process is energetically favorable -- it tells us nothing about the speed at which the process takes place. Many of the most familiar substances in our environment are unstable from a thermodynamic viewpoint. The fossil fuels (coal, petroleum and natural gas) should, according to thermodynamic calculations, be converted to carbon dioxide and water spontaneously on exposure to air. The same is true of the organic compounds that make up the living cells of our body. Life persists because some reactions that are in principle spontaneous occur at an infinitesimally slow rate under conditions of temperature and pressure that prevail on the earth's surface.

We must therefore conclude that there is no direct correlation between the rate of reaction and the thermodynamic driving force. In order to predict how rapidly a reaction will occur we must first become familiar with a different set of principles which fall in the area of chemical kinetics.

In order to discuss **reaction rate** in a meaningful way we must first know precisely what is meant by the term. The rate of a reaction is a quantity that tells us how the concentration of a reactant or product changes with time. To see what this statement means, consider the reaction between carbon monoxide and nitrogen dioxide.

$$CO\ (g)\ +\ NO_2\ (g)\ \longrightarrow\ CO_2\ (g)\ +\ NO\ (g)$$

The rate of this reaction can be taken as the change in concentration per unit time of one of the products, let us say, carbon dioxide:

$$\text{Rate} = \frac{\text{change in concentration of } CO_2}{\text{time interval}} = \frac{\Delta [CO_2]}{\Delta \text{ time}}$$

where the brackets, [ ], represent molar concentration.

Alternatively, the rate could be expressed as the disappearance of a reactant, i.e.,

$$\text{Rate} = \frac{\Delta [CO_2]}{\Delta \text{ time}}$$

Notice that because of the 1:1 stoichiometry these two expressions for the rate of the reaction are equivalent. For every mole of CO_2 that forms, one mole of CO disappears. If in one second the concentration of CO_2 were to increase by 0.02 moles per liter, the concentration of CO would have to decrease by the same amount ($\Delta [CO_2] = +0.02$ moles l^{-1}, $\Delta [CO] = -0.02$ moles l^{-1}). The rate would therefore be +0.02 moles l^{-1} sec^{-1} no matter which change in concentration we used.

Experimentally, we observe that the rate of the reaction decreases as the concentrations of CO and/or NO_2 decrease. Increasing the concentrations of the reactants increases the rate of reaction. This observation is generally valid for a variety of chemical reactions and can be interpreted quite simply: the higher the concentrations of reactant molecules, the more frequently they will collide and be converted to products. As the rate of this reaction is found experimentally to be directly proportional to the concentrations of both CO and NO_2 we may write

$$\text{Rate} \; \alpha \; [CO] \; [NO_2]$$

or

$$\text{Rate} = k \; [CO] \; [NO_2]$$

The constant of proportionality, k, in the previous equation is referred to as the **RATE CONSTANT** for the reaction. For a particular reaction, k is a function only of temperature and is independent of the concentrations of the reactants. It can, of course, be calculated from the observed rate at known reactant concentrations, i.e.,

$$k = \frac{\text{Rate (moles } l^{-1} \text{ sec}^{-1})}{[CO] \; [NO_2]}$$

$$k = \text{ units of } l \, \text{mole}^{-1} \, \text{sec}^{-1}$$

Notice that k is not dimensionless; it does possess units. Rate expressions have been established experimentally for a large number of reactions. In general, for the reaction

$$aA + bB \longrightarrow \text{products}$$

the rate expression takes the form

$$\text{Rate} = k\,[A]^x\,[B]^y \tag{1}$$

The powers (x and y) to which the concentrations of reactants are raised in the rate expression describe the **ORDER** of the reaction. For the above expression we say that x is the "order with respect to A" and that y is the "order with respect to B". The overall order for the reaction is x + y.

It is important to realize that the order of a reaction must be determined experimentally and cannot, in general, be deduced from the coefficients of the balanced stoichiometric equation, i.e., x may not equal a and y may not equal b. For example, take the reaction:

$$4HBr\,(g) + O_2\,(g) \longrightarrow 2Br_2\,(g) + 2H_2O\,(g)$$

Experimentally, it is found that the rate law for this reaction is

$$\text{Rate} = k\,[HBr]\,[O_2]$$

which bears no relation whatsoever to the stoichiometry of the reaction.

Frequently it is found that the exponents x and y in equation (**1**) are integers (0,1,2). However, in complex reactions they may be fractions. Remember that the order of a reaction is independent of temperature; only the rate constant, k, is temperature dependent.

Another important point to notice is that the rate of the reaction that we measure is the rate of the **SLOWEST STEP** in the reaction mechanism. In the reaction of HBr and O_2, the overall stoichiometry is 4:1, but the reaction takes place in a number of steps (mechanism), the slowest of which is the combination of one molecule of HBr and one of O_2. This shows one of the limitations of kinetic studies; one can only follow the slowest step in a sequence.

Just as a chain is only as strong as its weakest link, a reaction is only as fast as its slowest step and it is important to remember that a kinetic study only tells you the speed of the slowest step in a reaction mechanism, and gives no information about the other steps that give the overall reaction.

The next question that you may ask is, how do I determine the rate equation for a particular reaction? There are a number of different methods available to do this, but one of the most useful is outlined below.

Suppose we consider the general reaction that we discussed earlier,

$$aA + bB \longrightarrow \text{products}$$

The rate law will be of the form

$$\text{Rate} = k\,[A]^x\,[B]^y$$

What we have to determine are the values of x and y. To do this, we carry out a trial run with certain concentrations of A and B and measure the rate of the reaction (say we measure the disappearance of A with respect to time). We then keep, say, the concentrations of A constant and double the concentration of B and measure the new rate. Finally we keep the concentration of B constant and double the concentration of A and obtain this new rate, see **Table 1**.

TABLE 1			
Experiment	[A]	[B]	Time for Disappearance of A
#1	.05 M	.05 M	80 sec.
#2	.05 M	.10 M	20 sec.
#3	.10 M	.10 M	40 sec.

Let us say we start with 0.05 moles l^{-1} of A and 0.05 moles l^{-1} of B and we observe that all of A disappears in eighty (80) seconds. The rate for experiment #1 will therefore be

$$\text{Rate (1)} = \frac{-\Delta[A]}{\Delta t} = \frac{0.05 \text{ moles } l^{-1}}{80 \text{ seconds}} = k\,[0.05]^x\,[0.05]^y \qquad (2)$$

$$6.25 \times 10^{-4} \text{ moles } l^{-1}\text{ sec}^{-1} = k\,[0.05]^x\,[0.05]^y$$

We then double the concentration of B while keeping the concentration of A constant (experiment #2) and we observe that the new time taken is twenty (20) seconds. The new rate will therefore be:

$$\text{Rate (2)} = \frac{-\Delta[A]}{\Delta t} = \frac{0.05 \text{ moles } l^{-1}}{20 \text{ seconds}} = k\,[0.05]^x\,[0.10]^y$$

$$2.5 \times 10^{-3} \text{ moles } l^{-1}\text{ sec}^{-1} = k\,[0.05]^x\,[0.10]^y \qquad (3)$$

Finally, if we keep the concentration of B constant at 0.10 moles l^{-1} and double the concentration of A (experiment #3), the final time taken is measured as 40 seconds, and the final rate equation will be:

$$\text{Rate (3)} = \frac{-\Delta[A]}{\Delta t} = \frac{0.10 \text{ moles } l^{-1}}{40 \text{ seconds}} = k\,[0.10]^x\,[0.10]^y$$

ACID DISSOCIATION CONSTANT

PURPOSE

To determine the acid dissociation constant for an unknown acid and to identify the unknown acid using a pH titration.

PRINCIPLES

A weak acid, HX, will dissociate in water according to the reaction

$$HX\ (aq) \rightleftharpoons H^+\ (aq)\ +\ X^-\ (aq) \tag{1}$$

The equilibrium expression for this reaction is given by

$$K_a\ =\ \frac{[H^+]\,[X^-]}{[HX]} \tag{2}$$

where the brackets, [ ], represent molar concentrations.

Equation (2) can be recast into a very useful form by taking the log of both sides of the equation

$$\log K_a = \log [H^+]\ +\ \log \frac{[X^-]}{[HX]}$$

$$-\log [H^+]\ =\ -\log K_a + \log \frac{[X^-]}{[HX]} \tag{3}$$

Since $\qquad\qquad pH\ =\ -\log [H^+]$

and $\qquad\qquad pK_a\ =\ -\log K_a$

then equation (**3**) takes the form

$$pH = pK_a + \log \frac{[X^-]}{[HX]} \qquad (4)$$

You should recognize that equation (**4**) is simply equation (**2**) in a different form.

When a weak acid, HX, is titrated with a solution of a strong base, NaOH, the following reaction occurs

$$HX\ (aq) + OH^-\ (aq) \longrightarrow H_2O\ (l) + X^-\ (aq) \qquad (5)$$

If the acid dissociation constant, K_a, for the weak acid is greater than 1×10^{-11}, then the reaction given by equation (**5**) goes essentially to completion. All weak acids considered in this experiment will have K_a's greater than 1×10^{-11}.

The equivalence point in a titration is the point at which stoichiometric quantities of the acid and base are present. In other words, all of the HX has been neutralized.

Consider the situation where one-half of the HX has been neutralized by the sodium hydroxide. In this case, we are half way to the equivalence point and the concentration of [HX] will be equal to the concentration of [X^-]:

$$[HX] = [X^-] \qquad (6)$$

Under conditions where equation (**6**) is valid (at one-half the equivalence point), equation (**4**) simplifies to

$$pH = pK_a + \log 1$$

since $\log 1 = 0$

$$pH = pK_a \qquad (7)$$

at one-half the equivalence point. If we can find the equivalence point in an acid-base titration, we can then use equation (**7**) to determine the K_a for the unknown acid.

If we titrate a solution of HX with a NaOH solution and measure the pH as a function of the volume of NaOH added the data can be displayed as shown in **Figure 1**.

Reference Table

Acid	Formula	pK_{a_1}	pK_{a_2}
Acetic acid	$HC_2H_3O_2$	4.76	
Phenyl acetic acid	$HC_8H_7O_2$	4.28	
Chloroacetic acid	$HC_2H_2O_2Cl$	2.86	
trans-Crotonic acid	$HC_4H_5O_2$	4.69	
cis-Crotonic acid	$HC_4H_5O_2$	4.41	
Itaconic acid	$H_2C_5H_4O_4$	3.85	5.45
Maleic acid	$H_2C_4H_2O_4$	1.94	6.22
Malic acid	$H_2C_4H_4O_5$	3.40	5.05
Malonic acid	$H_2C_3H_2O_4$	2.86	5.70
Mandelic acid	$H_2C_8H_7O_3$	3.41	
Oxalic acid 2-hydrate	$H_2C_2O_4 \cdot 2H_2O$	1.27	4.27
Potassium hydrogen phthalate	$KHC_8H_5O_4$	5.41	
Sodium hydrogen sulfite	$NaHSO_3$	7.21	
Sodium hydrogen d-tartrate 1-hydrate	$NaHC_4H_4O_6 \cdot H_2O$	4.37	
meso-Tartaric acid	$H_2C_4H_4O_6$	3.22	4.81
d-Tartaric acid	$H_2C_4H_4O_6$	3.04	4.37

Lange's Handbook of Chemistry, (McGraw-Hill Book Company, New York, 12th Ed., 1979).

7.

$$\frac{.1_g}{2.45\,ml} = \frac{X_g}{25.0\,ml}$$

$$\frac{.1 \times 25.0}{2.45} = X = \boxed{1.02_g}$$

KINETICS OF A CHEMICAL REACTION: CONCENTRATION DEPENDENCE OF THE REACTION OF IODIDE WITH PERSULFATE

PURPOSE

The purpose of this experiment is to determine the rate law for the reaction between peroxydisulfate ion and iodide ion at constant temperature.

PRINCIPLES

When peroxydisulfate ion is added to a solution of iodide, the iodide ion is slowly oxidized to iodine according to the equation:

$$2\,I^{1-} + S_2O_8^{2-} \longrightarrow I_2 + 2\,SO_4^{2-} \tag{1}$$

The presumption is that the rate of the reaction can be expressed by an equation of the form

$$\text{Rate} = k\,[I^{-1}]^m\,[S_2O_8^{2-}]^n \tag{2}$$

where k is the specific rate constant, and the exponents m and n have certain values which we will assume to be integral or half integral. The experiment then involves determination of the values k, m and n.

This can be done by carrying out two sets of experiments. In the first set, the rate of the reaction is measured for several mixtures containinq the same concentration of $S_2O_8^{2-}$ and various concentrations of I^{1-} ion. The concentration of $S_2O_8^{2-}$ is constant and the rate expression above reduces to:

$$\text{rate} = k^{\text{I}} [I^{1-}]^m \tag{3}$$

The manner in which the rate varies with $[I^{1-}]$ may be determined by simple examination of the data, or better, by rewriting equation (3) in log form we obtain:

$$\log (\text{rate}) = m \log [I^{1-}] + \log k^{\text{I}} \tag{4}$$

Equation (4) is in the form $y = mx + b$, the equation of a straight line. A plot of the log (rate) against the corresponding experimental values for $\log [I^{1-}]$ should give a straight line having a slope equal to m.

In the second set of experiments the concentration of $[I^{1-}]$ is held constant and the manner in which the rate varies with the concentration of $S_2O_8^{2-}$ is determined. The rate expression (2) then reduces to rate $= k^{\text{II}} [S_2O_8^{2-}]^n$, or in log form to:

$$\log (\text{rate}) = \log k^{\text{II}} + n \log [S_2O_8^{2-}] \tag{5}$$

The value of n is then found in a manner similar to finding m.

We therefore determine the order of the reaction with respect to both $S_2O_8^{2-}$ and I^{1-}. Once we have determined the order of the reaction we may find the rate constant, k, by determining the rate, $\Delta [I_2]/ \Delta t$, over some time interval and by computing the **AVERAGE** concentration of the reactants over this time interval. The **AVERAGE** concentration of reactions may be found from the concentration of iodine found photometrically, the initial concentrations of the reactants, and the stoichiometry of the reaction. Knowing the values for m and n, the **AVERAGE** concentrations of the reactants, and the rate, $\Delta [I_2]/ \Delta t$, we may find k from equation (2).

In order to determine the concentration of I_2, we will make use of the fact that a species that exhibits color will absorb visible light of certain wave lengths and the amount of light absorbed is related to the concentration of the species. This is summarized by **Beer's Law**, which states that at a given wavelength, the absorption due to a given species is directly related to the concentration of the absorbing species.

$$A = \varepsilon bc \tag{6}$$

Where A is the absorbance; ε is the molar absorptivity, $M^{-1}cm^{-1}$, which is a constant characteristic of the absorbing material at the wavelength of measurement; b is the thickness of the sample cell, cm; and c is the concentration, mole / l.

On the instruments that you will use, it is more accurate to measure the percent transmittance, %T, rather than A. Since absorbance, A, is the negative log of transmittance, T,

$$A = -\log T \qquad\qquad (7)$$

NOTE: T is a decimal here, not % .

then the transmittance readings may be converted to absorbance readings or a plot of transmittance vs. concentration may be made directly on semi-log paper. If **Beer's Law** is obeyed this should give nearly a straight line plot. With this plot you can convert %T readings directly into concentrations for unknown solutions.

PROCEDURE

> ## PART 1. Preparation of a calibration curve.
> ## [I$_2$] vs. absorbance or % transmittance.

Place 8 six inch test tubes in a rack. Using the stock solution containing 5.00×10^{-4} M of iodine in 0.05 M KI, prepare a series of solutions containing various concentrations of I$_2$ as indicated on the Data Sheet. (Use a pipet.)

Turn on the power and allow a 10–15 minute warm-up. Set the wavelength dial to 415 nanometers. With the sample holder **empty** and its cover closed, set the needle to zero with the **ZERO** adjust knob. Fill a cuvet (a selected 13 × 100 mm test tube) two-thirds full of solution number 8 which serves as a "**blank**", (i.e., contains no iodine but is otherwise similar to the iodine solutions whose properties are to be measured) and insert this cuvet into the sample holder. Adjust the 100% control until the meter needle points to 100% T. Retain the blank: check the 0% and 100% settings from time to time.

Using a second cuvet, determine the percent transmittance of solutions 1 through 7. Be certain to rinse the cuvet out each time with the solution whose %T you are going to measure. **Plot log T vs. [I$_2$]** and draw the smoothest curve through your plotted points, even if it is not a straight line. This curve will be used later in the experiment to convert % transmittance readings directly into molarity of I$_2$.

> ## PART 2. Determination of the order with respect to I$^-$ and to S$_2$O$_8^{2-}$

Obtain 50 ml of .05 M KI, 75 ml of .05 M K$_2$S$_2$O$_8$, and 75 ml of 2 M KNO$_3$ in clean, **dry**, containers.

The rate of the reaction for solutions A – F will be studied **one at a time**.

Solution	Distilled H_2O	2 M KNO_3	0.05 M KI	0.05 M $K_2S_2O_8$	
A	3.5	5.0	1.5	15.0	⎫
B	2.0	5.0	3.0	15.0	⎬ CONSTANT [$S_2O_8^{2-}$]
C	0.5	5.0	4.5	15.0	⎭
D	3.5	5.0	15.0	1.5	⎫
E	2.0	5.0	15.0	3.0	⎬ CONSTANT [I^{1-}]
F	0.5	5.0	15.0	4.5	⎭

The first three substances (H_2O, KI, KNO_3) are measured in a clean, dry 7-inch test tube, the $S_2O_8^{2-}$ solution is measured in a second clean, dry 7-inch test tube and the two tubes placed in a thermostat. (A styrofoam cup containing water at room temperature.) The test tubes are allowed to remain in the thermostat for at least five minutes to adjust the temperature of the solutions. While the solutions are in the thermostat, the photometer is blanked (adjust to a read full scale) with a cuvet of 0.05 M KI solution. These solutions should be prepared one at a time.

The change in concentration of I_2 is going to be measured as a function of time (every 30 seconds), so at a convenient time the solutions in the two test tubes are quickly mixed by pouring the solution back and fourth several times, the cuvet is rinsed with one or two ml of the solution and then filled approximately half way. The cuvet is then placed in the thermostat, removed several seconds just prior to each reading (½ or 1 min.), wiped dry on the outside and placed in the photometer and at exactly the proper time the meter reading is taken. The cuvet is then immediately returned to the thermostat until the next time interval has passed. This procedure of analysis is continued for 6-8 minutes or until the readings decrease to less than 10% transmittance, whichever occurs first. The data should be recorded on the Data Sheet.

This procedure is followed for the six runs, A–F. From the calibration curve the concentration of I_2 corresponding to each transmittance reading is determined and plots of [I_2] (on the ordinate) vs. elapsed time (on the abscissa) are drawn. It is suggested that runs A, B, and C be drawn on one sheet and runs D, E, and F, on another sheet of paper.

CONCLUSIONS AND CALCULATIONS

All data and all calculated values must be presented in tabular form. Arrange the papers of your report in the order set forth by these notes. Begin with Data Sheet for the calibration curve, runs A, B, C, D, E, and F (in that order), followed by calculations and graph; Part A, and so on, ending with Calculation of the Average k, Statement of the General Rate Equation and your table of calculated data. Include units on all graphs and on all calculations.

1. Prepare a calibration curve by plotting A vs. $[I_2]$ on 10 mm/cm graph paper or plot transmittance vs. $[I_2]$ on Semilog paper.

2. Determine $[I_2]$ at each time interval for runs A through F by using your calibration curve.

3. Plot $[I_2]$ vs. time for runs A, B, and C on one sheet of graph paper and runs D, E, and F on a second sheet.

4. Determine the slope of each line from $[I_2]$ vs. time plots. These lines may begin to flatten when the reaction is almost over. Disregard flat portion when determining slopes. Since rate of a reaction is given by

$$\textbf{Rate} \ = \ \frac{\textbf{change in concentration}}{\textbf{change in time}}$$

the slope of each plot is the rate for that solution.

5. Calculate the initial concentrations of KI and $K_2S_2O_8$ in solutions A through F.

6. From the graphs of $[I_2]$ vs. time, determine $[I_2]$ after 90 seconds for each reaction ($[I_2]$ 90 sec.).

7. By making use of the reaction stoichiometry, determine $[I^{-1}]$ 90 sec. and $[S_2O_8^{2-}]$ 90 sec. for each solution.

8. Plot log (rate) vs. log $[I^-]$ 90 sec. and log (rate) vs. log $[S_2O_8^{2-}]$ 90 sec. on separate sheets of graph paper. Determine the order with respect to each component.

9. Determine k for each run, A-F, and calculate the average value of k using average values for n and m.

10. Determine the order with respect to each component by using relative concentrations and relative rates. That is, without using the plots.

11. Write the general rate equation using average values for k, m and n.

DATA SHEET: KINETICS OF A CHEMICAL REACTION

I. Calibration Curve

Test Tube	ml of 5.00 $\times 10^{-4}$ M I$_2$	ml of 0.05 M KI	Final Conc. I$_2$	% Trans.	Abs.
1	10.00	0.00	_____	_____	_____
2	8.00	2.00	_____	_____	_____
3	6.00	4.00	_____	_____	_____
4	4.00	6.00	_____	_____	_____
5	3.00	7.00	_____	_____	_____
6	2.00	8.00	_____	_____	_____
7	1.00	9.00	_____	_____	_____
8	0.00	10.00	_____	_____	_____

DATA SHEET: KINETICS OF A CHEMICAL REACTION

RUN A

Elapsed Time	Temperature	% Trans.	Calculated Absorbance	Conc. of I_2 from Calibration Curve	Initial Conc.	
					$[I^-]$	$[S_2O_8^{2-}]$

RUN B

Name _____ Lab Instructor: _____ Date: _____

DATA SHEET: KINETICS OF A CHEMICAL REACTION

RUN C

Elapsed Time	Temperature	% Trans.	Calculated Absorbance	Conc. of I_2 from Calibration Curve	Initial Conc.	
					[I^-]	[$S_2O_8^{2-}$]

RUN D

DATA SHEET: KINETICS OF A CHEMICAL REACTION

RUN E

Elapsed Time	Temperature	% Trans.	Calculated Absorbance	Conc. of I_2 from Calibration Curve	Initial Conc.	
					$[I^-]$	$[S_2O_8^{2-}]$

RUN F

DETERMINATION OF SOLUBILITY PRODUCT CONSTANT FOR PbI$_2$

PURPOSE

In this experiment you will determine the solubility product of lead iodide, PbI$_2$.

PRINCIPLES

Lead iodide is relatively insoluble, having a solubility of less than 0.002 mole per liter at 20°C. The equation for the solution reaction of PbI$_2$ is

$$\text{PbI}_2 \; (s) \; \rightleftharpoons \; \text{Pb}^{2+} \; (aq) \; + \; 2 \, \text{I}^- \; (aq) \tag{1}$$

The solubility product expression associated with this reaction is

$$K_{sp} = [\text{Pb}^{2+}] \, [\text{I}^-]^2 \tag{2}$$

Equation (2) implies that in any system containing solid PbI$_2$ in equilibrium with its ions, the product of [Pb^{2+}] times [I$^-$]^2 will at a given temperature have a fixed magnitude, independent of how the equilibrium system was initially made up.

In the first part of the experiment, known volumes of standard solutions of Pb(NO$_3$)$_2$ and KI will be mixed in several different proportions. The yellow precipitate of PbI$_2$ formed will be allowed to come to equilibrium with the solution. The value of [I$^-$] in the solution will be measured experimentally. The [Pb^{2+}] will be calculated from the initial composition of the system, the measured value of [I$^-$], and the stoichiometric relation between Pb^{2+} and I$^-$ in Equation (1).

By mixing the solutions as we have described, we approach equilibrium by precipitating PbI$_2$ and measuring the concentrations of I$^-$ and Pb^{2+} remaining in the solutions. We will also carry out the reaction in the other direction, by first precipitating PbI$_2$, washing it free of excess ions, and then dissolving the solid in an inert salt solution, KNO$_3$. Under such conditions the concentrations of Pb^{2+} and I^- in the saturated solution will be related by Equation (1), since both ions come from pure PbI_2. From the measured value of $[I^-]$ in the saturated solution we can calculate $[Pb^{2+}]$ immediately.

The concentration of I^- ion will be found spectrophotometrically, as in **Experiment 17**. Although the iodide ion is not colored, it is relatively easily oxidized to I_2 which is brown in water solution. Our procedure will be to separate the solid PbI_2 from the solution and then to oxidize the I^- in solution with potassium nitrite, KNO_2, under slightly acidic conditions, where the conversion to I_2 is quantitative. Although the concentration of I_2 will be rather low in the solutions you will prepare, the absorption of light by I_2 in the vicinity of 525 nm is sufficiently intense to make accurate analyses possible.

In all of the solutions prepared, potassium nitrate KNO_3, (note this distinction between KNO_2 and KNO_3!) will be present as an inert salt. This salt serves to keep the ionic strength of the solution essentially constant at 0.2 M and promotes the formation of well-defined crystalline precipitates of PbI_2.

PROCEDURE

Wash and dry 5 medium test tubes, 5 small test tubes and 3 small beakers.

From the stock solutions that are available, measure out about 35 ml of 0.012 M $Pb(NO_3)_2$ in 0.20 M KNO_3 in a small beaker. To a second small beaker add 30 ml 0.030 M KI in 0.20 M KNO_3 and, to a third, add 10 ml 0.20 M KNO_3. Use these reagent solutions in your experiment.

Label five regular test tubes 1 to 5. Into the first four tubes, pipet 5.0 ml of 0.012 M $Pb(NO_3)_2$ in KNO_3. Then, to test tube 1, add 2.0 ml 0.030 M KI in KNO_3. Add 3.0, 4.0, 5.0 ml of the same solution to test tubes 2, 3, and 4, respectively. Add enough 0.20 M KNO_3 to the first three tubes to make the total volume 10.0 ml in each tube. The composition of the final mixture in each tube is summarized in **Table 1**.

TABLE 1: VOLUMES OF REAGENTS USED IN PRECIPITATING PbI_2 (ML)		
Test Tube	0.012 M $Pb(NO_3)_2$	0.030 M KI	0.20 M KNO_3
1	5.0	2.0	3.0
2	5.0	3.0	2.0
3	5.0	4.0	1.0
4	5.0	5.0	0.0
5	10.0	10.0	0.0

In this experiment it is essential that the volumes of reagents used to make up the mixtures in test tubes 1 to 4 be measured accurately. It is also essential that all **five** mixtures be shaken thoroughly (15 minutes by the clock) so that equilibrium can be established. Insufficient shaking of the first four test tubes will result in not enough PbI_2 precipitating to reach true equilibrium; if the small test tube is not shaken sufficiently, not enough PbI_2 will dissolve to attain equilibrium.

Stopper each test tube and shake thoroughly at intervals of several minutes while you are proceeding with the next part of the experiment.

In the fifth test tube mix about 10 ml of 0.012 M $Pb(NO_3)_2$ in KNO_3 with 10 ml of 0.01 M KI in KNO_3. Shake the mixture vigorously for a minute or so. Let the solid settle for a few minutes and then decant and discard three-fourths of the supernatant solution. Transfer the solid PbI_2 and the rest of the solution to a small test tube and centrifuge. Discard the liquid, retaining the solid precipitate. Add 3 ml 0.20 M KNO_3 and shake to wash the solid free of excess Pb^{2+} or I^-. Centrifuge again, and discard the liquid. By this procedure you should now have prepared a small sample of essentially pure PbI_2 in a little KNO_3 solution. Add 0.20 M KNO_3 to the solid until the tube is about three-fourths full. Shake well at several one minute intervals to saturate the solutions with PbI_2.

When each of the mixtures has been shaken for at least 15 minutes, let the tubes stand for three to four minutes to let the solid settle. Pour the supernatant liquid in test tube 1 into a small dry test tube until it is three-fourths full and centrifuge for about three minutes to settle the solid PbI_2. Pour the liquid into another small dry test tube; if there are any solid particles or yellow color remaining in the liquid, centrifuge again. When you have a clear liquid, dip a small piece of clean, dry paper towel into the liquid to remove floating PbI_2 particles from the surface. Pipet 3.0 ml of 0.02 M KNO_2, potassium **NITRITE** (not KNO_3, potassium nitrate), into a clean, dry spectrophotometer tube and add 2 drops of 6 M HCl. Adjust the temperature of the centrifuged solution to 25°C by putting the tube in a water bath and heating. Then add 3.0 ml of the clear centrifuged solution to the spectrophotometer tube. Shake gently to mix the reagents then measure the absorbance of the solution as directed by your instructor.

The molar absorptivity of I_2 at 525 nm is 285.7 1 mol^{-1} cm^{-1}. Use this and Beer's Law to determine the concentration of I^- ion that was in equilibrium with PbI_2. Use the same procedure to analyze the solutions in test tubes 1 through 5, completing each analysis before you proceed to the next.

Waste containers will be provided for the disposal of all liquid waste.

CAUTION: Lead is poisonous. Wash hands after handling.

SUGGESTIONS REGARDING CALCULATIONS

In test tubes 1 to 4, calculations must be based on the amounts of reagents which were used. In test tube 5, Sections 1-6 do not apply; the solution is saturated with PbI_2, so initial amounts or reagents are not relevant. Several of the calculations depend upon the definition of molarity. For species A,

$$M_A = \frac{\text{\# moles of A}}{\text{volume (liters)}} \quad \text{or} \quad \text{\# moles of A} = M_A \times \text{volume (liters)} \qquad (3)$$

1.   The initial number of moles of Pb^{2+} is equal to the amount of the $Pb(NO_3)_2$ solution that was used. What is $[Pb^{2+}]$ in that solution? _____ M. What volume was used? _____ml; _____liters. Use Equation (3) to find the initial number of moles of Pb^{2+}. Since the volumes used were equal, each tube (1-4) contains the same number of moles of Pb^{2+}.

2.   What is $[I^-]$ in the KI solution? _____ M. What volumes were used? _____liters. Use Equation (3) to find the initial numbers of moles of I^- present. Since the solution volumes in test tubes 1 to 4 differ, the numbers of moles of I^- differ.

3.   Here we need to find the number of moles of I^- in each solution at equilibrium. What is the total volume of each solution? _____ ml; _____ liters (same for tubes 1 to 4). From $[I^-]$ as measured at equilibrium, and the solution volume, find the number of moles of I^- in each solution at equilibrium, again using Equation (3).

4.   The number of moles of I^- in solution at equilibrium is given by the equation

moles I^- in soln = initial no. moles I^- – # moles I^- precipitate

From the no. of moles in I^- you started with (Section 2) and the number remaining in solution (Section 3), you can easily obtain the number of moles of I^- that precipitated.

5.   The number of moles of Pb^{2+} that precipitated is related to the number of moles of I^- that precipitated, since they precipitate together as PbI_2. What is the relationship? _____. Calculate the number of moles Pb^{2+} that precipitated from the number of moles of I^- that precipitated.

6.   The number of moles Pb^{2+} in solution at equilibrium must equal the number initially present minus the number that precipitated. Make that calculation for tubes 1 to 4.

7.   What was the total volume of solution for each of the test tubes 1 to 4? _____ ml; _____liters. Use Equation (3) to find $[Pb^{2+}]$ in the solution in each test tube. In the solution in test tube 5, the Pb^{2+} and the I^- both came from dissolving PbI_2 so the concentrations of those two ions are related. What is the relationship? _____ Calculate $[Pb^{2+}]$ from $[I^-]$ in tube 5.

8.   From $[Pb^{2+}]$ and $[I^-]$ at equilibrium, find K_{sp} for PbI_2 for each of the solutions in test tubes 1 to 5, using Equation (2).

DATA AND CALCULATIONS:

DETERMINATION OF THE SOLUBILITY PRODUCT OF PbI_2

From the experimental data we obtain $[I^-]$ directly. To obtain K_{sp} for PbI_2 we must calculate $[Pb^{2+}]$ in each equilibrium system. This is most easily done by constructing an equilibrium table. We first find the initial amounts of I^- and Pb^{2+} ions in each system from the way the mixtures were made up. Knowing $[I^-]$ and the formula of lead iodide allows us to calculate $[Pb^{2+}]$. K_{sp} then follows directly. The calculations are similar to those in **Experiment 17**.

Test Tube No.	1	2	3	4	Saturated solution of PbI_2 5
ml 0.012 M $Pb(NO_3)_2$	_____	_____	_____	_____	_____
ml 0.030 M KI	_____	_____	_____	_____	_____
ml 0.20 M KNO_3	_____	_____	_____	_____	_____
Total volume in ml	_____	_____	_____	_____	_____
% T	_____	_____	_____	_____	_____
Absorbance of Solution	_____	_____	_____	_____	_____
$[I_2]$ in moles / liter	_____	_____	_____	_____	_____
$[I^-]$ in moles / liter at equilibrium	_____	_____	_____	_____	_____

CALCULATIONS

Test Tube No.	1	2	3	4	5
1. Initial no. moles Pb^{2+}	____ × 10^{-5}	____ × 10^{-5}	____ × 10^{-5}	____ × 10^{-5}	
2. Initial no. moles I^-	____ × 10^{-5}	____ × 10^{-5}	____ × 10^{-5}	____ × 10^{-5}	
3. No. Moles I^- at equilibrium	____ × 10^{-5}	____ × 10^{-5}	____ × 10^{-5}	____ × 10^{-5}	
4. No. moles I^- precipitated	____ × 10^{-5}	____ × 10^{-5}	____ × 10^{-5}	____ × 10^{-5}	
5. No. moles Pb^{2+} precipitated	____ × 10^{-5}	____ × 10^{-5}	____ × 10^{-5}	____ × 10^{-5}	
6. No. moles Pb^{2+} at equilibrium	____ × 10^{-5}	____ × 10^{-5}	____ × 10^{-5}	____ × 10^{-5}	
7. $[Pb^{2+}]$ at equilibrium	_____	_____	_____	_____	_____
8. $K_{sp}(PbI_2)$	_____	_____	_____	_____	_____

QUALITATIVE ANALYSIS OF CATIONS:
GROUP I

PURPOSE

To use a qualitative analysis scheme to separate and identify Group I cations Hg_2^{2+}, Pb^{2+}, and Ag^+.

PRINCIPLES

Several common cations can be separated from other cations by the addition of hydrochloric acid which results in the formation of insoluble chlorides. These cations include the common metal ions mercury (Hg_2^{2+}), silver (Ag^+), and lead (Pb^{2+}). All other common metal ions form soluble chlorides in acid solution. This form of separation is termed selective precipitation.

The solubilities and solubility product constants of the Group I chlorides are given in Table 1.

TABLE 1			
Salt	K_{sp}	Solubility moles/liter	Solubility g/ml
AgCl	1.2×10^{-10}	1.1×10^{-5}	1.6×10^{-6}
Hg_2Cl_2	1.1×10^{-18}	6.5×10^{-7}	3.1×10^{-7}
$PbCl_2$	1.7×10^{-5}	1.6×10^{-2}	4.5×10^{-3}

Since the solubility of the lead chloride is so much greater than that of the silver chloride and mercury (I) chloride, most of the $PbCl_2$ will remain in solution while most of the Hg_2^{2+} and the Ag^+ ions can be precipitated out of the solution.

A slight excess of chloride ions results in a more complete precipitation of the Hg_2Cl_2, AgCl and $PbCl_2$ (due to the common ion effect), but a large excess of chloride ions will result in the silver chloride and the lead chloride forming soluble salts of complex ions.

$$AgCl(s) + Cl^-(aq) \longrightarrow [AgCl_2]^-(aq)$$

$$PbCl_2(s) + 2Cl^-(aq) \longrightarrow [PbCl_4]^{2-}(aq)$$

When the concentration of lead ions is too low, or if the temperature is too high, the lead chloride may fail to precipitate. A test for the lead ion in the supernatant from the Group I precipitate is advisable for these two reasons. [*This test cannot be done if the supernatant is to be assayed for Group II cations.] After the silver and mercury precipitate out and are removed by centrifugation, the remaining solution can then be treated with potassium chromate (K_2CrO_4). The chromate ion will form a yellow precipitate with the lead ion ($PbCrO_4$). This yellow precipitate confirms the presence of lead.

$$PbCl_2(aq) + K_2CrO_4(aq) \longrightarrow PbCrO_4(s) + 2 KCl(aq)$$
$$\text{\textit{yellow}}$$

The white residue from the chloride precipitation contains AgCl, Hg_2Cl_2, and $PbCl_2$, and is separated from the supernatant by centrifugation. Hot water is used to dissolve the $PbCl_2$. AgCl and Hg_2Cl_2 are not as soluble in the hot water. The lead supernatant is separated from the other chlorides by centrifugation. The precipitate (AgCl and Hg_2Cl_2) is saved for later separation. The supernatant can be tested for the presence of Pb^{2+} by the addition of K_2CrO_4. If lead is present, a yellow precipitate will form.

$$Pb^{2+}(aq) + CrO_4^{2-}(aq) \rightleftharpoons PbCrO_4(s)$$
$$\text{\textit{yellow}}$$

To separate the silver chloride from the mercury chloride, aqueous ammonia (NH_3) is added to the precipitate from the second centrifugation, and the silver chloride forms a soluble diamminesilver chloride.

$$AgCl(s) + 2NH_3(aq) \longrightarrow [Ag(NH_3)]_2^+(aq) + Cl^-(aq)$$

At the same time, the mercury (I) chloride will undergo an auto-oxidation-reduction and two products will be formed: a black metallic mercury and a white mercury (II) amido chloride, $HgNH_2Cl$.

$$Hg_2Cl_2(s) + 2NH_3(aq) \longrightarrow Hg(s) + HgNH_2Cl(s) + NH_4^+(aq) + Cl^-(aq)$$
$$\quad\quad\quad\quad\quad\text{\textit{black}}\quad\quad\text{\textit{white}}$$

A gray or black precipitate indicates the presence of Hg_2^{2+}.

The presence of the silver ions can be confirmed by treating the aqueous ammonia extract of the AgCl and Hg_2Cl_2 with nitric acid. This will cause the reprecipitation of the silver chloride as a white solid.

The nitric acid supplies the hydrogen ion which unites with the free ammonia in equilibrium with the complex cation, $[Ag(NH_3)_2]^+$. This reaction shifts the equilibrium to the right, and the free silver ion can now unite with the free chloride ion and precipitate as AgCl.

$$[Ag(NH_3)_2]^+ \rightleftharpoons Ag^+ + 2NH_3$$

$$2NH_3 + 2H^+ \rightleftharpoons 2NH_4^+$$

$$Ag^+ + Cl^- \rightleftharpoons AgCl$$

$$[Ag(NH_3)_2]^+(aq) + Cl^-(aq) + 2H^+(aq) \rightleftharpoons AgCl(s) + 2NH_4^+(aq)$$

CAUTION: Substances used in qualitative analysis can be caustic, corrosive, toxic and/or suspected carcinogens. Handle all chemicals with care. Wash hands thoroughly before leaving the lab.

PROCEDURE

IMPORTANT: All glassware (test tubes, dropper pipets, etc.) should be clean. Wash with soap, rinse with tap water, and do a final rinse with distilled water.

Obtain a solution of known Group I cations from the instructor. Transfer 15 drops of the mixture to a clean 13-mm × 100-mm test tube with a clean dropper. While shaking the test tube, add 6 M HCl dropwise until precipitation is observed. Centrifuge the test tube and contents for 2 minutes, and then add one drop of 6 M HCl. If precipitate forms, repeat the centrifugation and retest the mixture with 6 M HCl for completeness of precipitation. After the final centrifugation, decant the supernatant. This supernatant should be kept if Group II cations are to be identified.

1.   Separation and Identification of Pb^{2+}

Add 15 drops of hot water to the residual solids from a previous step and shake (or stir thoroughly with a glass rod). Centrifuge immediately and decant the liquid as quickly as possible. Repeat this step one more time and combine both extracts. Save the solid residue for Step 2–separation and confirmation of Hg_2^{2+}. Add 4 drops of 0.5 M K_2CrO_4 to the combined extracts. The formation of a yellow precipitate, $PbCrO_4$ confirms the presence of lead.

Record all observations on the Data Sheet.

Note: If the original solution contains only Group I cations, the supernatant obtained from the HCl precipitation can be tested for the presence of Pb^{2+} by the addition of approximately 4 drops of 0.5 M K_2CrO_4 (potassium chromate). ***[If Group II cations are present (as in the general cations unknown), this test cannot be done.]** Since dichromate ions are formed from chromate ions in strongly acidic solutions, 6 M aqueous ammonia may be added dropwise to raise the pH of the supernatant. The dichromate ions are orange and the rise in pH will shift the equilibrium to the left and allow the chromate ions to combine with the lead ions (if present) to form a yellow precipitate.

$$2CrO_4^{2-}(aq) + 2H^+(aq) \rightleftharpoons Cr_2O_7^{2-}(aq) + H_2O(l)$$

yellow   *orange*

2. Separation and Identification of Hg_2^{2+}

Add 4 drops of 6 M NH_3 and 2 drops of distilled water to the residue from step 1 and shake or stir with a glass rod for one minute. Centrifuge and repeat this extraction. Save the combined extractions for Step 3, confirmation of Ag^+. If mercury (I) ions are present, a black residue will result from the ammonia extraction. If the removal of $PbCl_2$ was incomplete during the hot water extraction, a white precipitate will form. The $PbCl_2$ reacts with the aqueous ammonia to form lead hydroxide, $Pb(OH)_2$, and basic lead chloride. $Pb(OH)Cl$, which are white solids.

$$PbCl_2(aq) \xrightarrow[\text{unbalanced equation}]{NH_3(aq) + H_2O(l)} Pb(OH)_2(s) + Pb(OH)Cl(s) + NH_4^+(aq) + Cl^-(aq)$$

Record all observations on the Data Sheet.

3. Identification of Ag^+

Add 6 M HNO_3 dropwise to the ammonia extract from Step 2 until the mixture is acidic to litmus. Shake or stir the mixture thoroughly for complete neutralization of the ammonia. The presence of silver ions is confirmed by a white precipitate.

Record all observations on the Data Sheet.

GROUP I UNKNOWN

Obtain an unknown solution from the instructor. This solution may contain one or more of the Group I cations. Record the solution number of your unknown and proceed with the separation and identification scheme of the Group I cation analysis. Record all observations.

GROUP I CATION FLOW CHART

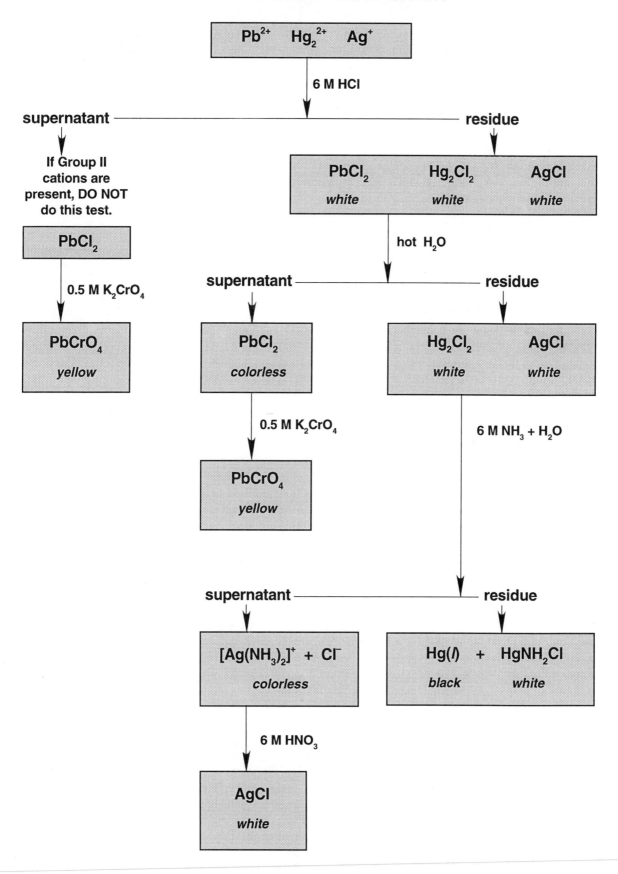

DATA SHEET: QUALITATIVE ANALYSIS OF GROUP I CATIONS

I. Observations for Group I Cation Analysis (Ag$^+$, Hg$_2^{2+}$, Pb^{2+})

A.   Precipitation of Group I chlorides

B.   Separation and Identification of Pb^{2+}

C.   Separation and Identification of Hg$_2^{2+}$

D.   Identification of Ag$^+$

DATA SHEET: QUALITATIVE ANALYSIS OF GROUP I CATIONS

II.   **Group I Unknown**

Unknown Number   _____

Cations found: _____

_____

_____

Indicate below all experimental evidence that supports the identification of cations found in the unknown solution.

QUESTIONS

1.   Write out a complete, <u>detailed</u> flow chart for Group I cation analysis.

2.   A large excess of chloride ion must be avoided in the precipitation of the Group I chlorides. Why?

3.   Explain the dissolution of silver chloride in aqueous ammonia and its reprecipitation with nitric acid. Include ionic equations.

4.   If only Group I cations are present in your unknown, why might it be useful to make a secondary identification of lead on the supernatant from the Group I chloride precipitation?

QUALITATIVE ANALYSIS OF CATIONS: GROUP II

PURPOSE

To use a qualitative analysis scheme to separate and identify Group II cations, Bi^{3+}, Cu^{2+}, Cd^{2+} and Sn^{4+}.

PRINCIPLES

Group II cations are known as the acid-insoluble sulfide group. The four cations studies in this experiment can be subdivided into two groups: Group A contains Bi^{3+}, Cu^{2+}, and Cd^{2+}, which do not form soluble complex ions with sulfides in alkaline sulfide solutions, and Group B, which contains Sn^{4+} (and mercury (II), arsenic and antimony) which does form soluble complex ions with sulfides in alkaline sulfide solutions.

The selective precipitation of these cations is done by regulation of the sulfide ion concentration in the solution. The anion, S^{2-}, is used for the precipitation of the Group II cation. The source of S^{2-} is hydrogen sulfide which is supplied by thioacetamide, CH_3CSNH_3. The thioacetamide hydrolyzes in hot acidic solutions and forms ammonium acetate and hydrogen sulfide.

$$CH_3CSNH_3(aq) + 2H_2O(l) \longrightarrow CH_3COO^-(aq) + NH_4^+(aq) + H_2S(g)$$

As predicted from Le Chatelier's principle, the equilibrium of this endothermic system can be shifted forward, with an increase in the concentration of the products, by the heat from the hot acidic solution.

The ionization of hydrogen sulfide is represented by the following equations:

$$H_2S \rightleftharpoons HS^- + H^+ \qquad K_I = 1.0 \times 10^{-7}$$

$$HS^- \rightleftharpoons H^+ + S^{2-} \qquad K_{II} = 1.3 \times 10^{-13}$$

The overall equilibrium which is the sum of the above equations is represented by the following equation:

$$H_2S \rightleftharpoons 2H^+ + S^{2-} \qquad K_{H_2S} = (K_I)(K_{II}) = 1.3 \times 10^{-20}$$

This equation may be used only if two of the three concentrations are known. for example, if the concentrations of H_2S and H^+ are known, then the S^{2-} concentration can be determined.

To reduce the hydrogen sulfide ionization, the saturated hydrogen sulfide solution is also 0.3 M in hydrogen ion (pH = 0.5). Hydrochloric acid furnishes the H^+. The hydrogen ion represses the hydrogen sulfide ionization, and this results in a decrease in the concentration of sulfide ion in the solution.

The equations which represent the precipitation of Group II cation are as follows:

$$2Bi^{3+}(aq) + 3H_2S(aq) \rightleftharpoons Bi_2S_3(s) + 6H^+(aq)$$

$$Cu^{2+}(aq) + H_2S(aq) \rightleftharpoons CuS(s) + 2H^+(aq)$$

$$Cd^{2+}(aq) + H_2S(aq) \rightleftharpoons CdS(s) + 2H^+(aq)$$

$$Sn^{4+}(aq) + 2H_2S(aq) \rightleftharpoons SnS_2(s) + 4H^+(aq)$$

The solubilities product constants for Group II sulfides are given in Table 1.

TABLE 1
Solubility Product Constants at 25°C
$SnS_2 = 1.0 \times 10^{-70}$
$Bi_2S_3 = 6.8 \times 10^{-96}$
$CuS = 8.7 \times 10^{-36}$
$CdS = 7.8 \times 10^{-27}$

Since SnS_2 is the only sulfide in this group which is soluble in concentrated alkaline solution, the precipitates are treated with sodium hydroxide (or potassium hydroxide) and thioacetamide. The thioacetamide hydrolyzes to produce hydrogen sulfide which reacts with the sodium hydroxide to for sodium sulfide. The sodium sulfide is responsible for the formation of the soluble complex sulfide.

$$2Na^+(aq) + 2OH^-(aq) + H_2S(aq) \rightleftharpoons 2Na^+(aq) + S^{2-}(aq) + 2H_2O(l)$$

An excess of the hydroxide ion represses the hydrolysis of the sulfide ion.

$$S^{2-}(aq) + H_2O(l) \rightleftharpoons HS^-(aq) + OH^-(aq)$$

A relatively high concentration of sulfide ion in excess base results in the dissolution of the SnS_2 into soluble $[SnS_3]^{2-}$ and $[Sn(OH)_6]^{2-}$.

$$SnS_2 + S^{2-} \rightleftharpoons [SnS_3]^{2-} \quad \text{(thiostannate)}$$

$$SnS_2 + 6\,OH^- \rightleftharpoons [Sn(OH)_6]^{2-} \quad \text{(hexahydroxostannate (IV))}$$

The Bi_2S_3, CuS and CdS fail to dissolve at this sulfide ion concentration in alkaline solution and can be separated from the soluble Sn^{4+} complex ion by centrifugation.

After the centrifugation, the tin has to be reprecipitated from the supernatant which contains the thiostannate and hexahydroxostannate (IV) ions. The formation of $Sn^{4+}(aq)$ is facilitated by the addition of hydrochloric acid.

$$[Sn(OH)_6]^{2-}(aq) + 6H^+(aq) \rightleftharpoons Sn^{4+}(aq) + 6H_2O(l)$$

$$[SnS_3]^{2-}(aq) + 6H^+(aq) \rightleftharpoons Sn^{4+}(aq) + 3H_2S(g)$$

The concentrations of the tin and sulfide ion increase because the H_2S which is formed escapes as a gas, and the equilibrium of the system is shifted towards the increased formation of these two ions.

$$[SnS_3]^{2-}(aq) \rightleftharpoons Sn^{4+}(aq) + 3S^{2-}(aq)$$

$$3S^{2-}(aq) + 6H^+(aq) \rightleftharpoons 3H_2S(g)$$

The product of the tin ion and sulfide ion becomes greater than the solubility product constant, and this results in the precipitation of yellow SnS_2. The net reaction would be:

$$[SnS_3]^{2-}(aq) + 6H^+(aq) \rightleftharpoons SnS_2(s) + 3H_2S(g)$$

The next step in the analytical scheme is the separation and identification of bismuth. Hot nitric acid dissolves the sulfides of bismuth, copper and cadmium.

$$Bi_2S_3 \longrightarrow 2Bi^{3+}(aq) + 3S^{2-}(aq)$$

$$CdS \longrightarrow Cd^{2+}(aq) + S^{2-}(aq)$$

$$CuS \longrightarrow Cu^{2+}(aq) + S^{2-}(aq)$$

The hydrogen ion combines with the free sulfide ion to form hydrogen sulfide, H_2S, while the nitrate ion oxidizes the sulfide ions, S^{2-}, to free sulfur which precipitates out of solution.

$$H^+(aq) + S^{2-}(aq) \rightleftharpoons H_2S(g)$$

$$3S^{2-}(aq) + 2NO_3^-(aq) + 8H^+(aq) \rightleftharpoons S(s) + 2NO(g) + 4H_2O(l)$$

The heating of the sulfide/HNO_3 mixtures lowers the solubility of the gas, NO, nitrogen monoxide. When the NO reacts with the oxygen in the air, nitrogen dioxide, $NO_2(g)$, is formed and can be identified b its red-brown color.

After centrifugation to remove the sulfur, the bismuth can be separated from the cadmium and copper in the supernatant by the addition of aqueous ammonia. When NH_3 is added to the supernatant, the bismuth, copper and cadmium form hydroxide compounds which precipitate out of solution.

$$Bi^{3+}(aq) + 3NH_3(aq) + 3H_2O(l) \longrightarrow Bi(OH)_3(s) + 3NH_4^+(aq)$$

$$Cu^{2+}(aq) + 2NH_3(aq) + 2H_2O(l) \longrightarrow Cu(OH)_2(s) + 2NH_4^+(aq)$$

$$Cd^{2+}(aq) + 2NH_3(aq) + 2H_2O(l) \longrightarrow Cd(OH)_2(s) + 2NH_4^+(aq)$$

When the NH_3 is added in excess, the copper and cadmium hydroxides dissolve by the formation of tetrammine complexes. Bismuth (III) hydroxide remains insoluble and can be removed by centrifugation.

$$Bi(OH)_3(s) + NH_3(aq) \longrightarrow \text{no reaction} \qquad \text{(white precipitate)}$$

$$Cu(OH)_2(s) + 4NH_3(aq) \longrightarrow [Cu(NH_3)_4]^{2+}(aq) + 2OH^-(aq) \quad \text{(blue)}$$

$$Cd(OH)_2(s) + 4NH_3(aq) \longrightarrow [Cd(NH_3)_4]^{2+}(aq) + 2OH^-(aq) \quad \text{(colorless)}$$

If the supernatant is blue, it's an indication of the presence of copper. Confirmation of the presence of bismuth can be accomplished by the addition of sodium stannite, which is a strong reducing agent. The sodium stannite is unstable and is prepared by adding an excess of sodium or potassium hydroxide to a tin (II) chloride solution.

$$Sn^{2+}(aq) + 4OH^-(aq) \rightleftharpoons [Sn(OH)_4]^{2-}(aq)$$

The tin ion and the hydroxide ions form the tetrahydroxostannate (II) ion, $Sn(OH)_4^{2-}$. This ion is oxidized by the bismuth hydroxide to form the hexahydroxostannate (IV) ion. The elemental bismuth which is formed precipitates out as a jet black metallic residue.

$$2Bi(OH)_3(s) + 3[Sn(OH)_4]^{2-}(aq) \rightleftharpoons 2Bi(s) + 3[Sn(OH)_6]^{2-}(aq)$$

Copper and cadmium hydroxides can also be reduced to their elemental states by this process, but their reduction occurs at a much slower rate than the bismuth hydroxide reduction which occurs quite rapidly.

The supernatant which results from the centrifugation and removal of the bismuth can now be tested for the presence of copper and cadmium. Copper is readily confirmed if the solution is blue, but usually there are only traces of copper, and the solution will be colorless.

A quick identification for the copper is the addition of potassium ferrocyanide to a few drops of the supernatant. If copper is present, a rose precipitate of copper (II) hexacyanoferrate (II) will form.

$$2[Cu(NH_3)_4]^{2+}(aq) + [Fe(CN)_6]^{4-}(aq) \longrightarrow Cu_2Fe(CN)_6(s) + 8NH_3(aq)$$

A white precipitate of cadmium hexacyanoferrate (II) will form if cadmium is present.

$$2[Cd(NH_3)_4]^{2+}(aq) + [Fe(CN)_6]^{4-}(aq) \longrightarrow Cd_2Fe(CN)_6(s) + 8NH_3(aq)$$

To confirm the presence of cadmium ions, the copper must be removed from the solution. Sodium dithionite, $Na_2S_2O_4$, is used as a reducing agent to convert the copper ion to its elemental form, which is a dark brown or black metallic residue.

$$[Cu(NH_3)_4]^{2+}(aq) \rightleftharpoons Cu^{2+}(aq) + 4NH_3(aq)$$

$$Cu^{2+}(aq) + S_2O_4^{2-}(aq) + 2H_2O(l) \rightleftharpoons Cu(s) + 2SO_3^{2+}(aq) + 4H^+(aq)$$

The tetraammine complex of cadmium remains in the supernatant after centrifugation. The supernatant can now be treated with thioacetamide, H_2S, and the formation of a yellow or yellow-orange precipitate (CdS) indicates the presence of cadmium.

$$Cd(NH_3)_4^{2+}(aq) + S^{2-}(aq) \rightleftharpoons CdS(s) + 4NH_3(aq)$$

If the copper was not completely removed before the addition of the H_2S, the black color of CuS will obscure the yellow color of the CdS.

CAUTION: Substances used in qualitative analysis can be caustic, corrosive, toxic and/or suspected carcinogens. Handle all chemicals with care. Wash hands thoroughly before leaving the lab.

PROCEDURE

IMPORTANT: All glassware (test tubes, dropper pipets, etc.) should be clean. Wash with soap, rinse with tap water, and do a final rinse with distilled water.

Obtain a solution of known Group II cations from the instructor. Transfer 15 drops of the mixture to a clean 13-mm × 100-mm test tube with a clean dropper. This solution should have a pH of 0.5 ± 0.3 ($[H^+] = 0.3$ M). Dip a clean glass rod into the solution and place the wet end of the rod on a piece of short range pH paper to determine acidity or basicity. If the pH is not within the specified range, add 6 M HCl or 6 M NH_3 dropwise to the solution until the pH is within the desired range. If the pH is too high (pH > 0.8 and $[H^+]$ < 0.2 M), then ions other than Group II cations might precipitate. If the pH is too low (pH < 0.2 and $[H^+]$ > 0.6 M), then there might be an incomplete precipitation of the Group II sulfides.

Add 10 drops of 1 M thioacetamide solution to the above mixture and stir. Heat this mixture in a hot water bath for 10 minutes with occasional stirring. While this mixture is heating, a dilute aqueous ammonia solution needs to be made for the next step in the procedure. The dilute ammonia is made by the addition of 3 drops of 6 M NH_3 to a test tube which contains 2 mL of distilled water.

After the 10-minute heating period, remove the mixture from the hot water bath, and cool the test tube under running water from the faucet. This cooling process helps the CdS precipitate. To help in the precipitation of both CdS and SnS_2, add one drop of the dilute aqueous ammonia to the mixture and stir. The test tube is now centrifuged for 2 minutes.

Five drops of the 1 M thioacetamide are now added to the test tube and the mixture is heated in the water bath for 2 minutes. After the heating, cool the test tube under running water from the faucet. Add another drop of the dilute aqueous ammonia to the mixture and stir. Centrifuge the mixture for another 2 minutes and decant the supernatant from the precipitate.

The precipitate must now be washed with 1 mL of 0.1 M ammonium chloride (HNH_4Cl). (The undissolved sulfides tend to become colloidal when washed with water, will not precipitate well, and often are lost when the supernatant is decanted.) Shake the test tube to thoroughly mix and wash. Centrifuge the mixture for 2 minutes and decant the supernatant. The precipitate which results from this last procedure is used for the separation and identification of the Group II cations.

1. Separation and Identification of Sn^{4+}.

Add 15 drops of 4 M NaOH and 3 drops of 1 M thioacetamide to the Group II sulfide precipitate. Stir the mixture constantly and heat in a hot water bath for exactly 2 minutes. Centrifuge for 2 minutes and decant the supernatant immediately into a 20-mm × 150-mm test tube.

Wash the precipitate with approximately 10 drops of distilled water. Shake well and centrifuge for 2 minutes. Decant and discard the supernatant, and repeat the washing procedure. Save the precipitate for the separation and identification of bismuth, copper and cadmium.

Add 6 M HCl dropwise to the supernatant in the 20-mm × 150-mm test tube and stir well. Test the solution for acidity (litmus paper test) after each drop of the hydrochloric acid. When the solution tests acidic, add 5 drops of 1 M thioacetamide and heat the mixture for 2 minutes in a hot water bath.

Record all observations on the Data Sheet.

2. Separation and Identification of Bi^{3+}

The precipitate from Step 1, above, contains Bi$_2$S$_3$, CuS, and CdS, which can be dissolved in hot nitric acid. The NO$_3^-$ ions oxidize the S^{2-} ions to free elemental sulfur which can be removed by centrifugation. The free metal ions, Bi^{3+}, Cu^{2+}, and Cd^{2+}, remain in the supernatant.

Add 15 drops of 6 M HNO$_3$ to the precipitate from Step 1, and heat the mixture in a hot water bath for 5 minutes. Separate from the supernatant, and discard, any residual sulfur which is formed from this procedure.

Add 6 M NH$_3$ dropwise to the supernatant until the mixture tests basic with litmus paper. Add 5 additional drops of the dilute aqueous ammonia to the mixture, shake well, and allow to cool. The formation of a blue solution is an indication of the presence of the tetraamminecopper (II) ion, [Cu(NH$_3$)$_4$]$^{2+}$. A white precipitate indicates the presence of Bi^{3+} as Bi(OH)$_3$.

After the mixture has cooled, centrifuge for 2 minutes and decant the supernatant from the precipitate. The supernatant contains the copper as [Cu(NH$_3$)$_4$]$^{2+}$ and the cadmium as [Cd(NH$_3$)$_4$]$^{2+}$. Save the supernatant for further separation.

Wash the precipitate with 10 drops of the 6 M NH$_3$ and centrifuge for 2 minutes. Decant and discard the supernatant. Add 8 drops of 4 M NaOH and 6 drops of 0.1 M SnCl$_2$ to the precipitate and mix well. The formation of a black precipitate confirms the presence of the Bi^{3+} ions.

Record all observations on the Data Sheet.

3. Separation and Identification of Cu²⁺

Transfer approximately 5 drops of the supernatant from Step 2 into a clean test tube and add 10 drops of 6 M CH_3COOH (acetic acid). The solution should be acidic to litmus. Add 6 drops of 0.1 M $K_4Fe(CN)_6$ (potassium ferrocyanide) to this mixture and shake. The formation of a rose-colored precipitate, $Cu_2[Fe(CN)_6]$, indicates the presence of copper ions. A white precipitate, $Cd_2[Fe(CN)_6]$, indicates the presence of cadmium ions and the absence of copper ions. A pink precipitate indicates a mixture of copper and cadmium ions, or a very low concentration of the copper ions.

Record all observations on the Data Sheet.

4. Separation and Identification of Cd²⁺

To the remainder of the solution that contains the $[Cu(NH_3)_4]^{2+}$ and $[Cd(NH_3)_4]^{2+}$ ions, add a small quantity of sodium dithionite, $Na_2S_2O_4$, about twice the size of a BB pellet or 2-3 grains of long rice. Stir well and heat in a hot water bath for 2 minutes. Centrifuge for 2 minutes and decant the supernatant off of the black precipitate. The black precipitate is metallic copper and may be discarded. Repeat this procedure with a smaller amount of the sodium dithionite (1 grain rice in size). When no black precipitate remains, add 3 drops of 1 M thioacetamide to the solution, stir well, and heat in a hot water bath for 2 minutes. The formation of a yellow precipitate, CdS, confirms the presence of cadmium. If a dark colored precipitate forms (olive, ochre, muddy brown), copper ions are still present. Centrifuge and discard the supernatant. Dissolve the precipitate in 6 drops 6 M HNO_3 and then neutralize with 6 M NH_3. Add the aqueous ammonia dropwise until the mixture is basic to litmus. Repeat the dithionite procedure. [Remember: the supernatant from this second dithionite procedure for removal of the copper ion now has a basic pH. The pH of this supernatant has to be made acidic (pH = 0.5) for the thioacetamide to hydrolyze and form the hydrogen sulfide that is necessary for the cadmium ion to react with and precipitate out of solution as CdS.] Record all observations on the Data Sheet.

GROUP II UNKNOWN

Obtain an unknown solution from the instructor. This solution may contain one or more of the Group II cations. Record the solution number of your unknown and proceed with the separation and identification scheme of the Group II cation analysis. Record all observations. These observations will support your identification of cations present in the unknown solution.

GENERAL UNKNOWN (may contain Group I, Group II, or a mixture of both)

The general unknown may contain both Group I and Group II cations, therefore, the supernatant from the Group I chloride precipitation must be kept for the Group II sulfide precipitation. Record all observations.

GROUP II CATION FLOW CHART

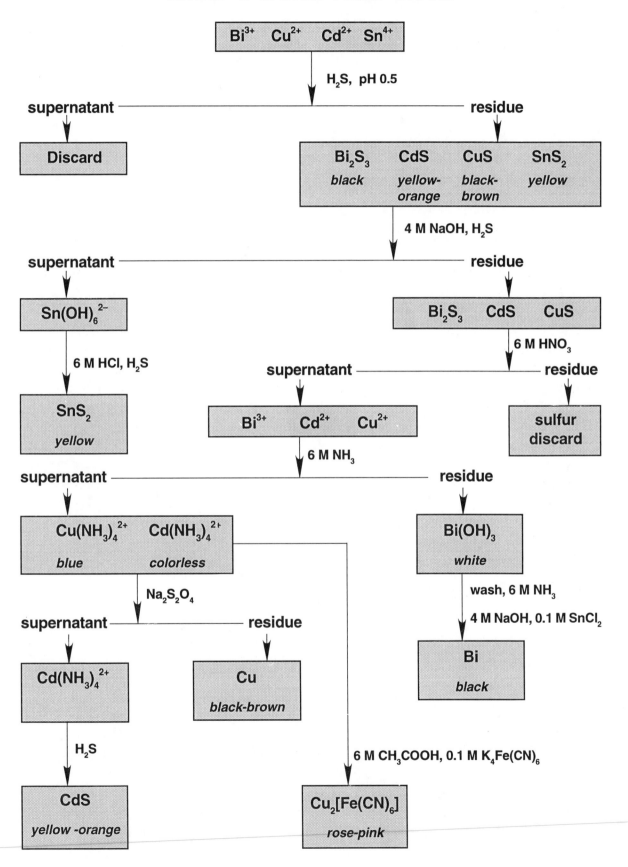

DATA SHEET: QUALITATIVE ANALYSIS OF GROUP II CATIONS

I. **Group II Cation Analysis (Bi^{3+}, Cu^{2+}, Cd^{2+}, Sn^{4+})**

A. Precipitation of Group II sulfides

B. Separation and Identification of Sn^{4+}

C. Separation and Identification of Bi^{3+}

D. Identification of Cu^{2+}

E. Separation and Identification of Cd^{2+}

DATA SHEET: QUALITATIVE ANALYSIS OF GROUP II CATIONS

II.   Group II Unknown

Unknown Number   _____

Cations found: _____

                            _____

                            _____

Indicate below all experimental evidence that supports the identification of cations found in the unknown solution.

QUESTIONS

1. Write out a complete, <u>detailed</u> flow chart for Group II cation analysis.

2. How would hydroxide ions influence the concentration of sulfide ions?

3. Explain the dissolution of the sulfides of copper, bismuth, and cadmium in nitric acid. Include ionic equations.

4. If a yellow precipitate is obtained upon addition of hydrogen sulfide to an unknown solution of Group II cations, which ions are probably present?

5. In the identification of bismuth, why must the sodium stannite be prepared just prior to use?

QUALITATIVE ANALYSIS OF ANIONS

PURPOSE

To use a qualitative analysis scheme to separate and identify anions.

PRINCIPLES

Nine of the more common negative ions included in this anion analysis scheme are carbonate (CO_3^{2-}), nitrate (NO_3^-), nitrite (NO_2^-), phosphate (PO_4^{3-}), sulfate (SO_4^{2-}), sulfite (SO_3^{2-}), bromide (Br^-), chloride (Cl^-), and iodide (I^-). The procedures used in this scheme are a series of elimination tests followed by a series of confirmation tests. Since some of the anions react with one another when in solution, the known and unknown anions are furnished as dry salts. Some of the anions will decompose upon standing in solution, but can be identified in a freshly prepared solution. Some anions react together in acidic solutions, while others react with one another in basic solutions. For example, strong reducing anions and strong oxidizing anions react together when placed in an acidic solution.

The carbonate, nitrite, and sulfite ions can be derived from the following weak acids: H_2CO_3, HNO_2, and H_2SO_3, respectively. When the salts of these anions are treated with acid, they form volatile acid anhydrides. Carbonic acid (H_2CO_3), nitrous acid (HNO_2), and sulfurous acid (H_2SO_3) are very unstable and decompose readily to gases. When the solubility in water of these gases is exceeded, they will escape from the solution as bubbles. A small increase in the temperature of the solution will help to decrease the solubility of the gases.

Sulfuric acid furnishes a large concentration of hydrogen ions, which shifts the equilibrium of the following reactions to the right.

$$CO_3^{2-}(aq) + H^+(aq) \rightleftharpoons HCO_3^-(aq)$$

$$HCO_3^-(aq) + H^+(aq) \rightleftharpoons H_2CO_3(aq)$$

$$H_2CO_3(aq) \rightleftharpoons H_2O(l) + CO_2(g)$$
$$\text{colorless gas}$$

A positive test for the presence of carbonate ion in a solution is the evolution of carbon dioxide (CO_2) upon the acidification of the solution.

$$3NO_2^-(aq) + 3H^+(aq) \rightleftharpoons 3HNO_2(aq)$$

$$3HNO_2(aq) \rightleftharpoons H_2O(l) + H^+(aq) + NO_3^-(aq) + 2NO(g)$$

$$2NO(g) + O_2(g) \rightleftharpoons 2NO_2(g)$$
$$\text{colorless gas} \qquad \text{red-brown gas}$$

A positive test for the presence of nitrite ion in a solution is the evolution of the red-brown gas, nitrogen dioxide, upon the acidification and heating of the solution.

$$SO_3^{2-}(aq) + H^+(aq) \rightleftharpoons HSO_3^-(aq)$$

$$HSO_3^-(aq) + H^+(aq) \rightleftharpoons H_2SO_3(aq)$$

$$H_2SO_3(aq) \rightleftharpoons H_2O(l) + SO_2(g)$$
$$\text{colorless gas, smells}$$

A positive test for the presence of sulfite ion in solution is the evolution of the acrid gas, sulfur dioxide, upon the acidification and heating of the solution.

The carbonate, phosphate, sulfate, and sulfite ions form insoluble salts with cations such as Ba^{2+} (barium).

The carbonate salt of barium forms a white precipitate in a basic solution.

$$CO_3^{2-}(aq) + Ba^{2+}(aq) \rightleftharpoons BaCO_3(s)$$

The sulfate salt of barium forms a white precipitate in an acidic solution or a neutral solution.

$$SO_4^{2-}(aq) + Ba^{2+}(aq) \rightleftharpoons BaSO_4(s)$$

The sulfite salt of barium forms a white precipitate in a neutral solution but is soluble in acidic solutions.

$$SO_3^{2-}(aq) + Ba^{2+}(aq) \rightleftharpoons BaSO_3(s)$$

The sulfite ion is readily oxidized to sulfate by atmospheric oxygen as shown in the following equation:

$$2SO_3^{2-}(aq) + O_2(g) \rightleftharpoons 2SO_4^{2-}(aq)$$

The phosphate salt of barium forms a white precipitate in a neutral solution, but dissolves in an acidic solution.

$$2PO_4^{3-}(aq) + 3Ba^{2+}(aq) \rightleftharpoons Ba_3(PO_4)_2(s)$$

Ammonium molybdate, $(NH_4)_2MoO_4$, will react with phosphate ions in an acidic solution to form a yellow ammonium molybdophosphate precipitate. This is a good confirmatory test for the presence of phosphate ions in a solution.

$$PO_4^{3-}(aq) + 3NH_4^+(aq) + 12MoO_4^{2-}(aq) + 24H^+(aq) \rightleftharpoons (NH_4)_3(PMo_{12}O_{40})(s) + 12H_2O(l)$$

The nitrate salt of barium is soluble, as are all nitrate salts. The nitrate ion, NO_3^-, does not form volatile acid anhydrides either. The ion cannot act as a reducing agent since the nitrogen in the ion is at its highest oxidation state (+5), but can act as a strong oxidizing agent (in a **strongly** acidic solution). A brownish-red gas, nitrogen dioxide, evolves when a reducing agent such as the iron(II) ion (Fe^{2+}) combines with the nitrate ion in a strongly acidic solution. The nitrite ion, NO_2^- also reacts as an oxidizing agent in acidic solution with one important difference — the nitrite ion does not require a separate reducing agent to produce the nitrogen dioxide gas.

$$NO_3^-(aq) + 3\,Fe^{2+}(aq) + 4H^+(aq) \rightleftharpoons 3Fe^{3+}(aq) + NO(aq) + 2H_2O(l)$$

$$2NO(g) + O_2(g) \rightleftharpoons 2NO_2(g)$$
colorless gas   red-brown gas

The halide ions are anions that form insoluble silver salts in acidic (or neutral) solutions. These anions include the chloride ion (Cl^-), the bromide ion (Br^-), and the iodide ion (I^-).

$$Cl^-(aq) + Ag^+(aq) \xleftarrow{\;HNO_3\;} AgCl(s)$$
white

$$Br^-(aq) + Ag^+(aq) \xleftarrow{\;HNO_3\;} AgBr(s)$$
cream

$$I^-(aq) + Ag^+(aq) \xleftarrow{\;HNO_3\;} AgI(s)$$
light yellow

The insoluble silver chloride becomes soluble in aqueous ammonia, whereas, the silver bromide and the silver iodide remain insoluble in the ammonia. The silver chloride will re-precipitate with the addition of nitric acid to the ammonia solution. This simple test serves as a secondary confirmation of the presence of chloride ions.

$$AgCl(s) + 2NH_3(aq) \rightleftharpoons [Ag(NH_3)_2]^+(aq) + Cl^-(aq)$$

$$[Ag(NH_3)_2]^+(aq) + Cl^-(aq) + 3NO_3^-(aq) + 2H^+(aq) \rightleftharpoons AgCl(s) + 4H_2O(l) + 5NO(g)$$

Another confirmatory test for the halide ions is based on a color change with each of the halides identified by a different color. The oxidizing agent, chlorine, will react with the halide ions to reduce them to their elemental forms. These elemental forms, Cl_2, Br_2, and I_2, are soluble in non-polar liquids such as toluene or carbon tetrachloride, and give the solution a characteristic color.

A clear solution is an indication of the chloride ion. A red-amber color is an indication of the presence of the bromide ion, while a violet color is an indication of the iodide ion.

Chlorine, Cl_2, can be provided by two different sources. One source is chlorine water made by bubbling chlorine gas through water. A second source is sodium hypochlorite, NaClO, commonly referred to as bleach. The elemental chlorine from the chlorine-water will dissolve in the non-polar carbon tetrachloride and will be readily available for reacting with the halide ions. Also, the elemental chlorine from a bleach-water solution will dissolve in the carbon tetrachloride and will react with the halide ions.

$$Cl_2(water) + CCl_4 \rightleftharpoons Cl_2(carbon\ tetrachloride) + H_2O(l)$$

$$ClO^-(aq) + 2H^+(aq) + Cl^-(aq) + CCl_4 \rightleftharpoons Cl_2(carbon\ tetrachloride) + H_2O(l)$$

The bromide ion is oxidized by the chlorine in the carbon tetrachloride to form a brownish-red bromine.

$$2Br^-(aq) + Cl_2(carbon\ tetrachloride) \rightleftharpoons 2Cl^-(aq) + Br_2(carbon\ tetrachloride)$$
$$brownish\text{-}red\ (red\text{-}amber)$$

The iodide ion is oxidized by the chlorine in the carbon tetrachloride to form a violet iodine.

$$2I^-(aq) + Cl_2(carbon\ tetrachloride) \rightleftharpoons 2Cl^-(aq) + I_2(carbon\ tetrachloride)$$
$$violet$$

CAUTION: Substances used in qualitative analysis can be caustic, corrosive, toxic, and/or suspected carcinogens. Handle all chemicals with care. Wash hands thoroughly before leaving the lab.

PROCEDURE

IMPORTANT: All glassware (test tubes, dropper pipets, etc.) should be clean. Wash with soap, rinse with tap water, and do a final rinse with distilled water.

Obtain a solution of anion salts from the instructor for the anion analysis. An unknown anion salt should also be obtained and the number of the unknown recorded on the Data Sheet. In the following procedures, use a quantity of anion salt that is approximately the size of two grains of rice or one BB (0.18 inch shot pellet). The procedures should be done on the known anion salts and the unknown anion salt at the same time.

There are two types of tests that help identify the anions. The two test types are as follows:

A) Elimination Test

B) Confirmation Test

The Elimination Test can be divided into three different types.

(1) Anions that form insoluble barium salts.

(2) Anions that form volatile products.

(3) Anions that form silver salts that are insoluble in acid solution.

The Confirmation Test for each anion can either be the same as one of the Elimination Test types, or the test can be unique for that anion (nitrite ion and phosphate ion).

1.   Sulfate Ion

A.   Elimination Test (1) and Confirmation Test
Place a quantity of Na_2SO_4 in a small test tube. Add 6 drops of 0.1 M $BaCl_2$ to the test tube and shake. Add 6 drops of 3 M HNO_3 to the mixture and stir with a clean glass stirring rod. Record all observations on the Data Sheet.

2.   Sulfite Ion

A.   Elimination Test (1)
Place a quantity of Na_2SO_3 in a small test tube. Add 6 drops of 0.1 M $BaCl_2$ to the test tube and shake. Add 6 drops of 3 M HNO_3 to the mixture and stir with a clean glass stirring rod. Record all observations on the Data Sheet.

B.   Elimination Test (2) and Confirmation Test
Place a quantity of Na_2SO_3 in a small test tube. Add 5 drops of 3 M H_2SO_4 and mix with a clean stirring rod. Note the color and odor of any gas evolved. It may be necessary to heat the mixture in a warm water bath. Record all observations on the Data Sheet.

3. Carbonate Ion

A. Elimination Test (1)

Place a quantity of Na_2CO_3 in a small test tube. Add 6 drops of 0.1 M $BaCl_2$ to the test tube and shake. Add 6 drops of 3 M HNO_3 to the mixture and stir with a clean glass stirring rod. Record all observations on the Data Sheet.

B. Elimination Test (2) and Confirmation Test

Place a quantity of Na_2CO_3 in a small test tube. Add 6 drops of 3 M H_2SO_4 and mix with a clean stirring rod. Note the color and odor of any gas evolved. Record all observations on the Data Sheet.

4. Phosphate Ion

A. Elimination Test (1)

Place a quantity of Na_3PO_4 in a small test tube. Add 6 drops of 0.1 M $BaCl_2$ to the test tube and shake. Add 6 drops of 3 M HNO_3 to the mixture and stir with a clean glass stirring rod. Record all observations on the Data Sheet.

B. Confirmation Test

Place a quantity of Na_3PO_4 in a small test tube. Add 10 drops of 3 M HNO_3 and 5 drops of 0.5 M $(NH_4)_2MoO_4$ solution. Record all observations on the Data Sheet.

5. Nitrite Ion

A. Elimination Test (2) and Confirmation Test

Place a quantity of $NaNO_2$ in a small test tube. Add 6 drops of 3 M H_2SO_4 and mix with a clean stirring rod. Note the color and odor of any gas evolved. It may be necessary to heat the mixture in a warm water bath. Record all observations on the Data Sheet.

6. Nitrate Ion

A. Confirmation Test

Place a quantity of $NaNO_3$ in a small test tube. Add 6 drops of a 1 M $FeSO_4$ solution (made in 6 M H_2SO_4) and warm the mixture in a warm water bath until a reaction takes place (approximately one minute). Be careful during this experiment as the gas may evolve quite rapidly. Record all observations on the Data Sheet.

7. Chloride Ion

A. Elimination Test (3) and Confirmation Test

Place a quantity of NaCl in a small test tube. Add 6 drops of chlorine water and 6 drops of carbon tetrachloride and shake thoroughly. Note the color of the lower (carbon tetrachloride) layer. Record all observations on the Data Sheet.

8. **Bromide Ion**

A.   Elimination Test (3) and Confirmation Test
Place a quantity of NaBr in a small test tube. Add 6 drops of chlorine water and 6 drops of carbon tetrachloride and shake thoroughly. Note the color of the lower (carbon tetrachloride) layer. Record all observations on the Data Sheet.

9. **Iodide Ion**

A.   Elimination Test (3) and Confirmation Test
Place a quantity of NaI in a small test tube. Add 6 drops of chlorine water and 6 drops of carbon tetrachloride and shake thoroughly. Note the color of the lower (carbon tetrachloride) layer. Record all observations on the Data Sheet.

UNKNOWN ANION

Each type of Elimination Test should be done for the unknown anion. On the basis of the results of these tests, the appropriate Confirmation Tests should then be performed.

DATA SHEET: QUALITATIVE ANALYSIS OF ANIONS

I. Observations for Anion Analysis

	Elimination Tests	Confirmation Tests
Sulfate Ion		
Sulfite Ion		
Carbonate Ion		
Phosphate Ion		
Nitrite Ion		

DATA SHEET: QUALITATIVE ANALYSIS OF ANIONS

I.   Observations for Anion Analysis (continued)

	Elimination Tests	**Confirmation Tests**
Nitrate Ion		
Chloride Ion		
Bromide Ion		
Iodide Ion		

DATA SHEET: QUALITATIVE ANALYSIS OF ANIONS

II.   Observations for Unknown Anion Analysis

	Elimination Tests	**Confirmation Tests**

Unknown #   _____

Anion found: _____

Write all pertinent chemical equations that support the identification of the unknown anion.

QUESTIONS

1.   Your unknown contains only the sulfite ion, but you obtain a positive test for the sulfate ion. Explain why you obtained these results. Include any pertinent chemical reactions.

2.   Describe a simple test to distinguish between the following anions. Include chemical equations.

   (a) PO_4^{3-} and Br^-

   (b) SO_4^{2-} and CO_3^{2-}

   (c) Cl^- and I^-

   (d) NO_3^- and NO_2^-

3.   Write all pertinent chemical equations which would demonstrate why the sulfite salt of barium forms a white precipitate in a neutral solution but is soluble in acidic solutions.

2.   Write all pertinent chemical equations which would demonstrate why the phosphate salt of barium forms a white precipitate in a neutral solution but is soluble in acidic solutions.

USE OF THE METTLER BALANCE

In a chemical experiment it is frequently necessary to determine the mass of a sample very accurately. The **Mettler Type H Analytical Balance** allows one to determine the mass of a sample to .001 g (1 milligram).

This balance is very sensitive and delicate and must be treated with care.

Remember that it is impossible to get good results in your experiment if you weigh your samples incorrectly. After your Lab Instructor has demostrated the use of the Mettler Balance, practice making weighings until you feel confident using the balance.

The following is a step-by-step procedure for using the balance.

PROCEDURE FOR WEIGHING:

METTLER TYPE H ANALYTICAL BALANCES

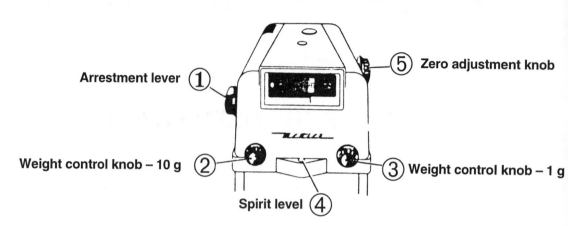

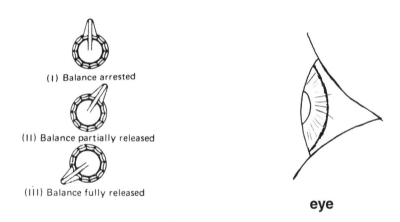

I. Check Zero

A.   Remove all material from balance pan and set all weights to zero. Then carefully push the lever (1), on the left side of the balance, all the way back to a reading position. Do not force the lever if you find difficulty in moving it.

B.   Align the zero marks on the illuminated scale using the knob (5) on the right side of the balance.

C.   Switch the balance off by turning lever (1), on the left side of the balance, to an upright vertical position.

II. Load Balance

A.   With the balance off, load the pan with the item to be weighed. Close the sliding glass door.

B.   Move the lever (1) forward to the partial release position. (Do not force it.)

C.   Add weights in l0 g units using knob (2) on the left front side of the balance. When the illuminated scale moves upward, turn the knob back one step.

D.   Repeat the step (C) for 1 g increments using the knob (3) on the right side front of the balance.

III. Reading the Balance

A.   When the required weight in grams has been selected, a reading can be taken. Move lever (1) back to the reading position (full release). If the correct weight in grams has been set then the zero mark on the stationary vernier scale will be between 0.00 g and 1.00 g on the movable scale (i.e. on scale).

B.   Read the balance (See page 18 - 4).

C.   Turn the balance off, set all weights back to zero and clean the pan.

FLOW SHEET FOR THE USE OF THE METTLER BALANCE

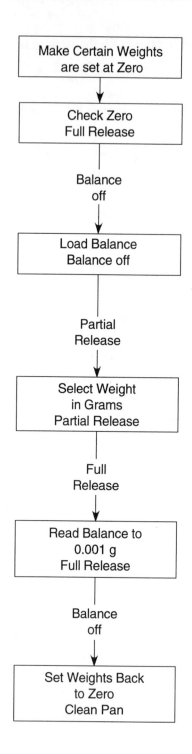

NOTE: 1. Never force the lever.

                2. Only dial weights to the balance when the lever is on partial release.

HOW TO READ AN ANALYTICAL BALANCE OPTICAL SCALE WITH VERNIER

A vernier scale is a common device on a balance that is used in conjunction with the optical scale to determine the final digit of the weight of an unknown without estimation. Depending upon the balance model used, the final three or four digits are read from the optical and vernier scales

The optical scale moves in relation to the vernier scale, which is stationary. Eleven vernier scale divisions (from 0 to 10) are printed on the readout-panel glass and are compressed into nine optical scale divisions. The vernier scale allows you to read one-tenth of a scale division very accurately.

The zero on the vernier scale is the reference used to read the optical scale. Always read the scale division immediately below the zero line of the vernier scale In the following example, you would read 50 from the optical scale.

The final digit is read from the vernier scale. Read the vernier scale division that is in perfect alignment with an optical scale division. In the example above, the fifth vernier line is in perfect alignment with an optical scale division line. The final digit, therefore, is 5. The correct reading from the optical and vernier scales combined is 505.

ERRORS AND SIGNIFICANT FIGURES

Errors

Measurements taken in the laboratory are subject to various uncertainties, generally known as errors. These errors may be **systematic** or **random**. Systematic errors are chiefly due to imperfections in the instruments employed and to some particular and persistent characteristic of the experimenter. An example of a systematic error is that uncertainty resulting from a measurement made with an instrument having an imperfectly calibrated scale. Such errors can usually be eliminated. However, if an instrument were perfect and the experimenter free from peculiar tendencies, errors of measurment would still arise due to limitations of the scale divisions on the instruments. Suppose, for example, that one uses a scale graduated in millimeters in determining the length of a line to the nearest 0.1 mm. If several measurements were made, there will be small differences among them due to estimation of the nearest 0.1 mm between the scale divisions. These differences vary irregularly and give rise to random errors.

It is the magnitude of the random errors that usually limits the accuracy of data taken in the laboratory. In these instructions some principles of accuracy will be given. These principles should be turned into **"working rules"** as quickly as possible by the student.

Errors are to be differentiated from mistakes. The latter are uncertainties due to **carelessness**, and usually are easily detected and eliminated. Mistakes can be avoided in the laboratory by constant and careful attention to the experimental procedure.

The nicety of automation when applied to the area of measurements is recognized. For example, voltages can now be read from the dials of an electronic apparatus which not only gives the magnitude of the voltage but also indicates the polarity (+ or −) of the signal being monitored. Analytical balances are available which automatically give the weight of a sample with no aid from experimenter except that of placing the specimen on the pan. However, the data derived from such devices is subject to the same limitations as that from the more usually employed voltmeters of balances whereon a scale reading is taken.

Significant Figures

In recording data in the laboratory, one should be careful to retain as many figures as actually represent a measurement but no more. Suppose one uses a ruler graduated in millimeters to measure the length of a line as shown in **Figure 1**.

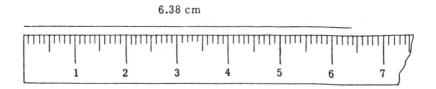

Figure 1.

Since estimations can be made between the millimeter markings of the ruler, the length can be recorded to 0.1 mm, as 6.38 cm. Here the 8 is an estimation and represents the last figure one can rightfully set down. The length has been determined to three **significant** figures, two known exactly and one estimated. Likewise, when recording measurments the **last** figure set down should be a trustworthy estimation. (This last figure is called an uncertain figure, again obtaining and handling data, all figures up to and including the **first uncertain one** are called **significant figures**.)

The length of the above line may be recorded as 63.8 m. 0.0638 km, 638×10^{-7} km, or 6.38×10^{-5} km. The decimal point fixes the magnitude of the length but does not indicate the number of significant figures of the measurement. The length is given to three significant figures in all cases.

If the line had been **"exactly"** 6.3 cm long, its length should be recorded as 6.30 cm, since one can estimate to 0.01 cm on the ruler. Recording the length as 6.3 cm means that the length must lie between 6.25 and 6.35 cm, or the measurement has an error of 0.1 part in 6.3, while recording the length as 6.30 cm means that the length lies between 6.295 and 6.305 cm, or the measurement has an error of 0.01 part in 6.30. Obviously recording the length as 6.30 cm more properly indicates the limit of precision possible with the ruler.

In arithmetical manipulations, due regard must be given the role that the significant figures of the individual quantities play. For instance, a box top measures 4.25 cm by 3.21 cm. To find its area one multiplies 4.25 cm by 3.21 cm. The product is 13.6425 cm^2, an area containing six figures. Is one justified in keeping these? The answer is obvious when the multiplication is performed by longhand underlining the uncertain products that arise when a certain figure is multiplied by an uncertain one. The 5 of the 4.25 and the 1 of the 3.21 is uncertain since they are recorded as the estimated value of the measurement. Therefore,

$$3.21$$
$$\underline{4.25}$$
$$\underline{\textbf{16 05}}$$
$$64\ \underline{\textbf{2}}$$
$$\underline{128\underline{4}}$$
$$13.\underline{\underline{64}\ \underline{25}}$$

Now it is seen that the last four figures are not trustworthy. Since the product should contain only one uncertain figure the area should be written as 13.6 cm^2. All arithmetic processes could be performed likewise, but this would involve a great expenditure of time.

The following rules concerning significant figures should be remembered:

1.   All nonzero numbers are significant figures.

2.   Zeros that do not appear after some other digit are called **leading zeros** and are never significant; these zeros simply locate the decimal point. For example, both 0.023 and 0.00023 have two significant figures.

3.   Zeros that are surrounded by nonzero digits are called **captive zeros** and are significant. For example, 0.002002 has four significant figures, three leading zeros, and two capitive zeros.

4.   Zeros following a nonzero digit in a number that has a decimal point are called **trailing zeros** and are significant. For example, 0.200 has three significant figures including two trailing zeros, while 2000. has four significant figures including three trailing zeros. If the zeros are not intended to be significant in a number larger than ten, the decimal point is omitted; if they are significant, the decimal point is used. For example, we may state that a town has a population of 133,000 to the nearest thousand and imply only three significant figures. The zeros only mark the decimal point. However, if the figure were written with a decimal point after it, as 133,000., then a count to the nearest person is implied and all six figures are significant.

Our next concern is what happens to significant figures when mathematical operations are carried out on numbers. **In addition or subtraction, the answer should be reported to the same number of decimal places as are contained in the number in the data set that has the fewest decimal places.**

In multiplication or division, the answer is rounded off to the same number of significant figures as in the number in the data set having the fewest significant figures. (Regardless of the position of the decimal point).

In carrying out a series of mathematical operations, at least one more significant figure should be kept than will appear in the answer. At the end of the calculation the answer is rounded off to the proper number of significant figures according to the following rules:

Rule 1. If the first digit to the right of the last significant figure is less than five, the preceding digit remains unchanged.

Rule 2. If this digit is more than five, the preceding digit is increased by one.

Rule 3. If this digit is five, the preceding digit is not changed if it is an even number but is increased by one if it is odd.

Accuracy

Frequently the percentage difference between two experimental values is desired since neither value may be considered standard. In such cases the percentage difference is given as:

$$\textbf{Percentage difference} = \frac{\textbf{difference}}{\textbf{average value}} \times \textbf{100\%}$$

Example: Two measurements of a track indicate its length as 100.8 yd. and 101.8 yd.

$$\textbf{Percentage difference} = \frac{(\ 101.8 - 100.8\ )}{\left(\frac{101.8 + 100.8}{2}\right)} \times 100\% = .9\%$$

The accuracy obtained in the laboratory experiments is usually judged by comparing the experimental values obtained to some standard values previously determined. The percentage error of the experimental value is given by:

$$\textbf{Percentage error} = \frac{\textbf{error}}{\textbf{accepted value}} \times \textbf{100\%}$$

Example: a 100.0 yd. track is measured to be 100.6 yards.

$$\textbf{Percentage error} = \left(\frac{100.6 - 100.0}{100.0}\right) \times 100\% = 0.6\%$$

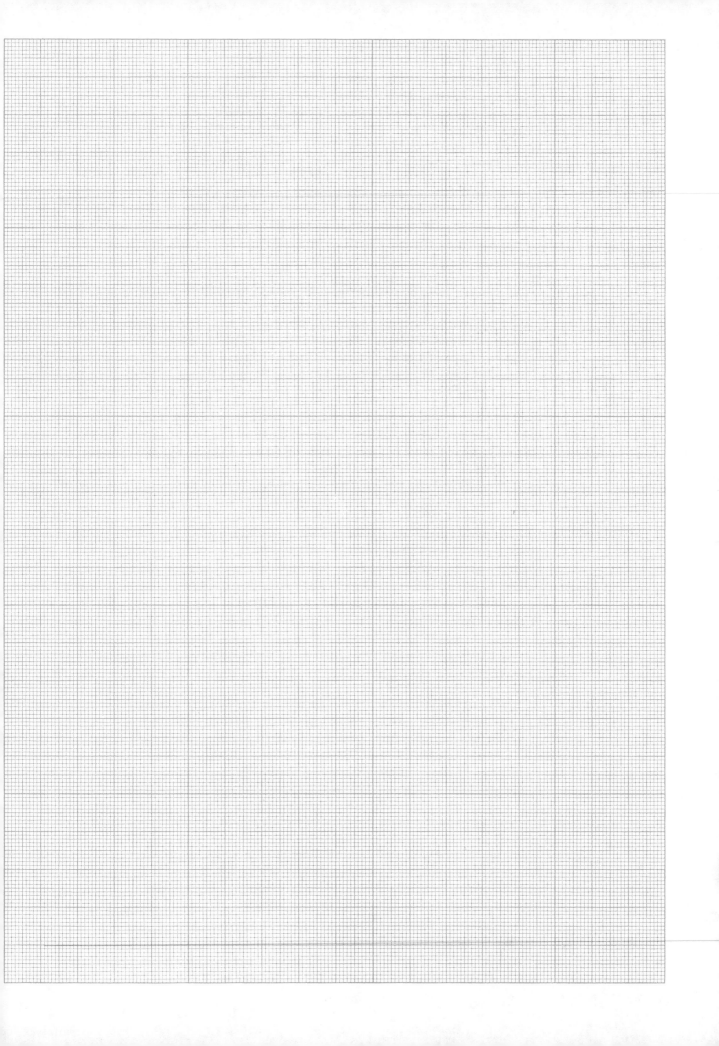

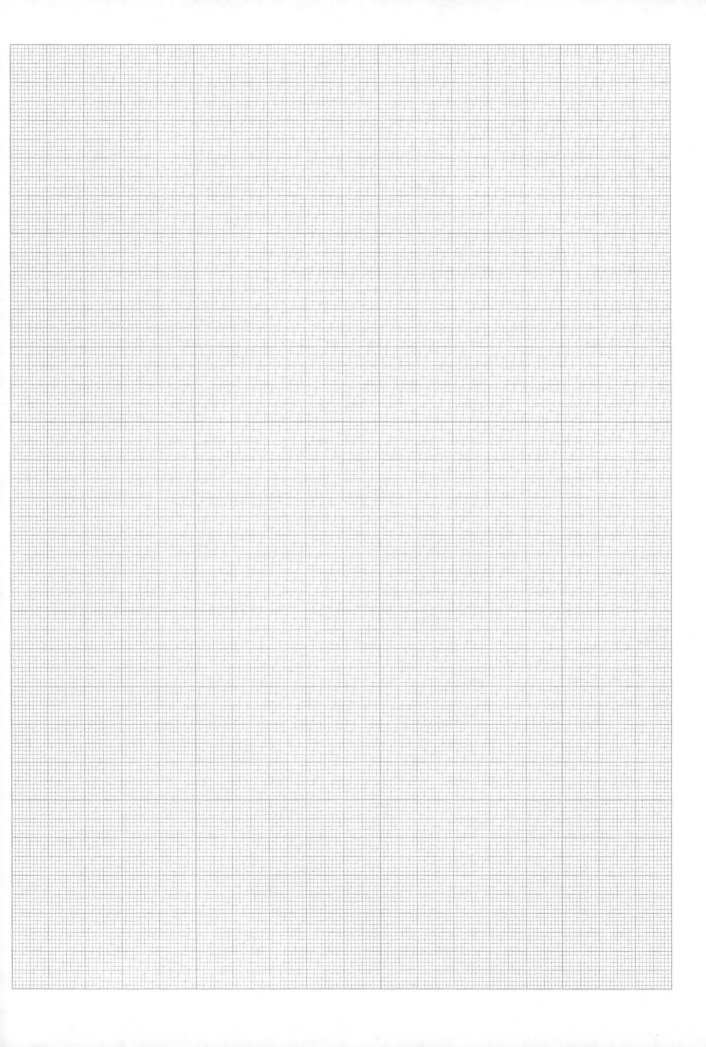

PERIODIC TABLE OF THE ELEMENTS

Table of Selected Radioactive Isotopes

SARGENT-WELCH®
SCIENTIFIC COMPANY
911 COMMERCE COURT, BUFFALO GROVE, ILLINOIS 60089

Catalog Number S-18806

Side 1

Selected Radioactive Isotopes

Naturally occurring radioactive isotopes are designated by a mass number in blue (although some are also manufactured). Letter *m* indicates nuclear or another isotope of the same mass number. Half-lives follow in parentheses, where s, min, h, d, and y stand respectively for seconds, minutes, hours, days, and years. The table includes mainly the longer-lived radioactive isotopes; many others have been prepared. Isotopes known to be radioactive but with half-lives exceeding 10^{15} y have not been included. Symbols describing the principal mode(s) of decay are as follows (these processes are generally accompanied by gamma radiation):

α   alpha particle emission
β^- beta particle (electron) emission
β^+ position emission
EC   orbital electron capture
IT   isomeric transition from upper to lower isomeric state
SF   spontaneous fission

* Estimated Values

The A & B subgroup designations, applicable to elements in rows 4, 5, 6, and 7, are those recommended by the International Union of Pure and Applied Chemistry. It should be noted that some authors and organizations use the opposite convention in distinguishing these subgroups.

[1] The names and symbols of elements 104 - 106 are those recommended by IUPAC as systematic alternatives to those suggested by the discoverers. Berkeley (USA) researchers have proposed Rutherfordium, Rf, for element 104 and Hahnium, Ha, for element 105.

KEY

ATOMIC NUMBER
ATOMIC WEIGHT (2)
OXIDATION STATES (Bold most stable)
SYMBOL (1)
ELECTRON CONFIGURATION
BOILING POINT, K
MELTING POINT, K
DENSITY at 300K (3) (g/cm³)
NAME

Example: 30 / 65.38 / 2 / Zn / [Ar]3d¹⁰4s² / 1180 / 692.73 / 7.14 / Zinc

NOTES:
(1) Black — solid.
    Red — gas.
    Blue — liquid.
    Outline — synthetically prepared.

(2) Based upon carbon-12. ( ) indicates most stable or best known isotope.

(3) Entries marked with asterisks refer to the gaseous state at 273 K and 1 atm and are given in units of g/l.

TABLE OF PERIODIC PROPERTIES OF THE ELEMENTS

Percent Ionic Character of a Single Chemical Bond

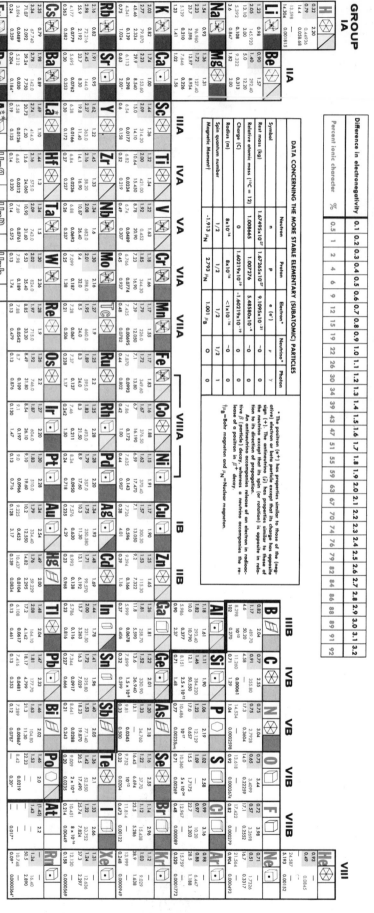

SARGENT-WELCH
S C I E N T I F I C   C O M P A N Y
911 COMMERCE COURT, BUFFALO GROVE, ILLINOIS 60089

Catalog Number S-18806

SIDE 2